11-27-61

CRITICAL
SOLUTION
TEMPERATURES

ALFRED W. FRANCIS

Socony Mobil Oil Co., Inc.

Paulsboro, N.J.

Number 31

ADVANCES IN CHEMISTRY SERIES

American Chemical Society

Washington, D. C.

1961

Copyright © 1961 by
AMERICAN CHEMICAL SOCIETY
All Rights Reserved

Library of Congress Catalog Card No. 61-11857
PRINTED IN THE UNITED STATES OF AMERICA

ADVANCES IN CHEMISTRY SERIES

Robert F. Gould, Editor

AMERICAN CHEMICAL SOCIETY APPLIED PUBLICATIONS

CONTENTS

Reference Marks in Tables vi

Introduction 1

Figures

1. Difference between Critical Solution Temperature and Aniline Point 7

2. Lower Critical Solution Temperature 8

3. Double Insolubility Areas Due to Allotropic Forms 8

4. Postulated CST Curve for Horizontal Melting Curve 9

5. Postulated CST Curve for Steep Melting Curve 9

6. Mutual Solubility of Liquids 10

Tables

I   Critical Solution Temperatures 11

II   Aniline and Furfural Points, High Molecular Weight Hydrocarbons 189

III   Lower Critical Solution Temperatures 209

IV   Mutual Miscibility of Liquids—Bingham 212

V   Mutual Miscibility of Liquids—Drury 213

VI   Mutual Miscibility of Liquids—Sample, et al. 214

VII   Mutual Miscibility of Liquids—Eslami & Dubois 215

VIII Mutual Miscibility of Liquids 218

Bibliography 218

REFERENCE MARKS IN TABLES

>	—Above (in temperature)
<	—Below (in temperature)
ca	—Approximately
m	—Metastable (observed, but below melting point)
e	—Extrapolated
E	—Estimated in a publication
?	—Considered doubtful by Francis
m.p.	—Melting point
b.p.	—Boiling point
crit. temp. or crit. t.	—Critical temperature
CST	—Critical solution temperature
LCST	—Lower critical solution temperature
Phase Pt.	—Phase Point (under Propane or Ethane, nearly the same as LCST)
isopycnic	—Temperature at which the two liquid phases have the same density
iso-optic	—Temperature at which the two liquid phases have the same refractive index (temperature sometimes omitted)

INTRODUCTION

This book contains a compilation of critical solution temperatures (CST); a description of the methods used to determine CST; a guide to the uses of CST data, especially for choosing extraction solvents; and a guide to methods for estimating the CST for untested systems.

More than 6000 CST observations are listed. The main interest of the author's work in this field and that of many others has been in hydrocarbon systems; 70% of the systems listed have a hydrocarbon as one component. However, nearly 1100 nonhydrocarbon solvents are listed.

Definitions

A critical solution temperature (CST) is the minimum temperature for mixing of two substances in all proportions *as liquid* (Figure 1); or it is the maximum temperature of a binary system for two liquid phases in equilibrium.

The term "lower" critical solution temperature (LCST) indicates that complete mixing occurs below the listed temperature but not immediately above it. For illustrations, see Figures 2 and 3. "Lower phase points"—e.g., the propane-lauric acid system in Table I—are nearly the same as LCST (*191, 192*).

Uses of Critical Solution Temperatures

1. The simplest use of CST is to answer the question, "Do two materials mix?" Chemical handbooks—e.g., (*193A*)—answer this question for water and sometimes for a few other solvents, usually only at room temperature. Some recent publications answer it for several other pairs (*17, 106, 121, 211, 372*). These are summarized in Tables IV to VIII of this book. CST answers the question for any temperature, since above the CST (or below the LCST) the liquids mix in all proportions, unless one component crystallizes out. CST also gives an approximate measure of liquid solubility at room temperature, or any other temperature below the CST, assuming the solubility curve is similar to Figure 1.

2. CST are used widely in screening possible solvents for selectivity between desired and undesired components. This aspect has been the basis of the author's chief interest in CST. A spread of 50° to 60° C. between CST of a solvent with a typical "paraffinic" lubricating oil and with a "naphthenic" oil of similar molecular weight was considered a criterion of good selectivity for extracting lubricating oil (*139, 140*). Similar CST differences are a measure of selectivity for pure naphthenes, olefins, or branched-chain paraffins, each with respect to normal paraffins.

CST differences between branched-chain and straight-chain paraffins are usually small. Stannic iodide is the most selective solvent found (*95*); but because of its high melting point, 143.5° C., it has not been considered practical.   Methanol has a fair selectivity for branched-chain hydrocarbons (*150*).

Spread in CST between aromatics and paraffins with the same solvent is usually so great that it cannot be observed (*140*).   Either one CST is below one of the freezing points, or the other is above one of the critical temperatures, or both. A rough estimate of such a spread would be 220° C. for a good selective solvent.

3. CST and aniline points characterize hydrocarbons in the same sense as do melting points and boiling points.

4. CST may be used for analysis, especially to estimate water in alcohols or other liquids, since CST is often very sensitive to traces of water or other impurities (*79–81, 220–223*).   Mixtures of *n*-butane and isobutane were analyzed easily and quantitatively by CST with *o*-nitrotoluene (*141*).

5. CST sometimes gives some insight into molecular structure.   Thus *o*-nitrophenol has a CST with hydrocarbons much lower and with water much higher than do *m*-nitrophenol and *p*-nitrophenol.   This indicates some hydrogen bonding in the ortho isomer, so that it resembles an ester in its solubility relationships.

Sometimes both CST and LCST are listed for the same pair of liquids. Separation occurs only between the two temperatures (Figure 2 and Table III). Sulfur with some aromatic hydrocarbons shows complete mixing only between the two temperatures (Figure 3) since the LCST of one allotropic form or molecular structure of sulfur is above the CST of another form.   The curves of Figure 3, especially the upper one, are not accurately reproducible because sulfur reacts with hydrocarbons at rates increasing with temperature above 150° C.

A separate compilation of 136 LCST's is given in Table III.   These are selected from Table I, which gives the references.

Terms Related to Critical Solution Temperature

Aniline point is the mixing temperature of equal volumes of pure aniline and the other liquid, usually a hydrocarbon.   The aniline point may be as much as 1° C. lower than the CST because the curve of mixing is unsymmetrical (Figure 1). Terms analogous to "aniline point" can be defined for other solvents—for example, "furfural points."   No distinction is made in the tables between critical solution temperatures and aniline points (or their analogs), because of the small difference mentioned.

Critical temperature, sometimes used in this discussion, is not to be confused with critical solution temperature.   Critical temperature has its usual meaning of maximum temperature for equilibrium of liquid and *vapor* phases, usually of a single component, under pressure.

Determination of Critical Solution Temperatures

The observation of CST with practical precision is usually very simple.   The two liquids are placed in a test tube and are stirred with a thermometer while heating or cooling until the liquids just mix (while heating) or just cloud (on cooling). Determinations of the cloud point are usually more precise than determinations of the temperature of disappearance of two phases.   There is very little risk of subcooling a liquid mixture below the CST, and having it remain homogeneous. When the upper layer becomes small before it disappears, more of the major component of the upper layer is added, and the observation is repeated until the interface disappears near the middle of the system.   This is necessary in order to find the maximum temperature of the miscibility curve (Figure 1). Similarly, it is sometimes necessary to add more of the major component of the lower layer when that layer is small. When the temperature is far removed from room temperature, a bath of heated water or glycerol, or a dry ice bath, may be used so as to make temperature change more gradual.

Greater refinements in observation of CST or aniline points or methods of expediting them have been described in numerous publications. Reference is made to ASTM Method D 97–57, to Brown (37), and to Rice and coworkers (5, 6, 355).

The presence of traces of insoluble impurities in a solvent or an oil may cause a turbidity which could be confused with a cloud point. The appearance of a real interface at a few degrees lower temperature may be necessary to confirm the reality of a cloud point.

Another optical illusion which could confuse the observation of a CST is an iso-optic or point at which the refractive indices of the two liquid phases are equal. Since the index varies with the wave length of the light (dispersion), observation in daylight of an iso-optic system normally results in a structural color, giving the appearance of a clear liquid with yellow, pink, purple, or blue bands (144). However, a few solvents—e.g., acetic anhydride, formic acid, and ethylene glycol— give practically no color at their iso-optics with some hydrocarbons because of equality in dispersion. Even experts in this field have been deceived by iso-optics. Lecat published a CST of formic acid and *n*-pentane that was at least 150° C. too low (268, 271; cf. 139, 144). Similar examples are acetamide–*m*-xylene and ethylene glycol–*n*-heptane.

The temperature of initial crystallization of one of the components of a binary system on cooling is not a CST or cloud point. Some confusion exists in the literature from reporting crystallization points as CST. Many such observations have been corrected for use in these tables by placing the prefix "<" before the temperature.

In Table I many CST are listed below the melting point of one of the two components. Some of these are true equilibria, since the melting points are lowered by mixing. Others are real observations, taking advantage of subcooling with respect to crystallization. Others are extrapolated values. These were observed with the help of a small amount of a third substance which raises the CST above the crystallization temperature.

Many CST are listed which were measured above the boiling point of one of the components. For temperatures up to 60° above the boiling point, a pierced stopper and thermometer wired into the test tube usually sufficed to hold the pressure while the phases mixed. Much higher CST observations were possible with sealed tubes attached to a thermometer in a bath, or by using a visual autoclave.

Near a critical temperature, however, solubility often decreases with rising temperature, so that there may actually be no CST at all—for example, see the systems of aniline with methane, ethane, or propane (Table I). One phase reaches its critical temperature below the CST. A few such critical temperatures of the upper layer are listed—e.g., for carbon dioxide, ethane, and ethyl ether (Table I).

For some pairs of substances three critical points are possible: the one just mentioned, which is always a little higher than the critical temperature of the more volatile component; a LCST, which is usually a few degrees below that temperature, and the real CST, which is extremely low. Original literature and other compilations are sometimes not clear as to which temperature is actually observed. Those listed in Table I are marked according to the present compiler's judgment on this point.

Many attempted observations of CST were stopped before reaching a. sufficiently high temperature—for example, see the acetonitrile-pentane system in Table I, where the CST had not been reached at 60° C.

Arrangement of Compilations

The "solvents" in Table I are listed with upper case letters alphabetically, with the names which seemed best known. Many solvents with two or more common names are listed in each place. Cross references save the repetition of the accompanying data, when more than five lines are required.

When both components are nonhydrocarbons, the observation is listed in both places unless a substantial saving of space would result from using a cross reference. Hydrocarbons are listed as "solvents" (names in upper case and not indented) only if two hydrocarbons are involved, or if they are included in the supplementary Tables III to VIII.

In the line giving the name of the solvent, or just below it, alternative names of the solvent are shown, and also its melting point if this is higher than some of the CST. Similarly, the critical temperature of the solvent is listed if it is a pertinent factor in the observations. Also listed are references to the supplementary tables. This furnishes an index to them.

With each solvent the hydrocarbons whose CST have been observed with it are indented and arranged in order of paraffins, olefins, naphthenes, alkylbenzenes, alkylnaphthalenes, other polycyclics, and hydrocarbon mixtures. In each class the hydrocarbons are arranged in order of increasing molecular weight. The order is approximately the same as that used by Ball (12) for aniline points, but may not be rigorous. Aniline points of 264 hydrocarbons of high molecular weight (382, 383) were not merged with the others. They were accompanied by furfural points, and could be presented more conveniently in Table II, especially in view of the very complex names and formulas of some of them. These were available from the 1958 report of A.P.I. Project 42. Permission for this from the director, J. A. Dixon, is gratefully acknowledged. Other important properties of these hydrocarbons, listed in the original papers, are omitted from Table II.

CST of nonhydrocarbons, if any, with each solvent in Table I are placed below those of the hydrocarbons, and in alphabetical order. Again melting points or critical temperatures, etc, are given when pertinent. These serve to explain the use of "<," since the actual CST are often not attainable. For paraffin wax the melting point may be merely a characterization.

The expression "<m.p.," used frequently for groups of substances, means "below melting point curve." In Figure 4 (196A) a nearly horizontal portion of the melting point curve indicates that a metastable liquid-liquid equilibrium curve (dashed line) is probably only slightly below the curve of equilibrium with crystals. These are shown usually in Table I by individual listing with "<" followed by the temperature at the 50% point. When the melting curves are steep, as in Figure 5, the hypothetical liquid-liquid equilibria may be far below the higher melting point, as much as 188° C. for camphor-phenols.

Some entries are "All hydrocarbons" with < or >. The former means that since high paraffins are miscible at the temperature listed, all other hydrocarbons · can be expected to be so. The latter means that the most miscible hydrocarbon, usually benzene, is not miscible with this solvent, and so no other could be expected to be miscible.

All temperatures in these tables are in degrees Centigrade. Some pairs of liquids show isopycnics or temperatures at which the two liquid phases are equal in density (*140A*). Some, but probably not all, of these systems are listed. A few iso-optics or pairs of liquids with equal refractive indices (giving opalescent colors) also are mentioned (*140A, 143, 144*).

An effort has been made to give a complete bibliography for each CST (or LCST, etc.). However, only one temperature is usually listed, a mean selected by the compiler. A few badly discrepant observations are listed separately, sometimes with question marks and with explanatory notes. The page numbers are given in compilations (*209, 210, 253–6, 296, 391–3, 445–6*) and a few others to facilitate location of data. In a few citations to (*210*), the original reference (given there) is omitted if difficultly accessible. Binary compositions at the CST are not listed because they are relatively unimportant, and because only a small portion of them are available.

A letter, A, B, or C, following a reference number has no significance except to indicate a different reference. The brief "abstracts" in the bibliography, though not comprehensive, were of much help in checking the references. They may help in using the book. Similar abstracts are given in some tables of (*256*).

Supplementary Tables

Tables IV to VIII present in concise form, though complete, the data from five papers (*17, 106, 121, 211, 372*), each giving miscibilities of a group of substances. The papers are in the form of triangular or rectangular charts similar to mileage charts on road maps. In each square is given M or S for miscible, I for immiscible, and usually R for reacts. This method is unsatisfactory for more than about 50 liquids because of the large area required. Since about 70% of the pairs are miscible, much of the space is largely wasted.

The five charts mentioned could be incorporated into the general Table I with the notations "<25" or ">25" (or 20) under CST; but this would expand that table considerably without giving much information. Instead they are presented in rearranged and condensed form. However, the large table serves as an index to these tables. The tables are arranged chronologically.

At one time it was hoped that any group of liquids could be arranged in an order such that the first is miscible with others part way down the list and immiscible with the remaining ones; the second is miscible a little farther down the list, etc., so that miscibility of any pair could be indicated approximately by the degree of separation of the two in the list. This was the basis of the "octagon figure" Figure 6 published in 1944 (*140*), and quoted by others—e.g., (*269*, p. 129) without a reference.

Each liquid in the figure is completely miscible with liquids of adjacent number, and with those having numbers two more or less. When the difference in number is three, solubility is still high but incomplete (with one exception). Liquids further apart around the octagon have low solubility, as indicated by the type of diagonal (or none).

However, in almost any larger group of liquids, there are incongruities with such an arrangement. For certain liquids there is no completely logical position in the list. Thus in Table V, nitromethane is miscible with most of the other liquids, yet immiscible with two liquids near it in the list, and with several at both ends of the list. An attempt was made to arrange Table VI also in a "logical" order so as to minimize the number of entries in column 3.

This arrangement would be very satisfactory if there were no gaps or errors in the original publications. Unfortunately, there are many gaps and some discrepancies in most of the papers. The tests are simple but numerous (1035 for a 46-liquid list). Discrepancies may arise through differences in the purity of reagents, especially water content, which is very important.

Many of the discrepancies were detected and most of the gaps filled, by other published data. In several doubtful cases tests were repeated. These "corrections" are indicated by parentheses or question marks, as shown in the footnotes. The presence of unnumbered liquids in Table VIII is due to the fact that Jackson and Drury (211) tested these liquids only with the numbered liquids and not with each other. It was impossible to fill all of the resulting gaps without having these liquids available.

In Table VII the arrangement used by the authors was retained, and in Tables IV and VIII an alphabetical order was used because of the larger number of liquids.

Extension of Data to Untested Systems

Many hundred CST could be added for pairs of liquids marked "miscible" or " ∞ " in handbooks. These could be listed with "CST <20," etc. Likewise many more given as "insoluble" or "slightly soluble" could be listed as "CST >20." The data of (15, 17, 106, 121, 211, 372) and some of those of (85, 296, 340, 341) are of this type and are referred to only in groups. The table thus furnishes an index for these compilations.

About 800 aniline points or CST of hydrocarbons with aniline are listed. Since CST of hydrocarbons with nitrobenzene are about 50° C. lower than aniline points with the same hydrocarbons, nitrobenzene CST can be estimated easily for these 800 hydrocarbons. CST of many other aromatic solvents with the same hydrocarbons may be approximated similarly. Nonaromatic solvents are not so nearly parallel in this respect, but certain generalities are apparent among similar groups of components (139, 140). Moreover, many more aniline points (and from them other CST) of unknown isomeric hydrocarbons could be estimated with reasonable confidence by one of six equations for aniline points of hydrocarbon classes (that section of Table I). Altogether this table might furnish a basis for estimates of about a million CST. Even so, combinations are encountered frequently which are not predictable from this table, and new observations are required.

Acknowledgment

The author is indebted to the Socony Mobil Oil Co. for support of the present compilation.

He is indebted also to his associates, especially R. W. Schiessler, S. L. Meisel, G. C. Johnson, and D. D. Neiswender, for valuable suggestions, and to Leroy G. Leap for extensive help in checking the references.

                                                              ALFRED W. FRANCIS
Research Department
Socony Mobil Oil Co., Inc.
Paulsboro, N.J.

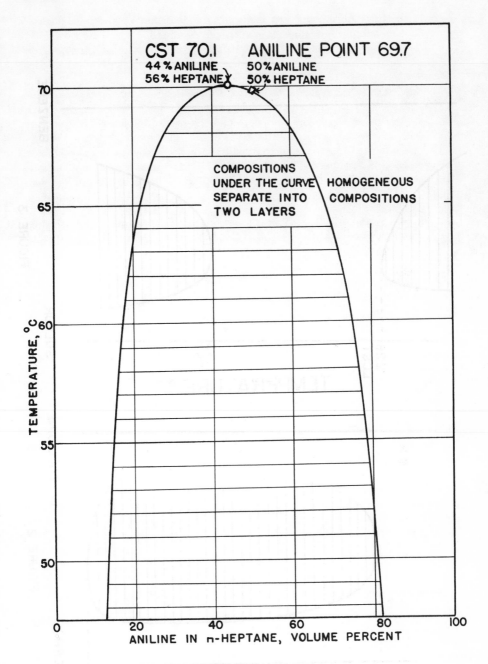

Figure 1

Difference between Aniline Point and

Critical Solution Temperature

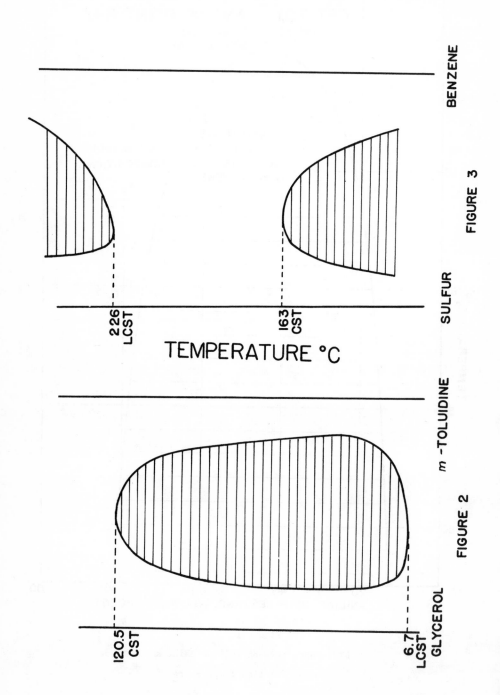

BENZENE

FIGURE 3

226
LCST

163
CST

TEMPERATURE °C

SULFUR

m -TOLUIDINE

FIGURE 2

120.5
CST

6.7
LCST

GLYCEROL

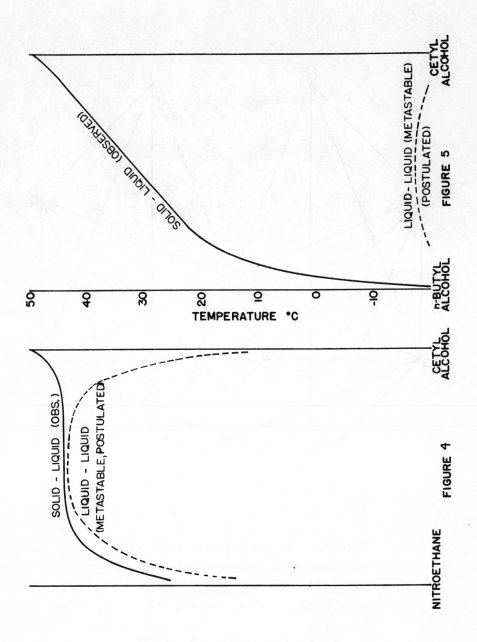

SOLID - LIQUID (OBSERVED)

LIQUID - LIQUID (METASTABLE)
(POSTULATED)

FIGURE 5

TEMPERATURE °C

CETYL ALCOHOL

n-BUTYL ALCOHOL

SOLID - LIQUID (OBS.)

LIQUID - LIQUID
(METASTABLE, POSTULATED)

CETYL ALCOHOL

NITROETHANE

FIGURE 4

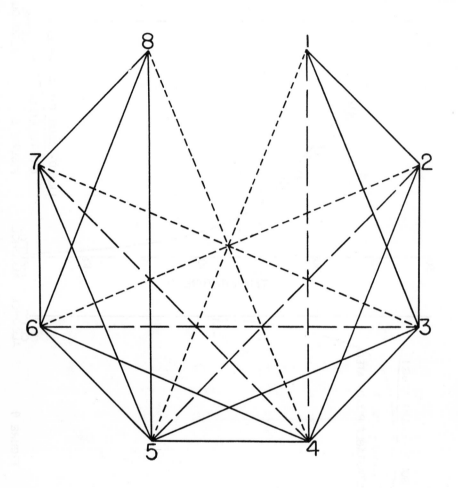

Figure 6. Mutual Solubility of Liquids

——————————   Complete miscibility
— — — —   High solubility
- - - - - -   Low solubility
No line   Very low solubility

1. Water   5. Ethyl ether
2. Diethylene glycol   6. Benzene
3. Triethylene glycol   7. Cyclohexane
4. Furfural   8. n-Heptane

TABLE I

Table I

Critical Solution Temperatures

	CST	References
ABIETIC ACID		
Propane	<50	192
ACETAL		
n-Heptane	-61E	149
Paraffinic lubricating oil	-16	139(p.766),145,149
Another oil	<0	131,149
Magnesium iodide	>77	210(p.204),301, 391(p.974)
ACETALDEHYDE (Table IV)		17
n-Hexane	-19	151
n-Heptane	-9	151
2,2,4-Trimethylpentane	-11	151
n-Decane	13	151
n-Dodecane	23	151
Cyclohexane	-16	151
Methylcyclohexane	-16	151
ACETAMIDE (m.p. 81)		15
Benzene	143	140,149,312
m-Xylene	79?200	140,256,268,271, 392(p.121),445(p.635)
Biphenyl	167	149,255,256,264,268,271, 445(p.639),392(p.121)
Bibenzyl	185	149,256,268,392(p.121)
Diphenylmethane	178	149,255,268,270, 392(p.121)
Naphthalene (m.p. 80)	148.5	149,256,260,268,271, 392(p.121)
1-Methylnaphthalene	169.5	149,255,256,268,270,271, 392(p.121)
2-Methylnaphthalene	171	271,445,(p.649)
Acenaphthene	178	149,255,256,264,268,271, 392(p.121),445(p.659)
Camphene	<74	271
Carvene	>169.2	260,271
Dipentene	>169	271
Indene	144	149,255,256,264,268, 271,445(p.655)
Acetophenone	<36.8	260,271,445(p.1021)
Anethole(p-Propenylanisole)	143.5	271,445(p.996)
Benzyl acetate	<56	255,270,271,392(p.121), 445(p.1039)
Borneol (m.p. 208)	<116	255,270,271,392(p.121)
Bornyl acetate	134	255,256,268,270,271,392 (p.121),445(p.1038)
Bromobenzene	110	255,256,264,268,271, 392(p.121)
1-Bromonaphthalene	175	255,256,265,268,271, 392(p.121),445(p.800)
m-Bromotoluene	>170	271
p-Bromotoluene	156	255,263,271,392(p.121), 445(p.799)
n-Butyl benzoate	132	255,256,263,268,271 392(p.121),445(p.1049)

	CST	References
ACETAMIDE (continued)		
Carvone	<67.8	260,271,445(p.1017)
1-Chloronaphthalene	168.3	255,256,264,268,271, 392(p.121)
p-Chlorophenol	<17	271
Cineole	<67	127,255,264,270,271, 392(p.121),445(p.995)
Citronellal	<50	255,263,271, 392(p.121)
p-Cresol methyl ether	107	256,264,268,271, 392(p.121),445(p.798)
n-Decyl alcohol	<75	271
p-Dibromobenzene	180	255,256,268,270,271, 392(p.121)
o-Dichlorobenzene	150	255,256,263,268,271, 392(p.121)
p-Dichlorobenzene	148.5	255,256,268,270,271, 392(p.121),445(p.797)
N,N-Diethylaniline	179	256,260,268,271,392 (p.121),445(p.1106)
N,N-Dimethylaniline	120.5	255,256,268,270,271, 392(p.121),445(p.1101)
N,N-Dimethyl-o-toluidine	174	255,256,264,268,271, 392(p.121),445(p.1109)
Ethyl benzoate	<70.8	255,270,271,392(p.121) 445(p.1049)
Ethyl cinnamate	75	271
Ethyl maleate	<63	271,445(p.1046)
Ethyl oxalate	<31.5	255,270,271,392(p.121), 445(p.1045)
Ethyl phenylacetate	<60.5	271,445(p.1050)
Ethyl salicylate	103.5	256,268,271,392(p.121)
Eugenol(2-Methoxy-4-allylphenol)	<59.5	255,270,271,392(p.121)
Eugenol methyl ether	<61.5	255,260,270,271, 392(p.121),445(p.1000)
Geraniol (see p. 98)	<58.6	255,270,271,392(p.121)
Guaiacol (o-Methoxyphenol)	<20.5	Ibid.
p-Iodotoluene	175	255,263,271,392(p.121), 445(p.800)
Isoamyl benzoate	140	255,256,268,270,271, 392(p.121),445(p.1050)
Isoamyl butyrate	126.8	256,268,271,392(p.121) 445(p.1041)
Isoamyl carbonate	186.5	271,445(p.1044)
Isoamyl ether	<71	271
Isoamyl isobutryate	100	271,445(p.1042)
Isoamyl isovalerate	163	256,268,271,392(p.121), 445(p.1043)
Isoamyl oxalate	113	255,265,271,392(p.121), 445(p.1045)
Isobutyl benzoate	126	255,256,268,270,271, 392(p.121)
Isobutyl carbonate	120	271,445(p.1044)
Isobutyl isovalerate	119	255,256,264,268,271, 392(p.121),445(p.1042)
Isobutyl valerate	163	255,264,392(p.121)
Isoeugenol methyl ether	<74	255,270,271,392(p.121), 445(p.1000)
Isosafrole	128.5	255,256,268,270,271,392 (p.121),445(p.1000)

TABLE I   13

	CST	References
ACETAMIDE (continued)		
Menthol (Hexahydrothymol)	<45	255,263,271,392(p.121)
p-Methylacetophenone	<54.4	255,256,270,271, 392(p.121),445(p.1021)
N-Methylaniline	<45.5	260,271,445(p.1100)
Methyl benzoate	<61.7	255,270,271,392(p.121), 445(p.1048)
Methyl caprylate	155	271,445(p.1043)
Methyl cinnamate	<60.8	255,270,271,392(p.121), 445(p.1050)
Methyl maleate	<42	271,445(p.1046)
Methyl salicylate	80.6	256,268,271,392(p.121)
Nitrobenzene	<54.6	260,271
p-Nitrochlorobenzene (m.p. 83)	<73.2	255,264,271,392(p.121)
o-Nitrophenol (m.p. 45)	<43	255,265,271,392(p.121)
o-Nitrotoluene	<70.5	271
p-Nitrotoluene	<60.8	271
n-Octyl alcohol	<21	271
Pentachloroethane	95	255,256,268,270,271, 392(pp.67,121)
Phenetole	108.5	Ibid.
Phenyl acetate	<30	255,270,271,392(p.121)
2-Phenylethanol	<38.5	271
Phenyl ether	160.8	255,256,268,270,271, 392(p.121),445(p.997)
Propionamide (m.p. 79)	<54	271,445(p.1145)
Propyl benzoate	115	255,263,271,392(p.121), 445(p.1049)
Pulegone (see p.158)	<66	256,260,268,271, 392(p.121),445(p.1017)
Safrole	136.5	255,256,268,270,271, 392(p.121),445(p.999)
α-Terpineol	<46	260,271
Tetrachloroethylene	>120	271
Thymol	<69	271
o-Toluidine	<24.3	255,270,271,392(p.121), 445(p.1108)
m-Toluidine	<-3	271
p-Toluidine	<65	318,392(p.121)
Urethane (Ethyl carbamate)	<44	Ibid.
Water	<25	318
ACETANILIDE (m.p. 114)		15
n-Hexane		
(no complete miscibility)	None	17,139
n-Heptane	204	139,149
2,2,4-Trimethylpentane	221	139
Diisobutene	145	139
Cyclohexane	103	139
Methylcyclohexane	123	139
Decalin	101	151
Benzene	<68	151
Toluene	<70	151,318
m-Xylene	<78	151
sec-Butylbenzene	<85	151
Di-sec-Butylbenzene	<86	151
Naphthalene	<88	151
Paraffin wax (m.p.53)	233	139
Paraffinic oil	232	139
Naphthenic oil	176	139

	CST	References
ACETANILIDE (continued)		
Acetic acid	<45e	30,392(pp.601-2)
Ethyl alcohol	<55	425
Methanol	<42	425
Phenol	<40	318,392(p.603)
Urethane (Ethyl carbamate)	<75	Ibid.
Water	144	153,209(p.392),385, 392(p.600)
ACETIC ACID (m.p.16.6)(Table IV)		15,17
n-Hexane	-4.0m	17,139,149,446(p.207) 491
n-Heptane	8.8m	139,147,149,491
n-Octane	18.5	491
2,2,4-Trimethylpentane	6.5	139
n-Nonane	29.3	491
n-Decane	40.6	491
n-Hendecane	52.2	491
n-Dodecane	64.0	491
n-Tetradecane	93	151
n-Hexadecane (Cetane)	109	151
Diisobutene	-37e	139
Cyclohexane	5	4A,139,220
Methylcyclohexane	7	139,147,149,220,254, 392(p.116)
Benzene, Toluene, Xylenes	<25	147,165,392(p.116), 393(p.1075),418A
Naphthalene (m.p. 80)	<60	452
Methylnaphthalene	<20	147
Paraffin waxes	178,200	17,139,340,446(p.212)
Petroleum (b.p. 185-95)	50.5	220,392(p.116)
Kerosene	>25	165,340,392(p.116)
Paraffinic oil	201	139
Naphthenic oils	100 to 153	131,139,340
Acetanilide (m.p.114)	<45e	30,392(pp.601-2)
Aniline	<0	4A,393(p.1099)
Bromoform	<25	165
1-Bromonaphthalene	42.4	153,209,443,446(p.379)
Camphor (m.p. 176)	<25	166,392(p.678),426
Carbon disulfide	3.9	17,153,165,209,220,247, 254,341B,392(p.116), 446(p.396) 446B
Carbon tetrachloride	<25	165,393(p.839),418A
Cottonseed oil	>25	165,392(p.116)
Dimethylaniline	ca 0	489A,393(p.1076)
Glycerol	<25	393(p.1075),418A
N-Methylacetanilide (m.p. 101)	<0e	30,392(p.636)
Methylaniline	ca 0	489A,393(p.1076),152,153
Methylene iodide	45? 94.8	17,446(p.355)
Propionanilide (m.p. 104)	<45e	30,392(p.636)
Resorcinol (m.p.110)	<60	318,392(p.394)
Triethylamine	130	393(p.594),446(p.815), 460
Water	<-27	129
Thirteen fatty acids	<m.p.	345
Five nitriles	<m.p.	194
24 Vegetable oils	60 to 104	168,392(p.830)

TABLE I

15

	CST	References
89.9% ACETIC ACID (m.p.2.77)		
Benzene	-3.3	324
Toluene	23.6	324
m-Xylene	52.9	324
Bromobenzene	34.5	324
p-Bromotoluene	65.4	324
ACETIC ANHYDRIDE		
n-Hexane	59	139
n-Heptane	68	139,149
2,2,4-Trimethylpentane	66	4,139,149
n-Decane	85.5	149,223,253
1-Heptene	24	139
Diisobutene	27	139
Cyclohexane	52	4,139,140,149,223,253, 341B,445(p.415)
Methylcyclohexane	56	4,139,140,149,445(p.415)
Decalin (cis)	83	4,140,149
Decalin (trans)	81.1	4,140,149
m-Xylene	<0	147
sec-Butylbenzene	<-78	140
Diethylbenzene	-50	140
p-Cymene	-50	140
Methyldiethylbenzene	-27	140
Ethylisopropylbenzene	-35	140
sec-Amylbenzene	-25	140
Triethylbenzene	-12	140
Diisopropylbenzene	-23	140
Methyldiisopropylbenzene	-6	140
Di-sec-amylbenzene	44	140
Isopropylnaphthalene	<-78	140
sec-Amylnaphthalene	-39	140
Diisopropylnaphthalene	-13	140
Di-sec-amylnaphthalene	44	140
Isopropyltetralin	3	140,445(p.424)
Gasoline (n=1.406)	54	149,315,445(p.401),449A
Paraffin waxes	160	139,340
Paraffinic oil	172	139
Naphthenic oils	143	131,139,340
Kerosene	85.5	223
Carbon disulfide	29.83	153,174,223,255,341B, 392(p.222),445(p.933)
Glycerol	High	339A,393(p.1086)
Water (reacts)	>40	151
ACETOACETANILIDE (m.p. 85)		
n-Heptane	182E	149
Decalin	144	140,149
sec-Amylbenzene	77	140
Triethylbenzene	77	140
Diisopropylbenzene	108	140
Di-sec-amylbenzene	162	140
Diisopropylnaphthalene	68	140,445(p.649)
Di-sec-amylnaphthalene	148	140

	CST	References
ACETONE (Tables IV to VIII)		17,106,121,211,372
Isopentane	-160	149,373
n-Hexane	-39	139
n-Heptane	-27.6	149,484
n-Octane	-5.5	149,346
2,2,4-Trimethylpentane	-34	139
n-Decane	-6	147,151,445(p.401), 449A
2,7-Dimethyloctane	-3.8,18?	149,175,209,443
n-Dodecane	16.5	149,346
n-Tetradecane	16	151
n-Hexadecane (Cetane)	35.8	149,346
n-Heptadecane	38	149,346
n-Octadecane	37	151
n-Dotriacontane	>56	346
Diisobutene	-67e	139
Cyclohexane	-29e	139
Methylcyclohexane	-21	139,445(p.419)
m-Xylene	<0	147
Di-sec-butylbenzene	25.9	151
Paraffin waxes	65,>87	139,149,340
Paraffinic oils	77,>87	139,340
Naphthenic oils	52,>87	139,340
Other oils	16 to 53.5	131,149,326,461
Eleven fatty Acids	<m.p.	345
Five higher Alcohols	<m.p.	196A
Fourteen Amides	<m.p.	348
Fifteen Amines	<m.p.	196,296,347,349
Benzoic acid (m.p. 122)	<60	318,392(p.514)
Carbon disulfide -39.5 to -51.4		144,153,209,365,392 (pp.10,183),427,443,464
Catechol (m.p. 104)	<20	392(p.391),471
Six Di-n-alkylamines	<m.p.	196
Diethyldiphenylurea (m.p. 71)	<50	93
2,4-Dinitroanisole (m.p. 95)	<20	88,392(p.534)
m-Dinitrobenzene (m.p. 89)	<20	90
2,4-Dinitrochlorobenzene (m.p. 53)	<0	89,392(p.322)
2,4-Dinitrophenetole (m.p. 86)	<15	88,392(p.578)
2,4-Dinitrophenol (m.p. 113)	<51	92
2,6-Dinitrophenol (m.p. 63)	<16	92
2,4-Dinitrotoluene (m.p. 70)	<20	90
Diphenylamine (m.p. 53)	<0	94,392(p.703)
Eight higher Esters	<m.p.	390A
Ethylene glycol	<22	393(p.1082-3),453A
Glycerol	95.7	153,209(p.395),286, 328,330,341B,392, (p.180),446(p.484)
Four higher Haloalkanes	<m.p.	194A
n-Hexadecylamine	<36	349
Hydroquinone (m.p. 170.5)	<65	392(p.396),471
Five Nitriles	<m.p.	194
o-Nitroaniline (m.p. 71)	<25	69,392(p.402)
m-Nitroaniline (m.p. 112)	<75	69,392(p.403)
p-Nitroaniline (m.p. 147.5)	<70	Ibid.
o-Nitrobenzoic acid (m.p. 147)	<30	70,392(p.488)
m-Nitrobenzoic acid (m.p. 141)	<35	70,392(p.489)

	CST	References
ACETONE (continued)		
p-Nitrobenzoic acid (m.p.242)	<160	70,392(p.490)
o-Nitrobenzyl chloride (m.p. 49)	<30	285,392(p.500)
m-Nitrobenzyl chloride (m.p. 47)	<30	Ibid.
p-Nitrobenzyl chloride (m.p. 71)	<25	170,285,392(pp.499-500)
p-Nitrochlorobenzene (m.p. 83)	<17	89,392(p.345)
o-Nitrophenol (m.p. 45)	<0	55,392(pp.364-5)
m-Nitrophenol (m.p. 97)	<0	55,92,392(p.365)
p-Nitrophenol (m.p. 114)	<0	55,92,392(pp.364-5)
p-Nitrotoluene (m.p. 52)	<15	90,392(p.537)
n-Octadecylamine	88e	349
Perfluorodimethylcyclohexane	>27	389
Perfluoromethylcyclohexane	>27	389
Picric acid (m.p. 121.6) (2,4,6-Trinitrophenol)	<16	92,392(pp.334-5)
Quinine iodobismuthate LCST,	<9	337
Resorcinol (m.p. 110)	<10	392(p.394),471
Tri-n-dodecylamine	>56	347
Triisobutylamine	-11	445(p.964)
2,4,6-Trinitroanisole (m.p. 68.4)	<0	88
1,3,5-Trinitrobenzene (m.p. 61)	<35	90
2,4,6-Trinitrochlorobenzene (Picryl chloride, m.p. 83)	<10	89
2,4,6-Trinitrophenetole (m.p. 78.5)	<15	88
2,4,6-Trinitrophenol (m.p. 121.6)	<16	92,392(pp.334-5)
Trinitrophenylethylnitroamine (m.p. 95.7)	25	91
2,4,6-Trinitrotoluene (m.p. 81)	<20	432
Tri-n-octadecylamine	<50	347
Tri-n-octylamine	48	347
Tri-n-propylamine	-40	444,445(p.964)
Undecylbenzothiazole (m.p. 44)	<10	108A
ACETONE OXIME (m.p. 61)		
n-Heptane	5e	151
n-Hexadecane (Cetane)	35	149
ACETONITRILE		
Propane	67	151
n-Pentane	60	149
n-Hexane	77	149,256
n-Heptane	84.6	73,130,139,149,491
2,2,3-Trimethylbutane	73.5	149
n-Octane	91.5	73,256,491
2,2,4-Trimethylpentane	81	73,139,149,311
n-Nonane	100	491
n-Decane	107.5	491
n-Undecane	112.5	491
n-Tetradecane (Isopycnic at 70)		151
Propylene	-50	151
1-Heptene	38	149

		CST	References

ACETONITRILE (continued)

Cyclohexane

	CST	References
(Isopycnic about 30)	76.5	139,140,149,445(p.540)
Methylcyclohexane	78	130,139,140,149, 445(p.534)
Decalin	106	140,149,445(p.542)
Isopropylbenzene (Cumene)	<-78	140
sec-Butylbenzene	-50	140
Diethylbenzene	-60	140
p-Isopropyltoluene (Cymene)	-60	140
Methyldiethylbenzene	-23	140
Ethylisopropylbenzene	-30	140
sec-Amylbenzene	-5	140
Triethylbenzene	-7	140
Diisopropylbenzene	-15	140
Methyldiisopropylbenzene	2	140
Di-sec-butylbenzene	29	151
Octyltoluene	42	151
Di-sec-amylbenzene	67	140
Isopropylnaphthalene	-30	140
sec-Amylnaphthalene	4	140
Diisopropylnaphthalene	12	140
Di-sec-amylnaphthalene	67	140
Isopropyltetralin	14	140,445(p.542)
Pinene	66	151
Limonene (Dipentene)	30	151
Lubricating oils	82 to 128	131,149
Eleven fatty Acids	<m.p.	197
Fourteen Amides	<m.p.	348
Four primary Amines	<m.p.	349
Carbon disulfide	51.5	144,153,226,341B, 392(p.10),445(p.944)446B
Carbon tetrachloride		
(m.p. -23)	<-23	365
n-Decyl alcohol	22.7	146,152,196A
Deuterium oxide	5.1	392(p.85),451
Six Dialkylamines		
(see pp. 69,76-79)	High	196
n-Dodecyl alcohol	35.2	146,152,196A
Ethylene glycol (m.p. -12.6)	-13.5	146,152
Ethyl stearate	65.5	390A
Glycerol	90	146,153
16-Hentriacontanone	High	153,393(pp.805-6)
14-Heptacosanone	>82	153,158,393(p.804)
2-Heptadecylbenzothiazole	>80	108A
n-Hexadecyl alcohol	58	196A
n-Hexadecylamine (m.p. 46.77)	<42	349
Hydrogen cyanide	<25	148
1-Iodododecane	High	194A,445(p.741)
Linoleic acid	39.5	195,446(p.1007)
Methyl myristate	<11	390A
Methyl palmitate	31.0	390A
Methyl stearate	53.1	390A
Methyl esters of three other		
fatty acids	<m.p.	390A
Five higher Nitriles	<m.p.	194
p-Nitrobenzyl chloride	<25	170,285,392(p.499)
2-Nonadecanone (m.p. 55)	<45	197A
10-Nonadecanone (m.p. 58)	70	153,158,393(p.792)
n-Octadecyl alcohol (m.p. 58)	63	196A
n-Octadecylamine (m.p. 53.06)	76	349

TABLE I   **19**

	CST	References
ACETONITRILE (continued)		
Oleic acid	61	195
18-Pentatriacontanone	High	158,393(p.808)
Propylene glycol	<0	151
Tetrachloroethylene	13	73,153,256(p.678), 392(p.66)
n-Tetradecyl alcohol	48	196A
12-Tricosanone	>82	153,158,393(p.799)
2-Tridecanone	<13	197A
Trimethylene glycol	-6	151
2-Undecylbenzothiazole	79	108A,445(p.1087)
Water	-0.9	119,126,153,392(p.85), 451
Not miscible with Acetonitrile: Benzene sulfonic acid, Crotonic and Oleic acids, Castor oil, Pentaerithritol, Triethanolamine		457A
Miscible with Acetonitrile: 23 other liquids including acids, alcohols, aldehydes, amines, aromatics, esters, ketones, nitroparaffins, etc.		457A
ACETONYLACETONE (2,5-HEXANEDIONE)		
n-Hexane	59	139
n-Heptane	68	130,139,149
2,2,4-Trimethylpentane	72	139
1-Heptene	11	139
Diisobutene	31	139
Methylcyclohexane	39	130,140,149,445(p.419)
Decalin	60	140,149,445(p.422)
Di-sec-amylbenzene	21	140,149
Di-sec-amylnaphthalene	0	140,149
Petroleum ether (42-62°)	>b.p.	140,343
Petroleum ether (80-100°)	>b.p.	149,343
Ethylene glycol	>180.5	271
Water	<20	193A,296(p.43)
ACETOPHENONE (m.p. 19.7)(Table IV)		15,17
n-Butane	10.6	141,149
Isobutane	24.5	141,149
n-Hexane	3	139
n-Heptane	4	139,149
2,2,4-Trimethylpentane	14	139
n-Decane	10	17,149,445(p.401)
Diisobutene	-28e	139
Cyclohexane	-16e	139
Methylcyclohexane	-17e	139
Paraffin wax (m.p. 53)	51	139
Paraffinic oil	47	139
Naphthenic oils	13,17	131,139,149
Acetamide (m.p. 81)	<36.8	260,271,445(p.1021)
Benzoic acid	<80	318,392(p.514)
Ethylene glycol	114.5	256,268,271,392(p.157)
Glycerol	185.5	153,209,(p.396),286,328, 330,392(p.579)
Propionamide (m.p. 79)	<33	271,445(p.1021)
Urethane (m.p. 50)	<41.5	Ibid.
Water (Isopycnic at 96°)	220	17,140A

	CST	References
ACETYLACETONE (2,4-PENTANEDIONE)		
(Table V)		106
n-Heptane	-14e	151
Lubricating oils	31.6	131,149
Water	87.7	153,209(p.388),253,271, 330,362,365,486
ACETYL CHLORIDE		
n-Heptane	-36E	149
n-Octadecane (m.p. 28)	<19	151
Paraffinic oil	9	139(p.766),149
Water (reacts)	>25	151
ACETYLDIETHYLAMINE		
(DIETHYLACETAMIDE)		
n-Heptane	6.25	149,309
2,2-Dimethylpentane	1.1	309
2,4-Dimethylpentane	2.95	309
2,2,3-Trimethylbutane		
(Triptane)	-11.95	309
2,2,4-Trimethylpentane	46	149,311
ACETYLDIMETHYLAMINE		
(DIMETHYLACETAMIDE)		
n-Heptane	65	149
2,2-Dimethylpentane	68	151
2,2,3-Trimethylbutane		
(Triptane)	68	151
Di-sec-butylbenzene	<25	145
Water	<25	151
ACETYLPHENYLENE DIAMINES		
(see AMINOACETANILIDES, p.22)		
ACETYLSALICYLIC ACID (ASPIRIN)		
(m.p. 135)		15
Decalin	115	149
Paraffin wax (m.p. 53)	>300	149
Water	89m	136,153,209(p.392),253, 362,392(p.630)
ACETYL-p-TOLUIDE (m.p. 148.5)		15
Water	>117.6	339
Eleven organic solvents	<120	339
ACROLEIN		
n-Heptane	43	151
Methylcyclohexane	<25	145
Water	88	28,153,209(p.387),255, (p.469),392(p.165)
ACRYLONITRILE		
n-Heptane	28	151
2,2,3-Trimethylbutane		
(Triptane)	15	151
n-Hexadecane (Cetane)	76	151
Methylcyclohexane	<25	145
Water	>95	84,393(p.603)

TABLE I   **21**

	CST	References
ADIPIC ACID (m.p. 153)		
Cumene (Isopropylbenzene)	198	140,446(p.246)
Bibenzyl	<147	140,446(p.252)
Isopropylnaphthalene	184	140,446(p.257)
sec-Amylnaphthalene	237	140,446(p.257)
Diisopropylnaphthalene	253	140,446(p.257)
ADIPONITRILE (Tables V and VII)		106,121
n-Amylalcohol	39	151
n-Decyl alcohol	85	151
n-Dodecyl alcohol	>100	151
Ethylene glycol	27	146,152
Water	101	493
ALANINE (1-AMINOPROPIONIC ACID)		15
ALBUMIN (egg)		
Water	<25	86
o-ALDEHYDOBENZOIC ACID (m.p. 98)		
(PHTHALDEHYDEHYDIC ACID)		
Benzene	<m.p.	392(p.572),408
Water	45.7	153,209(p.391),255, 392(p.571),408
m-ALDEHYDOBENZOIC ACID (m.p. 175)		
Water	<115	392(p.571),408
p-ALDEHYDOBENZOIC ACID (m.p. 250)		
Water	<m.p.	408
ALDOL		15
n-Hexane	23	139
n-Heptane	36	139
2,2,4-Trimethylpentane	37	139
1-Heptene	-26	139
Diisobutene	-27	139
Cyclohexane	-2	139,145
Methylcyclohexane	+1	139,145
Decalin	>85	151
Paraffin wax (m.p. 53)	116e	139
Paraffinic oil	122e	139
Naphthenic oil	86	139
ALIZARIN		15
ALLYL ALCOHOL		15
2,2'-Dichloroethyl ether (Chlorex)	<-35	455
Two lubricating oils	86,91	131,149
ALLYL IODIDE		
Nitromethane	-50	271,445(p.795)
ALLYL ISOTHIOCYANATE		
Formic acid	39.8	153,209,226,260, 392(p.32)
Sulfur (m.p. 113)	124	1,153,209(p.394),253, 392(p.221),393(p.1066)

	CST	References
ALUMINUM BROMIDE (m.p. 97.5)		
Ammonium bromide	>98	210(p.45),230
Silver bromide (m.p. 434)	186	18,153,209,230
Sodium bromide (m.p. 755)	232	153,209(p.393),230
Stannous bromide (m.p. 215.5)	204.5	Ibid.
$BaBr_2$,$CaBr_2$,KBr,$PbBr_2$,HgBr,		
TlBr	>260	210(pp.51-59),230

ALUMINUM CHLORIDE (m.p. 190)

  NH_4Cl,$BaCl_2$,KCl,AgCl,NaCl,

$SnCl_2$,TlCl	>192	210(pp.45-62),230

o-AMINOACETANILIDE (m.p. 144.8)		
Benzene	-20.7e	209,392(p.609)
Water	<m.p.	392(p.608),411

m-AMINOACETANILIDE HYDROCHLORIDE
(m.p. 280)
In the references this was
called "monoacetyl-m-
phenylenediamine", but the
m.p. was 210°C too high.

		Cf. 140(p.1097)
Benzene	266	140,149,209,210(p.134), 392(p.609),411

p-AMINOACETANILIDE (m.p. 161)		
Benzene	188	140,149,392(p.609),411
sec-Butylbenzene	>210	140
Naphthalene	<140	140
1-Methylnaphthalene	165	140
Isopropylnaphthalene	220	140
Water	<m.p.	392(p.608),411

p-AMINOACETOPHENONE (m.p. 106)		
n-Heptane	221E	149
Methylethylbenzene	95	140
Ethylisopropylbenzene	121	140
sec-Amylbenzene	125	140
Triethylbenzene	117	140
Diisopropylbenzene	147	140
Di-sec-amylbenzene	196	140
Diisopropylnaphthalene	98	140
Di-sec-amylnaphthalene	162	140
Isopropyltetralin	102	140

1-AMINOANTHRAQUINONE		15

o-AMINOBENZOIC ACID (m.p. 147)
  (see ANTHRANILIC ACID, p.38)

m-AMINOBENZOIC ACID (m.p. 174)		
n-Heptane	320E	149
Benzene	100	149
Butyl alcohol	<143	259,392(p.541)
Chloroform	<155	Ibid.
Ethyl acetate	<145	Ibid.
Ethyl alcohol	<118	Ibid.
Methanol	<108	Ibid.
Water	66m	136,153,392(p.539)

	CST	References
p-AMINOBENZOIC ACID (m.p. 187)		15
Benzene	<162	259,392(p.541)
Butyl alcohol	<136	Ibid.
Chloroform	<163	Ibid.
Ethyl acetate	<145	Ibid.
Ethyl alcohol	<105	Ibid.
Methanol	<90	Ibid.
Water	47m	136,153,392(p.539)
p-AMINOBENZOPHENONE (m.p. 124)		
n-Heptane	212E	149
Di-sec-amylbenzene	177	140,149,153
Di-sec-amylnaphthalene	130	Ibid.
o-AMINOBIPHENYL (m.p. 49)		
n-Hexane	45	139
n-Heptane	43	139,149
2,2,4-Trimethylpentane	60	139
n-Octadecane	68.5	151
Diisobutene	3e	139
1-Octadecene	<35	151
Paraffin wax (m.p. 53)	88	139
Paraffinic oil	82	139
Naphthenic oil	28e	139
p-AMINOBIPHENYL (m.p. 53)		
n-Hexane	134	139
n-Heptane	125	139,149
2,2,4-Trimethylpentane	140	139
1-Heptene	70	139
Diisobutene	82	139
Cyclohexane	63	139
Methylcyclohexane	72	139
Paraffin wax (m.p. 53)	155	139
Paraffinic oil	142	139
Naphthenic oil	93	139
p-AMINODIETHYLANILINE		
n-Heptane	0E	149
2,2,4-Trimethylpentane	0-20	149,311
p-AMINODIMETHYLANILINE (m.p. 53)		
n-Heptane	>100	149
1-AMINOETHANOL (ALDEHYDE AMMONIA) (m.p. 97)		
n-Heptane	320E	149
Naphthalene (m.p. 80)	100	149
2-AMINOETHANOL (see ETHANOLAMINE, p. 80)		
p-AMINOETHYLACETANILIDE (m.p. 70)		
n-Heptane	189E	149
sec-Amylbenzene	82	140
Triethylbenzene	84	140
Diisopropylbenzene	100	140
Methyldiisopropylbenzene	113	140
Di-sec-amylbenzene	154	140

	CST	References
p-AMINOETHYLACETANILIDE (continued)		
Isopropylnaphthalene	<57	140
sec-Amylnaphthalene	<50	140
Diisopropylnaphthalene	60	140
Di-sec-amylnaphthalene	135	140
Isopropyltetralin	70	140
2 (2-AMINOETHYLAMINO)-ETHANOL		
All hydrocarbons	High	145
2-AMINO-2-METHYL-1-PROPANOL		
(Table V)		106
n-Heptane	89	149
p-Cymene	23	151
sec-Butylbenzene	32	151
Di-sec-butylbenzene	74	151

AMINOPHENOLS

Isomer	Ortho	Meta	Para	
Melting point	174	123	186	
n-Heptane	150E	230E	255E	149
Benzene	<156	123	<145	210(p.132),392 (p.421),407, 446(p.164)
Triphenylmethane			91	210(p.143),244
Di-sec-amylnaphthalene	115	195	220	140,149,446(p.195)
Lubricating oil	<170			131
Glycerol		<120	<185	153,328
Water	<129	1.9	<106	392(p.421),407

	CST	References
p-AMINOPHENYLACETIC ACID		
n-Heptane	100e	149
1-AMINO-2-PROPANOL (Table VIII)		
(ISOPROPANOLAMINE)		211
Water	<20	284
2-AMINOPROPANOL		
Water	<20	284
AMINOSULFONIC ACID		15
AMMONIA (critical temp. 132.4)		
(Table IV)		17
Propane	28.3	151,430
n-Butane (Iso-optic at 18)	41	143,430
Isobutane	39	143
n-Hexane	56	139
n-Heptane	63	130,139,149
2,2,4-Trimethylpentane	61	139
Paraffins C_6 to C_{12}	60 to 80	149,276
Propylene	-5.5,11	151,430
1-Butene	+5,20	338A,430
Isobutene	6	430
2-Pentene	24.4	430
2-Methyl-2-butene	23	430
Diisobutene	46	139
1,3-Butadiene	-30	430
Cyclohexane	59	139,140
Methylcyclohexane	63	130,139,140

TABLE I **25**

	CST	References
AMMONIA (continued)		
Benzene	<-21	85,140
Toluene	-7	140,430
m-Xylene	14.7	140,149,209,242,276
o-and p-Xylene	<15	149,276
Ethylbenzene	<15	149,276
Isopropylbenzene (Cumene)	<25	140
p-Isopropyltoluene (Cymene)	<25	140
sec-Butylbenzene	31	151
Di-sec-Butylbenzene	73	151
Styrene (Phenyl ethylene)	-15.5	151
1-Methylnaphthalene	28	140
Paraffin wax (m.p. 53)	None	139
Two lubricating oils (no complete mixing below critical temp., 132.4)	None	139
Ammonium bicarbonate (m.p. 107)	118.5	213
Benzaldehyde	<25	85
Lithium (m.p. 186)	-35	167,367
Sodium (m.p. 97.5)	-41.6	2,153,167,209,241, 367,391(p.1146)
Water	<-30	368A,391(p.1032)
Miscibilities with 900 substances		15,85,153B
(Some of these solubilities are excessively low, perhaps because of water in the ammonia)		

AMMONIUM HALIDES
(see ALUMINUM HALIDES, p.22)

AMYL ACETATE (Table VII)		121
n-Heptane	<0	149
Paraffin wax (m.p. 50)	<51	340
Three lubricating oils	<10	131,149,340
ISOAMYL ACETATE (Table VIII)		211
Lubricating oils	<0	131,149,340
Ethylene glycol	26	271
n-AMYL ALCOHOL (Table VI)		372
Ethane (crit. temp., upper layer, 43.15)		250,446(p.2)
Paraffin wax (m.p. 50)	<50	340
Three lubricating oils	<10	131,149,340
Adiponitrile	39	151
2,2'-Dichloroethyl ether (Chlorex)	-14.7	446(p.417),455,455A, 456
1,1'-Dichloromethyl ether (M-Chlorex)	-41.2	455A
3,3'-Dichloro-n-propyl ether (P-Chlorex)	-71.0	455B
Glycerol	61.1	341B,446(p.1128)
Nitromethane	21	151
Trimethylamine	<25	170
Water	182	1,118,152,176,444

	CST	References
sec-AMYL ALCOHOL (2-PENTANOL)		
(see also DIETHYL CARBINOL		
p. 70 and METHYL ISOPROPYL		
CARBINOL, p. 122)		
Paraffin wax (m.p. 50)	<39	340
Paraffinic oils	-5	139(p.766),341
Water	>92.6	271
tert-AMYL ALCOHOL		15
Paraffinic oil	-10	139(p.766),145
2,2'-Dichloroethyl ether		
(Chlorex)	-16.9	446(p.417),455
Nitromethane	3	153,256(p.680),260,266, 268,271,392(p.36)
Water	>30	392(p.316)
ISOAMYL ALCOHOL (see p. 109)		
(Tables IV, V)		15,17,106
ISOAMYLAMINE		
Paraffinic oil	-6	139(p.766)
AMYL CHLORIDE		
Paraffin wax	<33	341
Two lubricating oils	<10	341
n-AMYL CYANIDE (Table VIII)		121
n-AMYL ETHER		
Urethane (Ethyl carbamate	<48	271
(m.p. 50)		
n-AMYL FORMATE		15
n-AMYL FUROATE		
n-Hexane	-36	139
n-Heptane	-32	139,149
2,2,4-Trimethylpentane	-28	139
Diisobutene	-82e	139
Cyclohexane	-56e	139
Methylcyclohexane	-70	139
Paraffin wax (m.p. 53)	51	139
Paraffinic oil	50	139
Naphthenic oil	9	139
AMYL MALONIC ACID		
Water	<25	392(p.618),462
ISOAMYL NITRITE		
Paraffinic oil	<0	139,149
AMYL OLEATE		
Propane (no lower phase		
point)	Mixed	149,191
tert-AMYLPHENOL (m.p. 92)		
Paraffinic oil	<90	139,149

TABLE I   **27**

	CST	References

n-AMYL PHTHALATE (Table III)
  Propane (lower phase point,
  105)   149,192

ISOAMYL PHTHALATE
  Propane (lower phase point,
  105)   192
  2,2,4-Trimethylpentane   <-40   149
  Decalin   <-35   149

AMYL STEARATE (Table III)
  Ethane (lower phase point,
  19)   149,191

ANETHOLE (m.p. 22)   15
  n-Heptane   <20   151
  Lubricating oil   <0   131
  Acetamide   143.5 271,445(p.996)
  Diethylene glycol   108   271

ANHYDROFORMALDEHYDEANILINE
(m.p. 141)   15

ANILINE (m.p. -6.2)
(Tables II, IV, V, VII)   12,17,100,106,121,211,
382,383
Since ref. 12 and 100
apply to 80% of the
aniline points, they are
usually omitted below.
  Methane (crit. temp.-82.5) None 138
  Ethane (crit. temp. 32) None 138
  Propane (crit. temp. 96) None 138
  n-Butane   84.1 138,141,188,209,276,282,
443,445(p.516),449A,485
  Isobutane   109   138,141,282,445(p.517),
485
  n-Pentane   71.7 31,48A,59,63,97,122,141,
159,188,203,209,253,276,
282,392(p.418),403,404,
440,442,445(p.517),480,
485
  Isopentane (2-Methylbutane) 78.9 31,48A,59,63,122,124,
141,159,203,209,253,282,
392(p.418),442,445
(p.517),449,480,485
  Neopentane   102E 12A,85,138,141
    (2,2-Dimethylpropane)
  n-Hexane   69.1 17,31,39,55,59,63,83,
87,97,104,114,122,139,
159,188,203,204,209,232,
246A,238,276,282,290,
293,310,320,321,370,371,
392(pp.417-8,457),403,
404,435,440,442,445
(p.517),480,485
  2-Methylpentane   73.9 59,63,114,159,188,203,
209,253,276,282,290,293,
310,392(p.418),435,442,
454,480,485

	CST	References
ANILINE (continued)		
3-Methylpentane	69.3	59,114,188,203,290,293, 310,392(p.418),435,442, 480,485
2,2-Dimethylbutane	81.0	59,114,188,203,290,293, 310,392(p.418),435,445 (p.524),480,485
2,3-Dimethylbutane	71.9	59,114,188,203,290,293, 310,442,454,480,485
n-Heptane (Figure 1)	70.1	31,39,42,53,54,63,97, 114,122,130,139,159, 165,180,188,203,204, 209,246B,253,276,282, 309,323,358,370,371, 376,392(p.418),403,404, 440,442,445(p.525),480, 485
2-Methylhexane	73.6·	39,44,63,97,114,122, 159,188,203,209,253, 276,282,309,375,392 (p.418),442,445(p.526), 480,485
3-Methylhexane	70.6	114,122,159,163,188,203, 392(p.418),442
2,2-Dimethylpentane	78.05	114,122,163,188,203,309, 392(p.418),442,445(p.526) 480
2,3-Dimethylpentane	67.95	114,122,159,163,188,203, 309,392(p.418),442,445 (p.526),480
2,4-Dimethylpentane	78.4	114,122,188,203,309,392 (p.418),442,445(p.526), 480
3,3-Dimethylpentane	70.3	114,122,163,188,203,392 (p.418),442,445(p.526), 480
3-Ethylpentane	66.3	114,124,188,203,392 (p.418)
2,2,3-Trimethylbutane (Triptane)	72.0	114,122,163,188,203,309, 442,445(p.526),480,485
n-Octane	72.0	31,54,63,64,97,114,122, 124,159,188,203,209,253, 276,282,291,293,321, 341B,370,371,392(p.418), 403,404,442,445(p.526), 480,485
2-Methylheptane	74.5	63,97,114,203,209,253, 276,282,291,293, 393(p.418),445(p.527)
3-Methylheptane	72.2	291,293,442,445(p.526), 480
4-Methylheptane	71.6	12A,138,291,293, 445(p.526)
2,2-Dimethylhexane	78E	138,292,445(p.526)
2,3-Dimethylhexane	70.6	200,291,293,442,445 (p.526),480
2,4-Dimethylhexane	76.0	138,291,293,445(p.526)
2,5-Dimethylhexane	77.8	97,200,291,293, 392(p.418,442,445(p.526) 447,480,485

TABLE I 29

	CST	References
ANILINE (continued)		
3,3-Dimethylhexane	72E	12A,138
3,4-Dimethylhexane	68.2	291,293,442,445(p.526), 480
3-Ethylhexane	72E	12A,138,291,293, 445(p.526)
2,2,3-Trimethylpentane	70.7	200,292,442,445(p.526), 480
2,2,4-Trimethylpentane (Isooctane)	80.0	12A,31,87,122,123,139, 200,203,204,292,321,442, 445(p.528),480,485
2,3,3-Trimethylpentane	67.0	200
2,3,4-Trimethylpentane	68.7	200,292,445(p.526)
2-Methyl-3-ethylpentane	67.2	291,293,445(p.526)
3-Methyl-3-ethylpentane	65.9	445(p.526),480
2,2,3,3-Tetramethylbutane (m.p. 102)	<80	138,292,445(p.526)
n-Nonane	74.5	9,53,54,122,159,188, 203,276,282,293,370,371, 392(p.418),403,404,440, 442,445(p.528),480,485
2-Methyloctane	77.5	97,100,282,476,478
3-Methyloctane	75.0	476
4-Methyloctane	74.5	476
2,2-Dimethylheptane	79E	12A,138
2,3-Dimethylheptane	73.2	138,477
2,4-Dimethylheptane	77E	12A,138
2,5-Dimethylheptane	77E	12A,138
2,6-Dimethylheptane	80.0	138,442,479,480
3,3-Dimethylheptane	75E	12A,138
3,4-Dimethylheptane	70E	138
3-Ethylheptane	73E	138
4-Ethylheptane	73E	138
2,2,3-Trimethylhexane	72E	138
2,2,4-Trimethylhexane	78E	138
2,2,5-Trimethylhexane	82.7	138
2,3,5-Trimethylhexane	76E	138
2,2,3,3-Tetramethylpentane	68E	138
2,2,4,4-Tetramethylpentane	75E	138
2,3-Dimethyl-3-ethylpentane	66E	138
3,3-Diethylpentane	65E	138
n-Decane	77.5	9,43,49,54,122,156,159, 188,203,276,282,293,321, 361,370,371,392(p.418), 403,404,442
2-Methylnonane	80.3	49,282,442,445(p.529)
3-Methylnonane	78.3	Ibid.
4-Methylnonane	78.3	Ibid.
5-Methylnonane	77.9	Ibid.
2,2-Dimethyloctane	81E	138
2,3-Dimethyloctane	75E	138
2,4-Dimethyloctane	78E	138
2,5-Dimethyloctane	77E	138
2,6-Dimethyloctane	78E	138
2,7-Dimethyloctane	79	31,39,54,97,122,138,159, 209,293,321,341B,370,403, 440,443,445(p.529)

	CST	References
ANILINE (continued)		
3,3-Dimethyloctane	75E	138
3,4-Dimethyloctane	73E	138
3,6-Dimethyloctane	76E	138
4,5-Dimethyloctane	74E	138
3-Ethyloctane	75E	138
4-n-Propylheptane	76E	138
2,2,3-Trimethylheptane	74E	138
2,2,6-Trimethylheptane	81E	138
2,4,6-Trimethylheptane	82E	138
3,3,5-Trimethylheptane	70E	138
3-Methyl-3-ethylheptane	73E	138
3,3-Diethylhexane	69E	138
3,4-Diethylhexane	73E	138
2,2,3,4-Tetramethylhexane	70E	138
2,2,5,5-Tetramethylhexane	83E	138
3,3,4,4-Tetramethylhexane	64E	138
n-Undecane	80.6	9,53,54,122,159,188,203, 276,282,293,370,371,379, 392(p.418),403,404,440, 442
n-Dodecane*	83.7	9,54,97,122,271,276,282, 293,370,371,392(p.418), 403,404,440,442
2-Methylundecane	82.3	97
n-Tridecane*	87	12A,54,282,370,371,379, 440
n-Tetradecane*	89.5	9,53,54,97,159,271,276, 282,289,293,321,370, 371,379,440
2,7-Dimethyl-4,5-diethyl-octane	83	336
n-Pentadecane*	92	12A,53,54,159,282,289, 370,371,379,440
n-Hexadecane* (Cetane)	95	54,97,122,159,282,370, 371,440,465,474,485
n-Heptadecane*	98	12A,53,54,156,389,379, 440
n-Octadecane*	100	54,440
7,8-Diethyltetradecane	93.8	333A,336
8-Propylpentadecane	94.8	333A,336
5,6-Dibutyldecane	94.8	333A,336
n-Nonadecane	108	54,440
n-Eicosane*	100.1	54,289,440
n-Heneicosane	107.3	53,289,295,440
n-Docosane	114	53,54,289,336,440
2,9-Dimethyl-5,6-diiso-amyldecane (Tetraiso-amylethane)	101.8	336
n-Tricosane	111.4	289,295,440
n-Tetracosane*	116	53,54,295,379,440
Paraffin wax (m.p. 53)	113	17,139,445(p.529)
n-Pentacosane	116E	289,440
n-Hexacosane*	116	53,54,156
n-Heptacosane	120E	289,440
n-Octacosane*	124	53,54,156,289,440
n-Nonacosane	122.0	289,440

(*) See also Table II (p. 189)

TABLE I   31

	CST	References
ANILINE (continued)		
n-Triacontane	126.8	54,440
n-Hentriacontane	117.2?126E	53,293,295,440
n-Dotriacontane*	127.6	53,54,156,234,289,440
11-Decyldocosane*	123	53,234
n-Tritriacontane	129E	156,234,289,440
n-Tetratriacontane	128.8	289,295
n-Pentatriacontane	130.4	289,295
n-Tetracontane	138E	54
n-Pentacontane	148E	54
n-Hexatriacontane*	132.8	289,474
A C_{43} paraffin	130.7	295
A C_{57} paraffin (m.p. 5)	154	53,54,295
n-Hexacontane	168E	54,156
A C_{73} paraffin (probably branched)	156	463,465

C_7 to C_{44} n-paraffins,
CST (estd.) $= 46 + 3.5n -0.03n^2$ Cf. 12A,138,289,440
Other paraffins (see Table II)   382,383

Propylene	47	149
Isobutene	15.8	282,445(p.530)
1-Pentene	19.3	122,124,161,178,209,239, 253,370,443,449,483
Amylene	0.7	31,321,445(p.530),464
2-Pentene (cis and trans)	18.3	122,124,239
2-Methyl-2-butene	11.0	31,122,124,159,203,204, 239,392(p.298), 445(p.531)
1-Hexene	22.9	122,124,159,161,203,321, 483
2-Hexene	26.0	122,124,159,203,370
3-Hexene	27.0	278A
4-Methyl-1-pentene	>20	321
2-Methyl-2-pentene	24.0	31,122,159,203
4-Methyl-2-pentene	41	321,445(p.531)
2,3-Dimethyl-1-butene	25	321,445(p.531)
2,3-Dimethyl-2-butene	12	321,445(p.531)
Hexene (b.p. 62)	16.4	31,159,203,445(p.531)
Isohexene (b.p. 66)	24	159
1-Heptene	26.6	122,124,139,161,321,483
2-Heptene	28	124,159,203,321, 445(p.531)
3-Heptene	39	278A,321,445(p.531)
4-Methyl-1-hexene	>25	321
5-Methyl-1-hexene	32	159,321,445(p.531)
3-Methyl-3-hexene (Ref. gives -40)	40	204
2,4-Dimethyl-2-pentene	>20	321
2,3,3-Trimethyl-1-butene	35.2	61A,442
1-Octene	32.8	9,122,161,483
2-Octene (cis)	33.5	12A,124,159,161,203, 278A,293,321,445(p.532)
2-Octene (trans)	36.2E	12A

(*) See also Table II (pp.189,192)

	CST	References
ANILINE (continued)		
4-Methyl-2-heptene	42	321,445(p.532)
2,4,4-Trimethyl-2-pentene	32.2	124,203
Diisobutene	42.5	12A,122,139,149,204,321
1-Nonene	38.4	9,122,124,161,293,321,
		445(p.532),483
4-Nonene	45	321,445(p.532)
4-Methyl-2-octene	50	321,445(p.532)
4,5-Dimethyl-2-heptene	52	321,445(p.532)
4,6-Dimethyl-2-heptene	55	321,445(p.532)
4,5,5-Trimethyl-2-hexene	52	321,445(p.532)
1-Decene	48	9,293,321,445(p.532)
1-Dodecene*	54.9	9,293
4-Butyl-2-octene	65	321,445(p.532)
1-Tetradecene*	60.2	9,293,321
1-Hexadecene* (Cetene)	69.4	9,124,159,203,293,321
8-Propylpentadecene	83.8	336
Other olefins (see Table II)		382,383
1,3-Pentadiene	<-10	321
1,5-Hexadiene	<-10	321
2,4-Heptadiene	<-10	321
2,4-Octadiene	-11	321,445(p.532)
4-Methyl-1,5-heptadiene	12	321,445(p.532)
5,5-Dimethyl-2,3-hexadiene	-14	321,445(p.532)
4,5-Dimethyl-2,6-octadiene	31	321,445(p.532)
4-Propyl-1,5-heptadiene	30	321,445(p.532)
1,10-Undecadiene	23.6	9,149,321
4-Butyl-1,5-heptadiene	32	321,445(p.532)
4,5-Dibutyl-2,6-octadiene	65	321,445(p.532)
1-Methyl-2-propylcyclopropane	48.5	277
Ethylcyclobutane	38.7	442,445(p.533),480
Cyclopentane	17.7	61,63,78,122,123,160,203,
		209,242,253,341B,344,355,
		361,370,392(p.418),435,
		442,445(p.533),449,450,
		480
Methylcyclopentane	34.4	41,61,63,64,83,122,123,
		152,159,160,180,203,209,
		253,276,333,341B,392
		(p.418),435,445(p.533),
		442,480
1,2-Dimethylcyclopentane		
(cis)	39.6	60,62,63,67,159,209,
		253,442
1,2-Dimethylcyclopentane		
(trans)	47.0	60,63,67,163,209,442
1,3-Dimethylcyclopentane	48.8	58,61,63,122,123,159,160,
(inac.)		203,253
1,3-Dimethylcyclopentane	49.9	
(trans)		163,442
Dimethylcyclopentane	45	63,370,392(p.418)
Ethylcyclopentane	38.7	61,122,123,159,160,203,
		392(p.418),435,445(p.533)
1,2,3-Trimethylcyclopentane	41.0	159,203

(*) See also Table II (p. 189)

TABLE I 33

	CST	References

ANILINE (continued)
1-Methyl-3-ethylcyclopentane

	CST	References
(cis)	47.5	65
(trans)	52.2	65
n-Propylcyclopentane	45.0	12A,61,122,123,159,160, 203,212,392(p.418),435, 445(p.533)

1-Methyl-2-propylcyclopentane

	CST	References
(cis)	52.5	66,67
(trans)	58.0	66,67
1,2-Diethylcyclopentane (cis)	50.9	65

1,2-Diethylcyclopentane

	CST	References
(trans)	56.6	65
n-Butylcyclopentane	50.5	61,122,123,124,159, 160,203,392(p.418),435, 445(p.533)
1-Methyl-3-butylcyclopentane	62.6	62,149

C_{11} to C_{37} n-Alkylcyclopentanes
CST (estd.)=$10+5.\ln -0.05n^2$ Cf. 12A,289

	CST	References
Cyclohexane	29.5	4A,5,6,40,41,46,47,61, 63,64,78,87,122,123,124, 139,140,152,159,160,203, 204,238,246A,253,276, 314,315,316,321,323,344, 355,362A,363,370,371,376, 384,392(pp.418,433),435, 442,443,445(pp.536-8), 448,449,449A,450,464, 480
Methylcyclohexane	41.0	4,12A,61,63,64,87,102, 122,123,124,130,139,140, 159,160,180,203,204,209, 276,321,333,371,376,392 (p.418),435,442,443, 445(p.541),450,480
1,1-Dimethylcyclohexane	45.4	61,63,122,149,209,253, 308,392(p.418),442
1,2-Dimethylcyclohexane (cis)	41.7	61,62,64,112,122,159, 160,203,209,442
1,2-Dimethylcyclohexane(trans)	48.3	308,442
1,3-Dimethylcyclohexane (cis)	46.3	61,62,64,112,122,123, 159,160,203,308,370,371, 442
1,3-Dimethylcyclohexane(trans)	51.7	112,122,308,442
1,4-Dimethylcyclohexane (cis)	46.9	61,62,64,122,123,159, 160,203,308,370,371, 442,445(p.542)
1,4-Dimethylcyclohexane(trans)	52.7	112,122,308,442
Ethylcyclohexane	44.1	123,160,276,360
1,2,3-Trimethylcyclohexane	53.6	122,203
1,2,4-Trimethylcyclohexane	59.0	159,203,281,371,442, 445(p.542),477
("Nonanaphthene")	56	276,477
1,3,5-Trimethylcyclohexane	56.9	102,122,149,276
n-Propylcyclohexane	49.8	112,122,123,160,442

	CST	References
ANILINE (continued)		
Isopropylcyclohexane	48.9	442,445(p.542),480
1-Methyl-2-n-propylcyclo-hexane	53.6	111,281,445(p.542)
1-Methyl-4-n-propylcyclo-hexane	57.95	Ibid.
1-Methyl-4-isopropylcyclo-hexane	56.5	159,203
n-Butylcyclohexane	54.7	111,122,123,124,160,281,445(p.542)
Isobutylcyclohexane	57.4	100
tert-Butylcyclohexane	53.6	100
1,1,3,5-Tetramethylcyclohexane	64.4E	371
1,2,4,5-Tetramethylcyclohexane	58.8	112
n-Amylcyclohexane	60.7	111,281,445(p.545)
Isoamylcyclohexane	61.6	111,281,445(p.542)
Pentamethylcyclohexane	57.75	112
Hexylcyclohexane	63E	289
Hexamethylcyclohexane	65.5	102,112,122,124
1-Cyclohexyloctane*	74.7	63,111,445(p.542),474

C_{12} to C_{37} n-Alkylcyclohexanes
   CST (estd.) = 10 = 5.1n -0.05n^2

	CST	References
Hexaethylcyclohexane	80.3	235
Tetraisopropylcyclohexane	82.2	235
n-Hexadecylcyclohexane	101.2	257
2-Methyl-2-cyclohexyl pentadecane	94.5	335
n-Octadecylcyclohexane	106.2	257,474
5-Cyclohexyldocosane	105.0	307
5-Cyclohexylhexacosane	111.7	307
2-Dodecyl-p-menthane	100.7	289,322,465
2-(2-Isoamylisoheptyl)-p-menthene	99.2	Ibid.
Octahydroindene	32.2	111,149
Bicyclopentyl*	35.8	122,123,164
cis-Decalin*	33.1	4,12A,122,123,124,140,159,203,271,281,321,371,445(p.542)
trans-Decalin*	36.1	4,12A,140,271
Pinene	10	151
d-α-Pinene	<0	321
l-α-Pinene	<20	321
d-Limonene	<-15	31,321
Camphene (m.p. 50)	<30	149,260,271
p-Menthane	>35	321
Cyclohexylcyclopentane	42.5	124
Bicyclohexyl*	145?47.7	12A,122,123,124,149,159,203,228,271
(The entry in ref.445(p.542) misquoted ref.139 or 140, which did not mention this hydrocarbon.)		
1,2-Dicarvacrylethane	-28.5	322
Dicyclohexylmethane	66.6	100

(*) See also Table II(pp.199,200,205)

TABLE I   35

	CST	References

ANILINE (continued)
1,2-Dicyclohexylethane	61.0	122,123,289
Methylcyclohexylcyclohexane	54E	159,203
n-Propyldecalin	55.2	334
n-Butyldecalin	55.5	333A,334
sec-Butyldecalin	60.1	334
tert-Butyldecalin	26.5?	334
2-n-Octyldecalin	16.7?	334
1-Dodecyldecalin	89.0	289,322,465
5-Decalyldodecane	111.0	307,322
1,2-Di-(-p-menthyl)-ethane	90.6	289,322,465
1,3-Dicyclopentylcyclopentane	54.9	149,164
3,3'-Dicyclopentylbicyclo-		
pentyl	67.8	149,164
1-(2-p-Menthyl)-1-		
decalylethane	86.7	281,322,465

C_{20} to C_{40} Alkyldecalins
CST (estd.) = $9.6 + 4.6n - 0.04n^2$

Cyclopentene	<-10	122,124,160,448
Cyclohexene	<-20	64,122,159,203,321
Methylcyclopentene	-7.0	122,124,160
Ethylcyclopentene	1.2	122,124,160
1-Methylcyclohexene	<20	321
n-Propylcyclopentene	14.2	122,124,149,160,474
3-Cyclohexyl-1-propene	9	124,149,321
n-Butylcyclopentene	25.0	122,149,160
1-Limonene (Dipentene)	<-15	31,100
1-Cyclopentyl-2-cyclopentene	8.6	149,164
4-Cyclohexyl-2-pentene	37	321
4-Cyclohexyl-2-heptene	44	149,321
3-(Cyclopentene-2-yl) bicyclo-		
pentyl	21.5	149,164
1,3-Dicyclopentylcyclopentene-1	37.5	149,164
Other naphthenes (see Table II)		382,383

Toluene	-95e	162
21 Alkylbenzenes up to C_{14}	<-17	12,31,100,124,149,160, 227,228,257,334,440, 441
n-Octylbenzene	<-5	474
Di-sec-butylbenzene	-6	151
1-Phenylnonane	-12.3	42,227,228
2-Phenylnonane	-10.1	227,440,441
2-Phenyldecane	-0.6	440,441
Diamylbenzene	16.5	42,440
Di-sec-amylbenzene	12	140
2-Phenylundecane	8.1	440,441
1-Phenyldodecane	13.7	149,227,228,289
1,2,4,5-Tetraisopropylbenzene	<76.2	100,235
(m.p. 117.5)		
Hexaethylbenzene (m.p. 127.4)	<95.4	100,235
1-Phenyltetradecane	27.3	227,228,417,440
Diheptylbenzene	41.2	440
1-Phenylhexadecane	40.4	257,289
2-Phenylhexadecane	41.1	440,441
1-Methyl-4-isopropyl-2-		
dodecylbenzene	43.2	289,322

	CST	References
ANILINE (continued)		
1-Phenyloctadecane (m.p. 36)	48.5	257,307,322,474
1-Phenyldocosane	66.0	307
5-Phenyldocosane	58.9	307

C_{20} to C_{56} n-Alkylbenzenes
  CST (estd.) = $-82 + 6.3n - 0.04n^2$

	CST	References
o-Dioctadecylbenzene	111.1	307
o-Di (5-docosyl) benzene		
(m.p. 65)	<65	307
Trioctadecylbenzene	131.1	307
o-Di (5-octadecyl) benzene		
(m.p. 64)	<m.p.	307
5-Phenyl-5-docosane	43.1	307
1-(1-Butyloctadecyl)-2-(1-Butyl-		
octadecene-1-yl)-benzene	113.9	307
4-Dodecylbiphenyl (m.p. 82)	<m.p.	307
4-Octadecylbiphenyl (m.p. 77)	<m.p.	307
1,1-Diphenyloctadecane	3.3	307
5,14-Diphenyloctadecane	6.9	307
1,1-Diphenyl-1-octadecene	9.4	149,307
5-Docosen-6-yl-4-biphenyl	37.2	307
5-Hexacosen-5-yl-5-biphenyl	52.0	307
4-Octadecylbiphenyl (m.p. 78)	<78	307
4-Docosylbiphenyl (m.p. 83)	<83	307
Higher alkylbenzenes (see Table II)		
Tetralin	<-20	149,159
Ethyl-,Propyl-,and four Butyl-		
tetralins	<0	149,159,334
Octyltetralin	10.8	149,334
n-Octadecyl-2-tetralin	60	257,289,307
1-Docosyl-2-tetralin	75	289,307
5-Docosyl-2-tetralin	73.9	307
5-Hexacosyl-2-tetralin	84.5	307
5-Hexacosen-5-yl-2-tetralin	77.0	307

C_{26} to C_{36} n-Alkyltetralins
  CST (estd.) = $4n - 55$

	CST	References
n-Butylnaphthalene	<0	307,322,333A,334
tert-Butylnaphthalene	<0	307,322,334
n-Hexylnaphthalene	<0	Ibid.
n-Heptylnaphthalene	<0	Ibid.
n-Octylnaphthalene	<0	307,322,333A,334
Di-sec-Amylnaphthalene	12	140
2,3-Dihexylnaphthalene	-3.3	149,307,322
1-Octadecylnaphthalene	40.8	257
2-Octadecylnaphthalene	36.1	289,307
2-(1-Docosyl)naphthalene	<57	307
2-(5-Docosyl)naphthalene	45.6	307
2-(5-Docosen-5-yl)-naphthalene	33.3	307
1-(2-Naphthyl)-1-phenyl-1-		
octadecene	-1.1	149,307
n-Pentacosylnaphthalene	60E	289
n-Hexacosylnaphthalene	64E	289
2-(5-Hexacosyl)naphthalene	68.0	307
3-(4-Butyldocosyl)-2-naphthalene	60.0	307

TABLE I 37

	CST	References

ANILINE (continued)
  3-(4-Butyldocosen-3-yl)-2-
    naphthalene .... 55.0 — 307
  5-Hexacosen-5-yl-2-naphthalene ...... 60.5 — 307
  Heptacosylnaphthalene .... 67E — 289
  $\underline{n}$-Octacosylnaphthalene .... 71E — 289
  5-Butyltetrascosyl-2-
    naphthalene .... 68.0 — 307
  $\underline{n}$-Nonacosylnaphthalene .... 75E — 289

  C_{22} to C_{39} $\underline{n}$-Alkylnaphthalenes
    CST (estd.)
    $= -191 + 10.7n - 0.1n^2$

  1-Heptyne .... <20 — 321
  1-Octyne .... <-10 — 321
  4-Nonyne .... <35 — 321
  Hexadecyne .... 2 — 321,445(p.532)

  Other high hydrocarbons (Table II) — 382,383
  Petroleum ether .... 46 — 279,323
  Turpentine .... <17 — 149,279,362A,445
                                              (p.544),463A
  Rosin spirit .... 10 — 279
  Paraffinic oil .... 115 — 139
  Three naphthenic oils .... 75 to 89 — 131,139,465

  Acetic and Butyric acids .... <0 — 4A,393(p.1099)
  $\underline{p}$-Dibromobenzene (m.p. 86.9) ...... <50 — 318,392(p.341)
  $\underline{p}$-Dichlorobenzene (m.p. 53) .... <45.5 — 255,270,271,392(p.342)
  Glycerol .... <0 — 153,328
  Hexachloroethane (m.p. 187) .... <101 — 260,271
  Hydrogen chloride LCST,10.5 — 210(p.186),275
  Hydrogen cyanide .... <25 — 148
  1-Iodododecane .... <-5 — 194A,445(p.741)

  Nitrochlorobenzenes .... <30 — 242A,392(p.346)
  Palmitic acid .... <45 — 342
  Phosphorus (yellow) .... 260 — 17
  Propionic acid .... <0 — 4A,393(p.1099)
  Sulfur (m.p. 113) .... 138 — 1,153,182,188,
                                              209(p.394),212,253,
                                              330,392(p.417),486

  Tri-$\underline{n}$-butylamine .... 43 — 151
  2,4,6-Trinitrotoluene (m.p. 81) .... <80 — 432
  Water (Isopycnic at 77) .... 167 — 1,27,46,140A,153,
                                              209(pp.389,393),253,
                                              303,315,330,387B,
                                              392(p.406),412,443,
                                              486

ANILINE BLUE — 15

ANILINE PHENOLATE (PHENYLAMMONIUM
  PHENOLATE)
  Water .... 140 — 1,153,209,389,
                                              392(pp.415,708)

	CST	References
ANISALDEHYDE (Table VIII)		211
n-Heptane	80E	149
2,2,4-Trimethylpentane	87	149,311
Petroleum ether (42–62°)	>b.p.	149,343
Petroleum ether (80–100°)	55	149,343
Lubricating oil	91.2	131,149
ANISIC ACID (m.p. 184.2)		
Ethyl alcohol	<8	392(p.591),452
Methanol	<0	Ibid.
Propyl alcohol	<30	Ibid.
Water	138.2m	136,153,209(p.392), 253,392(p.591)
o-ANISIDINE		
n-Heptane	70E	149
2,2,4-Trimethylpentane	77	1,3,4,149,393(p.1102)
Cyclohexane	31.4	Ibid.
Methylcyclohexane	36.5	Ibid.
cis-Decalin	27.7	Ibid.
trans-Decalin	28.9	Ibid.
Lubricating oil	69.5	151
Nine aromatic hydrocarbons	<20	393(pp.1100–1103)
Glycerol	145	153,209(p.396),328, 392(p.560),399
p-ANISIDINE (m.p. 58)		
n-Heptane	130E	149
cis-Decalin	87	4,149
trans-Decalin	89.2	4,149
Glycerol	<57.1	153,328
ANISOLE		
Lubricating oils	<0	131,149
Ethanolamine	76	271
Ethylene glycol	134.5	255,256,268,271,272, 392(p.157)
Glycerol	275.5	153,209(p.395),286, 328,392(p.546)
ANTHRANILIC ACID (m.p. 147)		
(o-AMINOBENZOIC ACID)		15
n-Hexane	219e	139
n-Heptane	204e	139,149
1-Heptene	149	139
2,2,4-Trimethylpentane	219e	139
Diisobutene	150	139
Cyclohexane	118e	139
Methylcyclohexane	132	139
Benzene	<112	259,392(p.540)
Paraffin wax	229e	139
Paraffinic oil	227e	139
Naphthenic oil	175	139
n-Butyl alcohol	<92	259,392(p.540)
Chloroform	<114	Ibid.
Ethyl acetate	<98	Ibid.
Ethyl alcohol	<75	Ibid.
Methanol	<65	Ibid.
Water	78m	136,153,209(p.391), 253,392(p.539

TABLE I 39

	CST	References
ANTHRAQUINONE		15
ANTIMONY		
Iodine	>169	210(p.24)
Sulfur	>615	210(p.25)
ANTIMONY BROMIDE (m.p. 96.6)		
n-Heptane	190E	149
Cyclohexane	175	149,209,210(p.195), 298
Cyclohexene	<78	210(p.195),298
ANTIMONY CHLORIDE (m.p. 73.4)		
n-Heptane	140E	149
Cyclohexane	125.5	149,210(p.191),298, 391(p.1477)
Cyclohexene	<m.p.	149,210(p.191),298, 391(p.1475)
Stannic chloride	65.9m	153,209(p.393),210 (p.46),230,330
Stannous chloride	>241	210(p.46),230,330
ANTIPYRINE (m.p. 114)		
n-Heptane	163E	149
Decalin	127	140,149
Di-sec-amylbenzene	128	140,149
Di-sec-amylnaphthalene	100	140,149,445(p.649)
Water	<25	86
ARSENIC		
Iodine (m.p. 114)	>135	210(p.24)
ASPIRIN (ACETYLSALICYLIC ACID) (m.p. 135)		15
n-Heptane	255E	149
Decalin	115	149
Paraffin wax (m.p. 53)	>300	149
Water	89m	136,153,209(p.392), 253,362,392(p.630)
ATOXYL		15
AURIN (ROSOLIC ACID)(m.p. 309d)		15
Pyridine	<20	86
AZOBENZENE (m.p. 68)		15
n-Heptane	20E	149
2,2,4-Trimethylpentane	<22	149
AZOXYBENZENE (m.p. 36)		15
BENZALACETONE (4-PHENYL-3-BUTENE-2-ONE, m.p. 42)		145
n-Heptane	41	149,151
n-Hexadecane (Cetane)	63	151
Cyclohexane	15	151
Methylcyclohexane	23	151
Decalin	22	151
Petroleum ether (42-62°)	43	149,343
Petroleum ether (80-100)	25.5	149,343
Tri-sec-butylbenzene	19	151
Naphthenic oil	143	151

	CST	References
BENZALACETOPHENONE (CHALCONE, m.p. 62)		15
BENZAL CHLORIDE (see αα DICHLOROTOLUENE, p. 69)		
BENZALDEHYDE (Tables IV, V, VII)		15,17,106,121,145
n-Hexane	3	139
n-Heptane	3	139,147
2,2,4-Trimethylpentane	16	139,149,311
1-Heptene	<-50	139
Diisobutene	-38	139
Cyclohexane	-22e	139
Methylcyclohexane	-15	139
Camphene (m.p. 50)	<18.5	271
Petroleum ether (42-62°)	-1.5	149,343
Petroleum ether (30-100°)	-13	149,343
Paraffin wax (m.p. 53)	49	139
Paraffinic oil	45	139
Naphthenic oils	14 to 25	131,139,149
Ammonia	<25	85
Dioxane	<25	393(p.992),418A
Ethylene glycol	20	151
Glycerol	160.7	17,153,209(p.395), 286,328,330
Hydrogen cyanide	<-65	332
Tri-n-butylamine	<25	151
BENZAMIDE (m.p. 130)		15
Carbon disulfide	<80	338,392(p.536)
Carbon tetrachloride	<112	Ibid.
Ethyl alcohol	<72	Ibid.
Water	<75	Ibid.
BENZENE (Tables IV to VIII)		17,106,121,211,372
Water	306.4	149,209,212,351,
(See Nonhydrocarbon solvents)		392(p.368)
BENZIDINE (m.p. 120)		15
m-Xylene	111	140
Methylethylbenzene	127	140
Cumene (Isopropylbenzene)	139	140
Pseudocumene	149	140
sec-Butylbenzene	158	140
Diethylbenzene	148	140
Cymene (p-Isopropyltoluene)	157	140
Triethylbenzene	185	140
Diisopropylbenzene	202	140
Isopropylnaphthalene	103	140
Diisopropylnaphthalene	144	140
Isopropyltetralin	145	140,445(p.543)
BENZIL (m.p. 95)		15
BENZOATE OF ACETOHYDROXAMIC ACID CST of two isomeric liquids (m.p. at 99° and at 70°)	>140	49A,445(p.1198)

TABLE I   **41**

	CST	References
BENZOIC ACID (m.p. 122)(Table IV)		17
Benzene	<60 ·	64A,392(p.514),410
Toluene	<80	64A,318,392(p.514)
Biphenyl	<87.5	255,264,271,392(p.516)
Diphenylmethane	<114	271
Naphthalene	<79	271
1-Methylnaphthalene	<67	271
Acetone	<60	318,392(p.514)
Acetophenone	<80	318,392(p.514)
1-Chloronaphthalene	<95.5	255,264,271, 392(p.516)
Ethyl salicylate	<25.5	271
Eugenol methyl ether	<117	271
Iodine	>115.5	210(p.34),322B
Isobutyl benzoate	<48.5	271
Isosafrole	<89	271
Methanol	<50	392(p.513),452
Nitrobenzene	<90	318,392(p.514)
p-Nitrochlorobenzene (m.p. 83.5)	<86	255,264,271,392(p.346)
p-Nitrotoluene (m.p. 51.3)	<47	271,446(p.1011)
Phenol	<80	318,392(p.514)
Phenyl ether	<99	271
Safrole	<47	271
Sulfur	>257.5	22A,173
Water	117	1,27,153,209 (pp.391,393),251,253, 392(pp.500-1),410, 443,473,486
BENZOIC ANHYDRIDE (m.p. 42)		
n-Hexane	79	139
n-Heptane	79	139,149
2,2,4-Trimethylpentane	91	139
Diisobutene	20e	139
Cyclohexane	11e	139
Methylcyclohexane	28e	139,145
Paraffin wax (m.p. 53)	123	139
Paraffinic oil	124	139
Naphthenic oil	66	139
Iodine	>110.2	210(p.34),322B
BENZOIC SULFINIDE		15
(see SACCHARIN, p. 162)		
BENZOIN (m.p. 137)		
n-Heptane	89E	149
Paraffin wax (m.p. 53)	134	149
BENZONITRILE (Tables V, VII)		106,121
n-Heptane	8	149,309
2-Methylhexane	8.45	149,309
2,2-Dimethylpentane	13.2	149,309
2,3-Dimethylpentane	3.0	149,309
2,4-Dimethylpentane	13.05	149,309
2,2,3-Trimethylbutane (Triptane)	7.35	149,309
n-Dodecane	17	151
n-Tetradecane	25	151
n-Octadecane	34	151
Cyclohexane	-9	151
Lubricating oil	26	131,149
Ethylene glycol	73	151
Water (Isopycnic at 34°)	High	140A,151,315

	CST	References
BENZOPHENONE (m.p. 50)		15
n-Heptane	<25	149
n-Hexadecane	44.5	151
Paraffin wax (m.p. 53)	66	151
BENZOTHIAZOLE (Table V)		106
BENZOTRICHLORIDE		
(1,1,1-TRICHLOROTOLUENE)		
n-Octadecane (m.p. 28)	<18	151
BENZOYL CHLORIDE		
Paraffinic oil	0	139,149
BENZOYL-2-NAPHTHYLAMINE (m.p. 161)		
n-Heptane	213E	149
Decalin	<120	149
Paraffin wax	258	149
BENZYL ACETATE		15
n-Heptane	-13.1	139,149,309
2,4-Dimethylpentane	-9.2	149,309
2,2,4-Trimethylpentane	9.5	149,309
Naphthalene (m.p. 80)	<33	271,445(p.509)
Petroleum ether (42-62°)	-11	149,343
Petroleum ether (80-100°)	<-20	149,343
Acetamide (m.p. 81)	<56	255,270,271, 392(p.121) 445(p.1039)
Ethylene glycol	100	256,268,271,392(p.157)
Propionamide (m.p. 79)	<50	255,270,271,392(p.198)
BENZYL ALCOHOL (Table V, VII)		15,106,121
n-Butane	>60	149
n-Pentane	68	110,149
n-Hexane	50.6	110,139,149,290,321, 446(p.13)
2-Methylpentane	58.8	290,446(p.14)
3-Methylpentane	50.1	Ibid.
2,2-Dimethylbutane	62.9	Ibid.
2,3-Dimethylbutane	54.4	Ibid.
n-Heptane	50.7	110,139,149,309,321
2-Methylhexane	57.25	309
2,2-Dimethylpentane	64.7	309
2,3-Dimethylpentane	46.4	309
2,4-Dimethylpentane	64.9	309
2,2,3-Trimethylbutane (Triptane)	53.5	309
n-Octane	54.5	149,291,321,446(p.24)
2-Methylheptane	59.9	291
3-Methylheptane	55.9	291
4-Methylheptane	54.9	291
2,3-Dimethylhexane	51.4	291
2,4-Dimethylhexane	57.3	291
2,5-Dimethylhexane	65.3	291
3,4-Dimethylhexane	46.4	291
3-Ethylhexane	49.2	291
2-Methyl-3-ethylpentane	46.6	291
2,2,4-Trimethylpentane	73	139,149,311,321
n-Nonane	57.4	293,321
n-Decane	62.2	293,321
2,7-Dimethyloctane	72	149,321
n-Undecane	66.2	110,293

TABLE I   **43**

	CST	References
BENZYL ALCOHOL (continued)		
n-Dodecane	71.9	110,293
n-Tridecane	77.3	110
n-Tetradecane	81.8	110,293,321
n-Pentadecane	86.5	110
n-Hexadecane (Cetane)	89.8	110
n-Heptadecane	92.8	110
1-Heptene	-8	139
2-Octene	-3.6	293
Diisobutene	15	139
1-Nonene	10.4	293
1-Decene	19.1	293
1-Dodecene	33.5	293
1-Tetradecene	40.4	293
1-Hexadecene (Cetene)	56.0	293
Cyclohexane	2	110,139,321
Methylcyclohexane	14	139,321
Decalin	1	151,321
p-Menthane	<50	321
2-Phenylhexadecane	27.9	149,441
Petroleum ether (42-62°)	>b.p.	149,343
Petroleum ether (80-100°)	25.2	149,343
Paraffin wax (m.p. 53)	123	139
Paraffinic oil	119	139
Naphthenic oils	76,84	131,139
Borneol	<-8	271
p-Dibromobenzene (m.p. 86.9)	<48	255,256,270,271, 392(p.341)
2,2'-Dichloroethyl ether (Chlorex)	<-35	455
Pyridine Zincichloride	<-78	133
Trimethylamine	<25	170
BENZYLAMINE		
Glycerol	<20	153,328
Miscibilities with 142 substances		15
BENZYLANILINE		
Glycerol	High	153,328
BENZYL BENZOATE		
n-Heptane	-2.05	149,309
2-Methylhexane	4.45	309
2,2-Dimethylpentane	12.35	309
2,3-Dimethylpentane	-3.65	309
2,4-Dimethylpentane	12.1	309
2,2,3-Trimethylbutane (Triptane)	2.55	309
2,2,4-Trimethylpentane	16	149,311
n-Dodecane	>25	145
Paraffinic oil	45	151
BENZYL CELLOSOLVE		
Water	>25	271,284
BENZYL CHLORIDE		
Lubricating oil	<0	131
Chloroacetic acid	32	271
Sulfur	134.2	22A,70A(p.898),153, 182,188

	CST	References
BENZYL CYANIDE (see PHENYLACETONITRILE, p.148)		
BENZYL ETHER (Table VIII)		211
BENZYLETHYLAMINE (Table III) Glycerol LCST, 50	281	153,209(p.396),328, 392(p.642)
BENZYL FORMATE Ethylene glycol	107.5	271
BENZYL p-HYDROXYBENZOATE (m.p.112)		
n-Heptane	206E	149
Decalin	92	140,149,446(p.149)
Di-sec-amylbenzene	99	140,149,446(p.173)
Di-sec-amylnaphthalene	<80	140,149,446(p.193)
BENZYL MERCAPTAN (Table V)		106
BENZYLMETHYLAMINE Glycerol	<20	153,328
o-BENZYLPHENOL (m.p. 21)		
n-Hexane	65	139
n-Heptane	67	139,149
2,2,4-Trimethylpentane	81	139
1-Heptene	3	139
Diisobutene	14	139
Cyclohexane	0	139
Methylcyclohexane	10	139
Paraffin wax (m.p. 53)	116	139
Paraffinic oil	108	139
Naphthenic oil	54	139
BENZYL PHTHALATE (m.p. 44)		
n-Heptane	125E	149
2,2,4-Trimethylpentane	132	149
Methylcyclohexane	27	149
Decalin	<25	149
Paraffin wax (m.p. 53)	173	149
BENZYL SULFIDE Paraffinic oil	<0	139,149
4,4'-BI-o-ANISIDINE n-Heptane	150e	139,149
4,4'-BIPYRIDINE		15
BISMUTH (m.p. 271)		
Bromine	>311	210(p.23)
Iodine (m.p. 114)	>340	210(p.24)
Selenium (m.p. 218)	>608	210(p.26)
BONE OIL Sulfur dioxide	35.75	475

TABLE I   **45**

	CST	References
BORNEOL (m.p. 208)		15
Acetamide	<116	255,270,271,392(p.121)
Benzyl alcohol	<-8	271
p-Chlorophenol	-15	271
Ethylene glycol	<99	260,271
Methyl maleate	<62.5	271
Nitrobenzene	<82	256,266,271,446(p.903)
o-Nitrophenol	<123	271
BORNYL ACETATE		
Naphthalene (m.p. 80)	<33	271
Acetamide (m.p. 132)	134	255,256,268,270,271, 392(p.121),445(p.1038)
Ethylene glycol	110	256,268,271,392(p.157)
Glycerol	200	153,256,268,271,392 (p.210)
BROMAL HYDRATE (m.p. 53.5)		
Water	107	116,153,209(p.387), 392(p.87),443
BROMINE (Table IV)		17
All hydrocarbons	<m.p.	17,145
Bismuth (m.p. 271)	>311	210(p.23)
Bromine trifluoride	55.5	132,152,277B(p.450)
(misquoted as Boron trifluoride)		277B(p.259)
Carbon disulfide	<20	70A(p.120)
Chloroform	<20	70A(p.120)
Ethylene oxide	<-50	283
Ethyl ether	<20	70A(p.120)
Nitrogen dioxide	<20	70A(p.120),153A
p-BROMOACETANILIDE (m.p. 168)		15
p-BROMOANILINE (m.p. 66)		15
BROMOBENZENE		
Lubricating oils	<10	131,341
Acetamide	110	255,256,264,268,271, 392(p.121)
89.9% Acetic acid	34.5	324
Chloroacetic acid (m.p. 62)	<24	271
Ethanolamine	59.5	271
Ethylene glycol	>150.2	271
o-Nitrophenol (m.p. 45)	<21	392(p.365),414
p-Nitrophenol (m.p. 114)	<86	Ibid.
Urethane (m.p. 50)	<22	271
p-BROMOBENZOIC ACID (m.p. 251)		
Water	170m	136,153,392(p.473)
BROMOCAMPHOR and BROMOCRESOL GREEN		15
p-BROMOCHLOROBENZENE (m.p. 67.4)		
Ethane LCST, 40m		381,445(p.179)
Ethylene glycol	>173.8	271
BROMODICHLOROMETHANE		
Formic acid	61.3	153,256(p.679),268,271, 392(p.16)
BROMOETHYL ACETATE (Table VIII)		211

	CST	References
BROMOFORM		
All hydrocarbons	<m.p.	145
Acetic, Propionic, Butyric acids	<25	165
Carbon dioxide	>25	45(pp.679-80),145
Ethylene glycol	142	255,256,262,268,271, 392(p.157)
Formic acid	>70	10,165,392(pp.12,25), 393(p.1069)
Phosphorus (m.p. 44)	<0	182,184
1-BROMONAPHTHALENE		
Acetamide (m.p. 81)	175	255,256,265,268,271, 392(p.121),445(p.800)
Acetic acid	42.4	153,209,443,446(p.379)
Ethylene glycol	>195	260,271
Isobutyl alcohol	8.6	153,209(p.397),238,443, 446(p.341)
Methanol	62	Ibid.
Phenylacetic acid (m.p. 77)	<55.3	255,264,271,392(p.584)
Resorcinol	135.2	153,255,256,265,268
o-BROMOPHENOL (m.p. 5)		
n-Heptane	-6E	149
2,2-Dimethylpentane	3.85	149,309
2,4-Dimethylpentane	3.15	149,309
2,2,3-Trimethylbutane (Triptane)	-3.80	149,309
2,2,4-Trimethylpentane	23	149,311
BROMOSUCCINIC ACID (m.p. 159)		
Methanol	<22	392(p.219),452
1-BROMOTETRADECANE		
95% Ethyl alcohol	ca 75	194A
o-BROMOTOLUENE		
Ethylene glycol and Glycerol	>168	271
m-BROMOTOLUENE		
Acetamide	>170	271
Ethylene glycol and Glycerol	>168	271
Urethane (Ethyl carbamate) (m.p. 50)	<35	271,445(p.799)
p-BROMOTOLUENE (m.p. 28)		
Lubricating oil	<13	131
Acetamide	156	255,263,271,392(p.121), 445(p.799)
Ethylene glycol	>166.8	260,271
Glycerol	>168	271
89.9% Acetic acid	65.4	324
1,3 BUTANEDIOL (Table VIII)		211
Benzene	75	149
Di-sec-butylbenzene	180	151
Naphthalene	89	149
1-Methylnaphthalene	103	149
2,2'-Dichloroethyl ether (Chlorex)	53.8	446(p.416),455
Water	<20	284
1,4-BUTANEDIOL		
Benzene	>80	218

TABLE I   **47**

	CST	References
2,3-BUTANEDIOL (Table VIII)		211
Benzene	30	218

BUTANOL (see BUTYL ALCOHOL, below)

2-BUTANONE (METHYL ETHYL KETONE)		121,372
(Tables III, VI, and VII)		
n-Octane	<-57	346
n-Dodecane	<-14	346
n-Hexadecane (Cetane, m.p. 20)	<0	149,341,346
n-Heptadecane (m.p. 22.5)	<15	346
n-Dotriacontane (m.p. 74)	<62	346
Paraffin wax (m.p. 50)	<50	340
Lubricating oils	<0 to 57	131,145,149,257,341
Nine fatty Acids	<m.p.	345
Fourteen Amides	<m.p.	348
Six secondary Amines	<m.p.	196
Glycerol	164.5	153,209,253,286,328,330, 362,365,392(p.244),418, 443,446(p.488),486
1-Iodododecane	<-10	194A,445(p.741)
Perfluorocyclic oxide ($C_8F_{16}O$)	96	252
Tri-n-dodecylamine (m.p. 15.7)	15	347
Tri-n-octadecylamine (m.p. 54)	<47	347
Tri-n-Octylamine	-17.5	347
Water LCST, -6 to -22; 139 to 151.8		153,209(pp.387,393),253, 330,362,365,392(p.243), 418,443,486

BUTOXYL (see 2-METHOXYBUTYL
ACETATE, p. 117)

n-BUTYL ACETATE (Tables V, VI, VII)		106,121,372
Paraffin wax (m.p. 50)	<50	340
Three lubricating oils	<10	131,340
Fourteen Amides	<m.p.	348
Five Methyl esters	<m.p.	390A

n-BUTYL ALCOHOL (Tables III,V,VI,VII)		15,106,121,372
Ethane (crit. temp., upper		
layer, 39.8) LCST, 38.1		149,248,250,446(p.2)
n-Heptane	<-78	139,147,149
Cyclohexane	<0	147
Decalin	<25	178
Tetralin	<25	178
Paraffin waxes	25e	139,149,340
Paraffinic oils	36,80	131,139,340
Naphthenic oils	1,10	Ibid.
Higher alcohols (Cf. Figure 5)	<m.p.	196A
Fourteen Amides	<m.p.	348
Five primary Amines	<m.p.	349
Six secondary Amines	<m.p.	196
Three tertiary Amines	<m.p.	347
m-Aminobenzoic acid (m.p. 174)	<143	259,392(pp.540-1)
p-Aminobenzoic acid (m.p. 187)	<136	Ibid.
Anthranilic acid (m.p. 147)	<92	Ibid.
Carbon dioxide	-18	45(p.677),446(p.381)
Carbon disulfide	-80	247B,446(p.393)
2,2'-Dichloroethyl ether		
(Chlorex)	-24.9	446(p.417),455,455A,456

	CST	References

n-BUTYL ALCOHOL (continued)

1,1'-Dichloromethyl ether (M-Chlorex)	-46.5	455A
3,3'-Dichloro-n-propyl ether (P-Chlorex)	-85.0	455B
Four higher Haloalkanes	<m.p.	194A
Hydrogen cyanide	<25	148
o-Hydroxybenzoic acid (m.p. 159)	<86	410
m- and p-Hydroxybenzoic acids	<140	410
Six Methyl esters	<m.p.	390A
Tri-n-octadecylamine	<52	347
Water	127	38,48,78,98,103,118,152 153,190,209(p.388),221, 254,255,296(p.492),325, 330,365,392(p.266),444

sec-BUTYL ALCOHOL

n-Heptane	<-78	139,149
Paraffin waxes	18e	139,341
Paraffinic oils	31,>40	139,341
Naphthenic oils	9,>40	139,341
Water	110	1,98,153,209 (pp.388,393),253,325, 365,392(pp.268-9), 442,442A,443,444,486

ISOBUTYL ALCOHOL (see p.110)

tert-BUTYL ALCOHOL

| | | 15,145 |
| Water | <0 | 151,325,365 |

n-BUTYLAMINE

| Glycerol | 20 | 153,328 |
| Miscibilities with 192 substances | | 15 |

n-BUTYL BENZOATE

Acetamide	132	255,256,263,268,271, 392(p.121),445(p.1049)
Diethylene glycol	102	271
Ethylene glycol	178	255,263,271,392(p.157)
Glycerol	243	153,256,268,271, 392(p.210)

n-BUTYL BUTYRATE

| Urethane (Ethyl carbamate,m.p.50) | 21 | 271 |

BUTYL CARBITOL (DIETHYLENE GLYCOL MONOBUTYL ETHER, Table VIII)

		211
Two lubricating oils	22,47.5	131,149
Water	<20	284

BUTYL CARBITOL ACETATE

| Water | >20 | 284 |

BUTYL CELLOSOLVE (ETHYLENE GLYCOL MONOBUTYL ETHER, Table VIII)

		211
n-Heptane	-38e	139
n-Octadecane (m.p. 28)	<24	151
Five lubricating oils	3 to 10	131,139,149,340
p-Dichlorobenzene (m.p. 53)	<28	271

n-BUTYL CHLORIDE

| Two Lubricating oils | <10 | 340 |

TABLE I 49

	CST	References
n-BUTYL CHLORAL HYDRATE		
Glycerol	<15	166,392(p.218)
n-BUTYL ETHER (Tables V and VI)		15,106,145,372
n-Octadecane (m.p. 28)	<24	151
Three lubricating oils	3	131,340
n-BUTYL FORMATE		15
Paraffin wax (m.p. 50)	<37	341
Two lubricating oils	<10	149,340
n-BUTYL FUROATE		
n-Hexane	-26	139
n-Heptane	-22	139,149
2,2,4-Trimethylpentane	-18	139
Diisobutene	-66e	139
Cyclohexane	-44e	139
Methyl cyclohexane	-50e	139
Paraffin wax (m.p. 53)	57	139
Paraffinic oil	58	139
Naphthenic oil	15	139
BUTYL LACTATE (Table VI)		372
n-BUTYL OXALATE		
n-Hexane	-58e	139
n-Heptane	-55e	139,149
2,2,4-Trimethylpentane	-58e	139
Paraffin wax (m.p. 53)	23e	139
Paraffinic oil	14	139
Naphthenic oil	-22e	139
p-n-BUTYLPHENOL		
Water	246.6	119,152
p-tert-BUTYLPHENOL (m.p. 99)		
Paraffinic oil	<90	139
n-BUTYL PHTHALATE		
Propane (Table III)		
(lower phase point, 106)		149,192
n-Heptane	20	149
Paraffin wax (m.p. 50)	60	340
Paraffinic lubricating oil	85	340
Naphthenic lubricating oil	<10	340
Sulfur	>197.8	35,153
n-BUTYL STEARATE (Table VI)		
(m.p. 26.6)		15,372
All hydrocarbons	<m.p.	145
Five organic solvents	<m.p.	390A
n-BUTYL TARTRATE (m.p. 23)		
n-Heptane	20E	149
2,2,4-Trimethylpentane	<20	149
n-BUTYRALDEHYDE		
Two lubricating oils	<10	149,340
Paraffin wax (m.p. 50)	<50	340

	CST	References
n–BUTYRAMIDE (m.p. 115)		
Propane(crit.pt.,upper layer,98)	None	22
n–Hexane	174	139
n–Heptane	178	139,149
2,2,4-Trimethylpentane	184	139
1-Heptene	141	139
Diisobutene	128	139
Cyclohexane	131	139
Methylcyclohexane	139	139
Naphthenic oil	231	139

n–BUTYRIC ACID

	CST	References
n–Heptane	-23E	149
Benzene, Toluene, Xylene	<25	135
Camphene (m.p. 50)	<15	271
Naphthalene (m.p. 80)	<60	171,451
Kerosene	<25	135
Lubricating oil	22	131,149
Aniline	<0	4A,393(p.1099)
Bromoform, Carbon disulfide	<25	165
Carbon tetrachloride	<25	165
Cottonseed oil	<25?	165
Deuterium oxide	19.65	331,392(p.251),451
p–Dichlorobenzene (m.p. 53)	<22	271
Water	-3	105,128,153,157,201,
		209(p.388),253,256,325,
		331,362,392(pp.250-1),
		422,442,444,447,451,486

ISOBUTYRIC ACID (see p.111)

	CST	References
CAFFEINE		15
CALCIUM		
Calcium chloride	600	33
Calcium fluoride	560	33
CALCIUM ACETATE, BUTYRATE, and FORMATE		15
CAMPHOR (m.p. 176)		15
All hydrocarbons	<m.p.	145
Acetic acid	<25	166,392(p.678),426
Carbon disulfide	<25	Ibid.
Chloroform	<25	Ibid.
Three cresols	<-18	142
Ethyl alcohol	<25	166,392(p.678),426
Ethylene glycol	<117	271
Ethyl ether	<25	166,392(p.678),426
Phenol	<-12	142,168B,446,484A
Thymol (m.p. 51.5)	<34	271
CAMPHORIC ACID (m.p. 187)		
Ethyl alcohol	<15	392(p.681)
Ethyl ether	<30	392(p.681)
Methanol	<0	392(p.681)

TABLE I   **51**

	CST	References
CAPRIC ACID (m.p. 31.5)		
Nitromethane	54.8	198,446(p.1005)
15 Organic solvents	<m.p.	197,345
CAPRINITRILE (n-NONYL CYANIDE)		
16 Organic solvents	<m.p.	194
CAPROAMIDE (m.p. 101)		
Propane(Crit.pt.upper layer,98)	None	22
CAPROIC ACID		
All hydrocarbons	<m.p.	145
Naphthalene	<37	271
p-Dichlorobenzene (m.p. 53)	<30	271
Nitromethane	-3.40	35A,446(p.1005)
15 Organic solvents	<0	197,345
ISOCAPROIC ACID		
All hydrocarbons	<m.p.	145
CAPRYL ALCOHOL (Table V)		106
CAPRYLIC ACID (m.p. 16)		
All hydrocarbons	<m.p.	145
Nitromethane	34.85	446(p.1005)
14 other solvents	<m.p.	197,345
CARBITOL		
(DIETHYLENE GLYCOL MONOETHYL ETHER)		
(Tables VII and VIII)		121,211,284
n-Hexane	12	139
n-Heptane	25	139,149,150
2,2-Dimethylpentane	20	149,150
2,3-Dimethylpentane	14	149,150
2,4-Dimethylpentane	20	149,150
2,2,3-Trimethylbutane (Triptane)	9	149,150
2,2,4-Trimethylpentane	28	139,149,311
n-Dodecane	57	151
n-Hexadecane (Cetane)	73	151
1-Heptene	-25	139
Diisobutene	-25	139
Cyclohexane (m.p. 6)	<-1	139
Methylcyclohexane	<-40	139
Decalin	12	151
Toluene	<0	147
Paraffin wax (m.p. 53)	125	139
Paraffinic oil	133	139
Naphthenic oils	109	131,139
Two other lubricating oils	>180?	131,139
(Carbitol may contain glycol)		
Water	<20	45,46,284
CARBITOL ACETATE		
Water	<20	284
CARBON DIOXIDE (crit. temp. 31.04)		
(Cf. Tables III and IV)		17
n-Hexane	-61	139
n-Heptane	-51	139,149

	LCST	CST	References
CARBON DIOXIDE (continued)			
2,2,4-Trimethylpentane		-61	139
n-Tetradecane LCST, <15.5			277B(p.489)
n-Hexadecane LCST, <15.5			277B(p.489)
Diisobutene		<-78	139
Cyclohexane (m.p. 6)		-37e	139
Methylcyclohexane		-41	139
Paraffin wax (m.p. 53)		None	139
Two lubricating oils		None	139
Bromoform		>25	45(pp.679-80),145
n-Butyl alcohol		-18	45(p.677),446(p.381)
1-Chloropropionic acid	12		145
Diphenylamine (crit.temp., upper layer, 38.8)			46
Ethyl alcohol	Miscible		11A,45(p.677),145
Ethyl phthalate	25		145
Hydrogen bromide		<0	147
Hydrogen chloride		<0	70A(p.219),147
Hydrogen disulfide		<20	19A,70A(p.384)
Isoamyl alcohol		-24	45,446(p.381)
Isobutyl alcohol		-22	45(p.677),145,446(p.381)
Nitrobenzene (crit.temp., upper layer, 40)	30	-53	17,45,237,365,445(p.941)
o-Nitrobromobenzene (m.p. 42)	0		45(p.683),145,445(p.944)
o-Nitrochlorobenzene (m.p. 32)(crit.temp., upper layer, 34.5)	<3		45(p.682),379,445(p.942)
m-Nitrochlorobenzene (m.p. 45)(crit.temp., upper layer, 37.5)	8.5		Ibid.
p-Nitrochlorobenzene (m.p. 83)(crit.temp., upper layer, 37)			Ibid.
Nitrodichlorobenzenes	<0		45(p.684),445(p.943)
o-Nitrophenol (m.p. 45) (crit.temp.upper layer, 39)	25.9		45(p.685),153,209,365, 379,392(p.364),443, 445(p.942)
p-Nitrotoluene (m.p. 51)	15		145,392(p.205)
n-Propyl alcohol		-28	45(p.677),392(p.205)
Urethane (m.p. 50)(crit. temp.,upper layer, 37)	30.5		45(p.678),392(p.203), 445(p.940)
Water (crit.temp.,upper layer, 31.5)			45,250
3,4-Xylidine (m.p. 49)	31.0		378
252 Substances, 128 miscible			145
CARBON DISULFIDE (Tables IV,VII)			17,121
Isopentane		-160	149,373
n-Tetradecane		-14	151
Three lubricating oils		<0	131,139,149
Acetic acid		3.9	17,153,165,209,220,247, 254,341B,392(p.116), 446(p.396),446B
Acetic anhydride		29.8	153,174,223,255,341B, 392(p.222),445(p.933)
Acetone		-39.5 to -51.4	144,153,209,365,392 · (pp.10,183),427,443,464
Acetonitrile		51.5	144,153,226,341B, 392(p.10),445(p.944)446B

TABLE I   **53**

	CST	References
CARBON DISULFIDE (continued)		
Benzamide (m.p. 130)	<80	338,392(p.536)
Bromine	<20	70A(p.120)
n-Butyl alcohol	-80	247B,446(p.393)
Butyric acid	<25	165
Camphor (m.p. 176)	<25	166,392(p.678),426
Diethyldiphenylurea(m.p.71)	<50	93
Diphenylamine (m.p. 53)	<0	94,392(p.703)
Ethyl alcohol	-24.4	17,153,169,209(p.394),223,
		247B,254,256,288,294A,386,
		391(p.240),446(p.388),464
Ethylene chloride		
(Dichloroethane)	-33	153,174,255,256
Formic acid	>42.5	165,271
Glycerol (Isopycnic at 20)	High	140A,151
Hydrogen disulfide	<20	19A,70A(p.384)
Methanol	36	17,73,104,152,153,209,246A,
		253,254,256,288,294A,344,
		362,362A,391(pp.239-40),
		392(p.10),442,443,446
		(p.386),446B,486
p-Nitrochlorobenzene		
(m.p. 83)	<50	89,392(p.345)
Nitromethane	63.4	144,146,152,153,209,226,
		256,341B,344,392(p.10),
		444,445(p.946),447
Perfluorodimethylcyclohexane	High	151
Phosphorus (yellow)		
(m.p. 44.1)	-6.5	73,153,182,184,188,189,209,
		210(p.36),253
Propionic acid	<25	165
Propionitrile	-13.5	445(p.944)
n-Propyl alcohol	-52	247B,446(p.392)
Sulfur chloride	<20	70A(p.899)
Sulfur dioxide	-2.3	151
Sulfur hexafluoride (crit.		
temp. 45.5)(Incomplete		
mixing)	None	151
Sulfuric acid	>180	17
Sulfur trioxide	Between 15 and 30	70A(p.907),388
CARBON HEXAFLUORIDE (C_2F_6)		
(see HEXAFLUOROETHANE, p.103)		
CARBON TETRABROMIDE (m.p. 90)		
n-Hexadecane (Cetane)	<65	149
Crystal oil (Nujol)	<60	151
CARBON TETRACHLORIDE(m.p. -23)		
(Tables IV,V,VI,VII)		17,106,121,372
All hydrocarbons	<m.p.	131,139,145,149,340,346
Acetic acid	<25	393(p.839),418A
Acetonitrile	<-23	365
Fourteen Amides and		
fifteen Amines	<m.p.	195,347,348
Benzamide (m.p. 130)	<112	338,392(p.536)
Butyric acid	<25	165
Catechol (m.p. 104)	<95	392(p.391),471
Diethyldiphenylurea (m.p. 71)	<50	93
Diphenylamine (m.p. 53)	<28	94,392(p.703)

	CST	References
CARBON TETRACHLORIDE (continued)		
Ethanolamine (Iso-optic)	220	17,151
Ethyl alcohol	<-39	391(p.217),392(p.152), 446(p.282),464
Formic acid	220	17,446(p.359)
Glycerol	270	17
Hydrogen cyanide	>25	148
Hydroquinone	>163.2	392(p.396),471
Iodine	160.5	181,277B(p.1275)
Iodine monochloride	14m	73A
Five Methyl esters	<m.p.	390A
o-Nitroaniline (m.p. 71)	<55	69,392(p.402)
m-Nitroaniline (m.p. 112)	<95	69,392(p.403)
o-Nitrobenzoic acid (m.p. 147)	>127.2	70
m-Nitrobenzoic acid (m.p. 141)	<119	70,392(p.489)
p-Nitrobenzoic acid (m.p. 242)(explodes)	>170	70,392(p.490)
p-Nitrochlorobenzene (m.p. 83)	<50	89,392(p.345)
Nitromethane	2	341B,445(p.785)
Nitrous oxide (crit.temp., 32)	<27	143
Perfluorocyclic oxide ($C_8F_{16}O$)	48	252
Perfluorodimethylcyclohexane	>27	389
Perfluoro-n-heptane	58.7	50,152,153,186,219A,252,390
Perfluoromethylcyclohexane	>27	78,152,153,183,185,219A,390 495
Propionic acid	<25	165
Resorcinol (m.p. 110)	>103.7	17,392(p.394),446,471
Sulfur (m.p. 113)	>220	17
Sulfur dioxide	-29.27	23,153,180,188,210(p.187), 255(p.473),391(p.216), 392(p.4)
Water	>220	17
CARBON TETRAFLUORIDE		
Methane	-178.7	82,365
Ethane	-122	179,390
Fluoroform	-142.7	365,390,438
Methylene fluoride	>-118	365,439
CARBONYL CHLORIDE (see PHOSGENE, p.152)		
CARVACROL (2-METHYL-5-ISOPROPYLPHENOL)		
Propane (miscible)	None	192
Glycerol	>200	153,328
CARVONE		
Acetamide (m.p. 81)	<67.8	260,271,445(p.1017)
Ethylene glycol	97.8	256,268,271,392(p.157)
Propionamide (m.p. 79)	<63	271,445(p.1017)
Thymol (m.p. 51.5)	<-10	271
CASEIN		15

TABLE I   **55**

	CST	References
CASTOR OIL (Table IV)		17
n-Hexane	35	17,149
n-Heptane	44.5	149
Methylcyclohexane	<25	145
Naphthenic oil	50	151
Sulfur dioxide	-8	475
CATECHOL (m.p. 104)		
n-Heptane	181e	149
Diisobutene	162	149
Cyclohexane	120	140,149,446(p.149)
Decalin	146	Ibid.
Benzene	<85	149,392(p.391),471
Methyldiisopropylbenzene	100	140,446(p.173)
Diphenyl methane	<96	271
Di-sec-amylbenzene	144	140,446(p.173)
Hexaethylbenzene (m.p. 129)	119	Ibid.
1-Methylnaphthalene	<86	271
Di-tert-butylnaphthalene	<100	140,446(p.195)
Di-sec-amylnaphthalene	136	Ibid.
Phenanthrene (m.p. 100)	94	16,140
Acetone	<20	392(p.391),471
Carbon tetrachloride	<95	Ibid.
Chloroform	<85	Ibid.
1-Chloronaphthalene	<90	271
p-Dibromobenzene (m.p. 87)	<83	271
Ethyl alcohol	<20	392(p.391),471
Ethyl ether	<38	Ibid.
Glycerol	<100	153,209,286,328
p-Phenetidine	<38.5	271
Phenyl ether	<92	271
Quinoline	<58	271,446(p.796)
Safrole	<71	271
Water	<35	392(p.391),471
CATECHOL DIETHYL ETHER		
Glycerol	>240	153,328
CATECHOL DIMETHYL ETHER (VERATROL)		
Glycerol	>240	153,328
CATECHOL MONOETHYL ETHER		
Glycerol	192.9	153,209(p.396),328,392 (p.209)
CELLOSOLVE (2-ETHOXYETHANOL) (Tables VII and VIII)		121,211
n-Hexane	-32	139
n-Heptane	-12	139,147,149
2,2,4-Trimethylpentane	-15	139
n-Hexadecane (Cetane)	40	151
Cyclohexane	-60e	139
Methylcyclohexane	-40	139,147
Paraffin wax (m.p. 53)	98	139
Another paraffin wax	92	340
Paraffinic oils	106,90	131,139,340
Naphthenic oils	74,56	Ibid.
Two other lubricating oils	61,65	Ibid.
Water	<20	284

	CST	References
CELLOSOLVE ACETATE		284
2,2,4-Trimethylpentane	<0	149,311
Two lubricating oils	27,29.5	131,149
Water	181	296(p.722)

CELLULOSE, CELLULOSE ACETATE
and NITRATE   15

	CST	References
CESIUM		
Cesium fluoride	<670	32
Sulfur	>172.8	210(p.26)

CETYL ALCOHOL (n-HEXADECYL		
ALCOHOL)		15
Acetonitrile	58	196A
Nitroethane (Figure 4)	<45	196A
Pyridine zincichloride	241	133
Sulfur dioxide	<25	210(p.188),392(p.767),396

| CETYL STEARATE (Table III) | | |
| Propane (LCST, 95.2) | | 22,101,149 |

CHLORAL HYDRATE (m.p. 52)		
n-Heptane	>102	149
Cyclohexane	<50	151
Methylcyclohexane	ca 63	151
Benzene	<28	149
Toluene	<28	149,392(p.92),425
Di-sec-butylbenzene	<45	151
Chloroform	<35	392(p.92),425
Ethyl alcohol	<0	Ibid.
Ethyl ether, Glycerol,		
Olive oil	<25	392(p.93),426
Water	<0	86,392(p.92),425,485

CHLOREX (see 2,2'-DICHLOROETHYL
ETHER, p.67)

CHLORINE		
Ethylene oxide	<-80	283
Water	>72	151

o-,m-,p-CHLOROACETANILIDES		
Benzene	<50	392(p.581),413
Water	>180	153,392(p.580),413,425

CHLOROACETIC ACID (m.p. 62)		15
n-Hexane	137	139
n-Heptane	137	139,149
2,2,4-Trimethylpentane	139	139
1-Heptene	70	139
Di-isobutene	67	139
Cyclohexane	86	139,140
Methylcyclohexane	98	139,140,446(p.215)
Di-sec-amylbenzene	56	140,446(pp.250-1)
Naphthalene (m.p. 80)	<49.7	271
sec-Amylnaphthalene	<33	140,446(p.257)
Diisopropylnaphthalene	<38	Ibid.
Di-sec-amylnaphthalene	108	140
Camphene (m.p. 50)	<4.8	271
Paraffin wax (m.p. 53)	238	139
Paraffinic oil	220	139

TABLE I 57

	CST	References

CHLOROACETIC ACID (continued)
| Naphthenic oil | 187 | 139 |

Benzyl chloride	32	271
Bromobenzene	<24	271
o-Cresol	<37	255,262
p-Dibromobenzene (m.p. 87)	<61	271
Isoamyl isovalerate	<44	271
Pentachloroethane	43	271

CHLOROACETONE
n-Heptane	47.5	151
Methylcyclohexane	32	151
Two lubricating oils	70,85	131,151

o-CHLOROANILINE (m.p. -14)
n-Butane	29.8	141,149
Isobutane	50.5	141,149
n-Pentane	23	149
n-Hexane	14	139
n-Heptane	13	139,149
2,2,4-Trimethylpentane	26.5	139

Diisobutene	-27e	139
Cyclohexane	-25e	139
Methylcyclohexane	-17	139
Paraffin wax (m.p. 53)	50	139
Paraffinic oil	46	139
Naphthenic oil	6	139
Water	>158	392(p.371),413

m-CHLOROANILINE
n-Heptane	69.5	151
n-Hexadecane (Cetane)	83	151
n-Octadecane	86	151
Cyclohexane	28.3	151
Methylcyclohexane	39.5	151
Decalin	18	151
Naphthenic oil	48	151
Water	>150	392(p.371),413

p-CHLOROANILINE (m.p. 70)
n-Heptane	80	139,149
2,2,4-Trimethylpentane	86	139,149
Water	>160	392(p.371),413

CHLOROBENZENE (Tables IV and VII) — 17,121
All hydrocarbons	<m.p.	131,145,340
Ethanolamine	120	271
Ethylene glycol	>130.8	271
Formic acid	106.6	17,209,443,446(p.374)
Glycerol	>200	17
Methanol	<25	393(p.863),418A
Perfluoromethylcyclohexane	126.8	153,185,390
Phosgene	<17	8
Phosphorus (yellow)	264	153,182,184,188,209(p.394)
Pyruvic acid	25	260,267,271
Resorcinol (m.p. 110)	227	17,446(p.348)
Silver nitrate (m.p. 212)	>280	17
Sulfur	116	1,38A,153,182,188,209,253 330,392(p.353),443,486
Water	>220	17

	CST	References
o-CHLOROBENZOIC ACID (m.p.142)		
n-Heptane	99E	149,410
Benzene	-52E	149,410
Water	126.2	136,153,209(p.390),253,
		392(p.473)
m-CHLOROBENZOIC ACID (m.p.158)		
n-Heptane	75E	149,410
Benzene	-36E	149,410
Water	142.8	136,153,209(p.390),253,
		392(p.473)
p-CHLOROBENZOIC ACID (m.p.243)		
n-Heptane	123E	149,410
Benzene	-13E	149,410
Water	167m	136,153,209(p.390),253,
		392(p.473)
p-CHLOROBIPHENYL		15
p-CHLOROBROMOBENZENE (m.p. 65)		
(Table III)		
Ethane (crit.temp.,upper layer,		
47.2) LCST, 40m		381,445(p.179)
Ethylene glycol	>173.8	271
1-CHLORODODECANE		
95% Ethyl alcohol	38	194A
2-CHLOROETHANOL (ETHYLENE		
CHLOROHYDRIN)(Table VIII)		211,284
n-Hexane	101	139
n-Heptane	115	73,139,149,256
2,2,4-Trimethylpentane	115	Ibid.
1-Heptene	74	139
Diisobutene	72	139
Cyclohexane	65.6	139,140,153,216,446(p.40)
Methylcyclohexane	89	139,140
Decalin	82	140
Limonene (Dipentene)	28	151
Methyldiethylbenzene	-50	140,446(p.129)
Ethylisopropylbenzene	-60	140,446(p.130)
sec-Amylbenzene	-22	Ibid.
Triethylbenzene	-15	Ibid.
Diisopropylbenzene	-5	Ibid.
Methyldiisopropylbenzene	13	Ibid.
Di-sec-butylbenzene	65	151
Di-sec-amylbenzene	70	140,446(p.130)
sec-Amylnaphthalene	<-78	140,446(p.143)
Diisopropylnaphthalene	-28	Ibid.
Di-sec-amylnaphthalene	68	140
Isopropyltetralin	-27	140,446(p.45)
Paraffin wax (m.p. 53)	170	139
Paraffinic oil	171	139
Naphthenic oils	141	131,139
Tetrachloroethylene	30	73,153,256(p.678),392(p.66)
Water	20	284

TABLE I   **59**

	CST	References

2-CHLOROETHYL ACETATE
| n-Heptane | 10E | 145,149 |
| 2,2,4-Trimethylpentane | 16 | 149,311 |

CHLOROFORM
(Tables IV,VI,VII, and VIII)   17,121,211,372
All hydrocarbons	<m.p.	131,145,341,346
m-Aminobenzoic acid		
(m.p. 174)	<155	259,392(pp.540-1)
p-Aminobenzoic acid		
(m.p. 187)	<163	Ibid.
Anthranilic acid (m.p.147)	<114	Ibid.
Bromine	<20	70A(p.120)
Camphor (m.p. 176)	<25	166,392(p.678),426
Catechol (m.p. 104)	<85	392(p.391),471
Chloral hydrate (m.p. 52)	<35	392(p.92),425
Diethyldiphenylurea(m.p.71)	<50	93
2,4-Dinitroanisole(m.p.95)	<50	88,392(p.534)
2,4-Dinitrochlorobenzene		
(m.p. 53)	<16	89,392(p.322)
2,4-Dinitrophenetole		
(m.p. 86)	<25	88,392(p.578)
Diphenylamine (m.p. 53)	<5	94,392(p.703)
Formamide (Iso-optic)	High	144
Hydrogen cyanide	<25	148
Five Methyl esters	<m.p.	390A
o-Nitroaniline (m.p. 71)	<43	69,392(p.402)
m-Nitroaniline (m.p. 112)	<86	69,392(p.403)
p-Nitroaniline (m.p. 147.5)	<115	Ibid.
o-Nitrobenzoic acid		
(m.p. 147)	<110	70,392(p.488)
m-Nitrobenzoic acid		
(m.p. 141)	<100	70,392(p.489)
p-Nitrobenzoic acid		
(m.p. 242.2)(explodes)	>170	70,392(p.490)
p-Nitrochlorobenzene		
(m.p. 83)	<30	89,392(p.345)
o-Nitrophenol (m.p. 45)	<16	69,92,392(p.364)
p-Nitrotoluene (m.p. 52)	<15	90,392(p.537)
Perfluorodimethylcyclohexane	>27	389
Perfluoro-n-heptane	78.5	153,186,219A,390
Perfluoromethylcyclohexane	50.3	153,185,219A,390
Phenylacetic acid (m.p. 77)	<25	177,392(p.584)
Resorcinol (m.p. 110)	>94.8	17,392(p.394),445(p.345),
		471
Sulfur (m.p. 113)	164	182
Trimethyl amine	<25	170
2,4,6-Trinitroanisole		
(m.p. 68.4)	<35	88,392(p.495)
2,4,6-Trinitrochlorobenzene		
(Picryl chloride,m.p. 83)	<40	89
2,4,6-Trinitrophenetole		
(m.p. 78.5)	<40	88
2,4,6-Trinitrotoluene		
(m.p. 81)	<45	432
Urethane (Ethyl carbamate,		
(m.p. 50)	<23	392(p.202),425

	CST	References

p-CHLOROIODOBENZENE (m.p. 57)
(Table III)
Ethane (crit.temp., upper
    layer, 38.5), LCST, 34.4m   381,445(p.179)

CHLOROMALEIC ANHYDRIDE (m.p. 30)

	CST	References
n-Heptane	150	149
Cyclohexane	115	149
Methylcyclohexane	124	149
Benzene	<25	145
Tetraisopropylbenzene (m.p. 118)	122	149
1-Methylnaphthalene	<-30	149

1-CHLORONAPHTHALENE (m.p. 55)

	CST	References
Practically all hydrocarbons	<m.p.	145
Acetamide (m.p. 81)	168.3	255,256,264,268,271, 392(p.121)
Benzoic acid (m.p. 122)	<95.5	255,264,271,392(p.516)
Catechol (m.p. 104)	<90	271
Ethylene glycol	>193.1	271
Phenylacetic acid (m.p. 77)	<36	255,264,271,392(p.584)
Phosgene	<17	8

CHLORONITRO-(see NITROCHLORO-,p.132)

o- and p-CHLOROPHENOLS

	Ortho	Para	References
			417
Melting points	7	43	
n-Hexane	5	69	139
n-Heptane	6	67	139,149
2,2,4-Trimethylpentane	18	80	139
Diisobutene	-43e	6	139
Cyclohexane	-44e	13	139
Methylcyclohexane	-27e	21	139
Benzene	-14	6	417
Naphthalene (m.p. 80)		<58.2	255,270,392(p.355)
Paraffin wax (m.p. 53)	58	111	139
Paraffinic oil	50	103	139
Naphthenic oil	6	55	139
Acetamide (m.p. 81)		<17	271
Borneol (m.p. 208)		-15	271
p-Dibromobenzene (m.p. 87)		<66.5	255,270,271
Ethylbenzoate		<-8	270,271
p-Methylacetophenone		<-12	270,271
Methyl benzoate		<17.5	271
2-Phenylethanol		<20	270,271
Water	173	129	153,209(p.389), 392(p.355),417

m-CHLOROPHENOL

	CST	References
Water	130.8	Ibid.

2-CHLORO-6-PHENYLPHENOL

	CST	References
n-Heptane	30	151

CHLOROPICRIN (TRINITROCHLOROMETHANE)

	CST	References
n-Heptane	<-60	149

3-CHLOROPROPANEDIOL (Table VIII)   211

TABLE I 61

	CST	References
1-CHLOROPROPIONIC ACID (Table III)		
n-Heptane	97	151
Cyclohexane	55	151
Decalin	100	151
Benzene	<25	145
Di-sec-butylbenzene	58	151
Tetralin	<0	151
Limonene	14	151
Carbon dioxide LCST, 12		145
o-CHLOROTOLUENE		
Ethylene glycol	>152.5	271
Urethane (Ethyl carbamate)	<35	271,445(p.799)
(m.p. 50)		
p-CHLOROTOLUENE (Table VI)		15,372
Ethylene glycol	>154.8	271
CHOLESTEROL,		15
CHROMOTROPIC SALT		15
CINCHONINE		15
CINEOLE (1,8-EPOXY-p-MENTHANE)		
2,2,4-Trimethylpentane	<-20	149
Lubricating oil	<0	131,149
Acetamide (m.p. 81)	<67	127,255,264,271,392(p.121)
		445(p.995)
Ethanolamine	150.4	267,271
Ethylene glycol	>164.7	260,271
Methyl fumarate (m.p. 102)	<70	271
Methyl oxalate (m.p. 54)	<46.8	271
Propionamide (m.p. 79)	<60	271,445(p.995)
CINNAMALDEHYDE (m.p. 30)		
(Table VIII)		211
n-Heptane	65	149,151
2,2,-Dimethylpentane	77	151
2,2,3-Trimethylbutane (Triptane)	68	151
2,2,4-Trimethylpentane	82	149,311
Cyclohexane	31	151
Methylcyclohexane	36	151
Di-sec-butylbenzene	-46	151
Petroleum ether (42-62°)	>b.p.	149,343
Petroleum ether (80-100°)	56.5	149,343
Lubricating oil	87	131,149
Other oils	65.5,74,102	151
CINNAMIC ACID (m.p. 133)		15
n-Heptane	70E	149
Paraffin wax (m.p. 53)	<120	149
Water	140.5	153,251,392(p.626)
CINNAMYL ALCOHOL (m.p. 33)		
n-Hexane	100	139
n-Heptane	102	139,149
2,2,4-Trimethylpentane	115	139
1-Heptene	47	139
Diisobutene	60	139
Cyclohexane	39	139
Methylcyclohexane	51	139
Five primary amines	<m.p.	349

	CST	References
CINNAMYL ALCOHOL (continued)		
Di-<u>sec</u>-butylbenzene	<25	145
Paraffin wax (m.p. 53)	152	139
Petroleum ether (42–62°)	>b.p.	149,343
Petroleum ether (80–100°)	56.5	149,343
Paraffinic oil	145	139
Naphthenic oil	97	139
α–CITRAL (GERANIAL)		
2,2,4-Trimethylpentane	<0	149,311
CITRONELLAL		
Acetamide (m.p. 81)	<50	255,263,271, 392(p.121)
Ethylene glycol	165	255,256,268,270,271 392(p.157)
Guaiacol (<u>o</u>-Methoxyphenol (m.p. 28)	<18	255,270,271, 392(p.551)
CITRONELLAL HYDRATE		
Petroleum ether (42–62°)	20.5	149,343
Petroleum ether (80–100°)	9.5	149,343
CITRONELLAL HYDRATE OXIME		
Petroleum ether (42–62°)	>b.p.	149,343
Petroleum ether (80–100°)	>b.p.	149,343
COCONUT OIL		15
COLLIDINE (2,4,6-TRIMETHYLPYRIDINE)		
Water LCST, 3.5	>180	153,209(p.393),253, 341A,362,392(p.616) 443
COPAL		15
COPPER (m.p. 1083)		
Sulfur	>1485	210(p.25)
COTTONSEED OIL (Table III)		
Propane Lower phase pt., 66.2		101,149,191
Isobutane Lower phase pt., 126		149,191
Acetic acid	<25	165,392(p.116)
Ethyl alcohol	60	152,350
Propionic and Butyric acids	<25	165

CRESOLS (Table III)	ortho	meta	para	211
Melting point	30	12	36	
Propane		(insoluble)		192
n-Hexane	5	12	11	139
n-Heptane	9	14	12	139
2,2,4-Trimethyl- pentane	21	29.5	28	139
n-Tetradecane		27.5		151
n-Hexadecane	26	41.7	42.0	151
1-Heptene		<-52		139
Diisobutene	-45e	-39	-40e	139
Cyclohexane	-36e	-53e	-51e	139
Methylcyclohexane	-29e	-27	-38e	139
Paraffin wax (m.p.53)	82	94	97	139
Paraffinic oil	76	93	98	139,149

TABLE I   63

		CST	References

CRESOLS (continued)

	ortho	meta	para	
Naphthenic oils	28	43	48	131,139,149
Another oil	19	40.5	42.5	131,149
Camphor	<-18	<-18	<-18	142
Chloroacetic acid	<37			255,262
Ethylene glycol	<4.5			255,270,271
Glycerol	below melting points			153,328
Hexachloroethane	<122			260,271
Hydrogen cyanide		<25		148
2-Methoxybutyl acetate	<12			271
Methyl maleate			<15	271
Urethane (m.p. 50)	<8			271,446(p.926)
Water (CST)	166	148	143	119,152,153,209,255 305,306,392(p.547) 414,431,433
(Isopycnics)	(145)	(148)	(138)	306

p-CRESOL METHYL ETHER

Acetamide (m.p. 81)		107	256,264,268,271,392 (p.121),445(p.789)
Ethylene glycol		156	255,256,266,268,271 272,392(p.157)
Urethane (Ethyl carbamate) (m.p. 50)		<23.5	271,445(p.997)

CRESYLIC ACID (mixture of cresols and phenol)

n-Butane	14.2	141,149
Isobutane	45.5	141,149
n-Pentane	15	151
n-Hexane	0	139
n-Heptane	0	139,149
2,2,4-Trimethylpentane	15	139,149,311
1-Heptene	-60	139
Diisobutene	-45	139
Cyclohexane	-51e	139
Methylcyclohexane	-37	139
Paraffin wax (m.p. 53)	74	139
Paraffinic oil	74	139,149
Naphthenic oils	23	131,139,149

CROTONALDEHYDE

n-Hexane	-21	139
n-Heptane	-14	139,149
2,2,4-Trimethylpentane	-14	139
n-Octadecane (m.p. 28)	<23	151
Diisobutene	-70	139
Cyclohexane (m.p. 6.5)	-31e	139
Methylcyclohexane	-25	139
Paraffin wax (m.p. 53)	63	139
Paraffinic oils	53,69	139,149,341
Naphthenic oils	<21,32	Ibid.

CROTYL ALCOHOL (2-BUTENE-1-OL)

Water	>100	271

CRYSTAL VIOLET (m.p. 195)   15

	CST	References
CYANOACETIC ACID (m.p. 70)		
Benzene	>90	149
CYCLOHEXANE (Tables VI,VII)		121,372
(see nonhydrocarbon solvents)		
CYCLOHEXANOL (Tables VI,VII)		
(m.p. 24)		15,121,372
Lubricating oils	<0	131,139,149
Water	184.7	152,153,256,392(p.435), 415,493
CYCLOHEXANONE (Table VII)		121
All hydrocarbons	<m.p.	145
CYCLOHEXYLAMINE		
2,2,4-Trimethylpentane	<0	149,311
o-CYCLOHEXYLPHENOL (m.p. 57)		
Paraffinic oil	<0	139,149
p-CYCLOHEXYLPHENOL (m.p. 133)	<m.p.	139,149
n-DECANE (Table IV)		17
n-DECYL ALCOHOL (m.p. 6)		
All hydrocarbons	<m.p.	145
Acetamide (m.p. 81)	<75	271
Acetonitrile	22.7	146,152,196A
Adiponitrile	85	151
Ethylene glycol (Iso-optic)	60,105?	146,152,255,262, 392(p.157)
Nitroethane	19	146,152,196A
Nitromethane	56.3	146,152
Propylene glycol	<0	151
Trimethylene glycol	-13	151
Water	296e	118,152,176

DEUTERIUM OXIDE (Table III)

	LCST	CST	References
Acetonitrile		5.1	392(p.85),451
Butyric acid		19.65	331,392(p.251),451
2,4-Dimethylpyridine	16.2	196.0	76
2,5-Dimethylpyridine	8.5	211.6	76
2,6-Dimethylpyridine	28.7	228	76,78
Isobutyric acid		41.4	331,392(p.251)
2-Methylpyridine (α-Picolin)	93.8	111.8	76,341A
3-Methylpyridine (β-Picolin)	38.5	117	76,78,152
4-Methylpyridine	Miscible		76
Nicotine	54		171,451
Phenol		78.7	171,341A,451
Triethylamine		14.45	341A,451

DIACETONE ALCOHOL (4-HYDROXY-
4-METHYL-2-PENTANONE, Table V)

	CST	References
		106
n-Hexane	10	139
n-Heptane	8	139,149
n-Dodecane	>25	145
2,2,4-Trimethylpentane	4,21.5	139,149,311
1-Heptene	-32	139

TABLE I   **65**

	CST	References
DIACETONE ALCOHOL (continued)		
Diisobutene	-48	139
Cyclohexane	-6	139
Methylcyclohexane	-5	139
Paraffin waxes	88,94	139,149,341
Paraffinic oils	95	Ibid.
Naphthenic oils	>65	Ibid.
DI-n-ALKYLAMINES (see under ACETONE, METHANOL, pp.16,116-7)		196
DIAMINOBENZENES (see PHENYL-ENEDIAMINES, p.149)		
2,4-DIAMINOTOLUENE (m.p. 99)		
n-Heptane	220E	149
Benzene	60	151
Octyltoluene	140	151
Tetraisopropylbenzene	185	149,151
DI-n-AMYLAMINE (Table VIII)		211
DIAMYLHYDROQUINONE		
Paraffinic oil	<0	139,149
DIANISIDINE (4,4'-BI-o-ANISIDINE)		
n-Heptane	150e	139,149
DIAZOAMINOBENZENE (m.p. 99)		15
Pyridine	<25	86
DIBROMOACETYLENE (C_2Br_2)		
o-Nitroaniline (m.p. 71)	<50	69,392(p.402)
m-Nitroaniline (m.p. 111.8)	<95	69,392(p.403)
p-Nitroaniline (m.p. 147.5)	<125	Ibid.
p-DIBROMOBENZENE (m.p. 86.9)		15
Lubricating oil	<72	131
Acetamide	180	255,256,268,270,271, 392(p.121)
Aniline	<50	318,392(p.341)
Benzyl alcohol	<48	255,256,270,271,392 (p.341)
Catechol (m.p. 104)	<83	271
Chloroacetic acid (m.p. 63)	<61	271
p-Chlorophenol	<66.5	255,270,271
Ethylene glycol	>183.9	271
Menthol (Hexahydrothymol)	<55	255,270,271,392(p.341)
Methyl salicylate	<69	255,270,392(p.341)
o-Nitrophenol	<46	271
o-Nitrotoluene	<64.5	271,445(p.798)
Phenol	<40	318,392(p.341)
2-Phenylethanol	<67	255,270,271,392(p.341)
Phosphorus (yellow)	163	153,182,184,188, 209(p.394)
Propionamide (m.p. 79)	<70	271,445(p.798)
Sulfur (m.p. 113)	<100	151,182,188
Urethane	<70	271,445(p.798)

1,2-DIBROMOETHANE (see ETHYLENE BROMIDE, p 85)

	CST	References
DIBROMOMETHANE (METHYLENE BROMIDE)		
Ethylene glycol	>168.6	271
1,3-DIBROMOPROPANE		
Ethylene glycol	85.7	271
2,3-DIBROMOPROPANOL		15
DIBUTOXYTETRAETHYLENE GLYCOL (Table V)		106
DI-n-BUTYLAMINE (Table VIII)		211
Miscibilities with 148 substances		15
Di-n-BUTYL CARBONATE (Table VIII)		211
DIBUTYL HYDROGEN PHOSPHITE (Table VIII)		211
2,6-DI-tert-BUTYL-4-METHYLPHENOL		
Diethylene glycol	190.2	428
4,6-DI-tert-BUTYL-3-METHYLPHENOL		
50% Glycerol, 50% Ethylene glycol	178.7	428
DIBUTYL PHTHALATE (see BUTYL PHTHALATE, p.49)		
DICHLORAMINE T (m.p. 83)		15
DICHLOROACETIC ACID		
Isopentane	0	239,446(p.206)
Lubricating oils	0	131,149
2,5-DICHLOROANILINE (m.p. 50)		
n-Hexadecane	<36	151
Paraffin wax (m.p. 53)	<40	149,151
Nujol	<40	151
o-DICHLOROBENZENE (Table VI)		372
All hydrocarbons	<m.p.	145
Acetamide	150	255,256,263,268,271, 392(p.121)
Ethylene glycol	>165.8	271
Urethane	<45	271,445(p.797)
p-DICHLOROBENZENE (m.p. 53)		
Ethane	<m.p.	381
Ethylene (Table III) LCST, 26		96,365
Dipentene	<43	271
Lubricating oil	<35	131
Acetamide (m.p. 81)	148.5	255,256,268,270,271, 392(p.121),445(p.797)
Aniline	<45.5	255,270,271,392(p.342)
Butyl Cellosolve	<28	271
Butyric acid	<22	271
Caproic acid	<30	271
Dichlorohydrin	<39	271

TABLE I   **67**

	CST	References
p-DICHLOROBENZENE (continued)		
Ethanolamine	104.5	267,271
Ethylene glycol	>163	271
Furfural	<19.4	271
Isovaleric acid	<40	271
Methyl oxalate (m.p. 54)	<43	271
2-Octanol	<45	271
Phenol (m.p. 41)	<42.4	271
Propionamide (m.p. 70)	<65	271,445(p.797)
Sulfur	103.5	38A,210(p.35),391
Urethane (m.p. 50)	<48	271,445(p.797)
Valeric acid	<47	271
DICHLOROETHANE		
(see ETHYLENE CHLORIDE, p.86)		
1,2-DICHLOROETHYLENE		
Paraffin wax (m.p. 50)	<29	341
Lubricating oil	<10	341
2,2'-DICHLOROETHYL ETHER		
(CHLOREX)		
n-Butane	13.1	149
n-Pentane	10.85	149,188,485
n-Hexane	12.7	139,149,188,485
n-Heptane	15.5	139,149,188,455A,456, 485
n-Octane	19.7	149,153,188,455A,456, 457,485
2,2,4-Trimethylpentane	18.6	78,139,153,455A,457,485
n-Nonane	24	149,188,455A,485
n-Hexadecane (Cetane)	47.93	149,188,445(p.403),485
n-Octadecane	53.5	151
1-Heptene	-22	139
Diisobutene	-19	139
1-Nonene	-15.1	455A
Cyclohexane	-10.3	139,153,454A,455A,456
Methylcyclohexane	-8.6	Ibid.
Decalin	0	151
Paraffin wax (m.p. 53)	70	139
Paraffinic oils	68	139,149
Naphthenic oils	34,49	139,149,326
Allyl alcohol	<-35	455
n-Amyl alcohol	-14.7	446(p.417),455,455A,456
tert-Amyl alcohol	-16.9	446(p.417),455
Benzyl alcohol	<-35	455
1,3-Butanediol	53.8	446(p.417),455
n-Butyl alcohol	-24.9	446(p.417),455,455A,456
1,4-Dimethyl-1-pentanol	-4.0	446(p.417),455
Ethyl alcohol	-32.1	455,456
Ethylene glycol	115	267,271,446(p.416),455
Glycerol	>178	455
1,7-Heptanediol	60.5	446(p.417),455
n-Heptyl alcohol	-3	455,456
n-Hexyl alcohol	-12	455,456
Hydrogen cyanide	<25	148
Isoamyl alcohol	-12.9	446(p.416),455
Isobutyl alcohol	-12.3	446(p.416),455,455A
Isopropyl alcohol	-16.8	Ibid.

	CST	References

2,2'-DICHLOROETHYL ETHER (continued)

	CST	References
Methanol	<-53	455,456
2-Methyl-1-butanol	-9.4	446(p.416),455
2-Methyl-1-pentanol	-6.7	446(p.416),455
n-Octyl alcohol	-1.0	455,456
2-Phenylethanol	<-35	455
n-Propyl alcohol	-32.9	455,455A,456
Water	>20	284
Fourteen halogen hydrocarbons	<25	457A

2,2'-DICHLOROETHYL SULFIDE
(MUSTARD GAS)

	CST	References
Petroleum ether	19	149,209(p.395),392 (p.242),436
Gasoline	20.4	Ibid.
Kerosene	25.6	Ibid.
R. R. light oil	37	Ibid.
Ethyl alcohol	15.6	153,209,392(p.242),436
Sulfur	143	153,182,188,210(p.35), 482

DICHLOROGALEIN   15

DICHLOROHEXAFLUOROCYCLOBUTANE

	CST	References
Furfural	29.5	151

DICHLOROHYDRIN

	CST	References
p-Dichlorobenzene (m.p. 53)	<39	271

2,2'-DICHLOROISOPROPYL ETHER

	CST	References
All hydrocarbons	<m.p.	145
Water	>20	284

1,1'-DICHLOROMETHYL ETHER
(M—CHLOREX)   455A

3,3'-DICHLORO-n-PROPYL ETHER
(P—CHLOREX)   455B

	M—CHLOREX	P—CHLOREX
Melting point	-41.5	<-80
n-Heptane	-44	-61.6
n-Octane	-39.4	-56.4
n-Nonane	-35.9	-52.4
2,2,4-Trimethyl- pentane	-48.2	-63.8
1-Nonene	-79.1	<-80
Cyclohexane	-40.6	-41.0
Methylcyclohexane	54.8	-92.5
n-Amyl alcohol	-41.2	-71.0
n-Butyl alcohol	-46.5	-85.0
Isobutyl alcohol	-30.5	-62.0
Isopropyl alcohol	-37.3	-59.4
n-Propyl alcohol	-46.2	-90.5

2,4-DICHLOROPHENOL (m.p. 45)

	CST	References
Lubricating oils	<40	131,149

TABLE I   **69**

	CST	References

1,2-DICHLOROTETRAFLUOROETHANE
(see FREON 114)
α,α-DICHLOROTOLUENE
(BENZAL CHLORIDE)

All hydrocarbons	<m.p.	145

DICROTON

n-Hexane	-22	139
n-Heptane	-24	139,149
2,2,4-Trimethylpentane	-16	139
1-Heptene	<-78	139
Diisobutene	-56	139
Cyclohexane	-36e	139
Methylcyclohexane	-41	139
Paraffin wax (m.p. 53)	35e	139
Paraffinic oil	27	139
Naphthenic oil	-8	139

DI-(2-CYANOETHYL) AMINE

Cyclohexane	>80	151
Benzene	0	151
Toluene	41	151
sec-Butylbenzene	170	151
Di-sec-butylbenzene	>220	151

DICYCLOHEXYLAMINE

2,2,4-Trimethylpentane	0	149, 311

DIDODECYLAMINE

Acetone	<43	196
Acetonitrile	High	196
n-Butyl alcohol	<38	196
2-Butanone	<42	196
Methanol	38	196
Nine other solvents	<m.p.	196

DIETHANOLAMINE (2,2'-
IMINODIETHANOL)(Tables V and VIII)   106,121,284

Benzene	161	140
Biphenyl	183	140,446(p.133)
Bibenzyl	206	140,446(p.134)
Naphthalene	161	140,446(p.140)
1-Methylnaphthalene	182	140
2-Methylnaphthalene	182	140,446(p.142)
Isopropylnaphthalene	217	140,446(p.143)
sec-Amylnaphthalene	239	140,446(p.143)
Diisopropylnaphthalene	258	140,446(p.45)
Tetralin	181	140,446(p.45)
Isopropyltetralin	248	140,446(p.45)
Fluorene	179	140,446(p.144)
Anthracene (m.p. 216)	<195	140,446(p.144)
Phenanthrene	182	140,446(p.143)
Water	<20	284

N,N-DIETHYLACETAMIDE
(see ACETYLDIETHYLAMINE,p. 20)

DIETHYLACETIC ACID (Table VIII)   211

	CST	References
DIETHYLAMINE (Table III)		
n-Heptane	<-60	149,258
Water LCST, 143.5		1,135,153,169A,209
		253,258,392(p.278)
Miscibilities with 212		
substances		15
DIETHYLAMINOETHANOL		
Water	<20	284
N,N-DIETHYLANILINE		
Lubricating oil	<0	131,149
Acetamide	179	256,260,268,271,
		392(p.121),445(p.1106)
Ethylene glycol	>183.4	271
Glycerol	>300	153,328
DIETHYLCARBINOL (Table VI)		372
Paraffin wax (m.p. 50)	<38	341
Lubricating oils	<10	341
Water	>91.8	271,341
DIETHYLCARBITOL		
Water	<20	284
DIETHYL CELLOSOLVE (Table V)		106
Water	<20	284
DIETHYLCYCLOHEXYLAMINE		
2,2,4-Trimethylpentane	<0	149,311
DIETHYLDIPHENYLUREA (m.p. 71.5)		
Benzene, Toluene, m-Xylene	<50	93
Acetone, Carbon disulfide,		
Carbon tetrachloride,		
Chloroform, Ethyl acetate,		
Ethyl alcohol, Ethyl ether,		
Methanol and Pyridine	<50	93
DIETHYLENE GLYCOL		
(2,2'-DIHYDROXYETHYL ETHER)		284
n-Heptane	High	219
Benzene	88.5	140,152,218,219,421,
		446(p.95)
Toluene	134	140,421,446(p.113)
o-Xylene	153	152,421
m-Xylene	162	140,421,446(p.123)
p-Xylene	162	152,421
Ethylbenzene	155	140,421,446(p.116)
Cumene (Isopropylbenzene)	178	140,446(p.117)
Pseudocumene	187	140
Methylethylbenzene	176	140,446(p.128)
sec-Butylbenzene	191	140,446(p.119)
tert-Butylbenzene	189	140,446(p.119)
Diethylbenzene	193	140,446(p.128)
p-Cymene	194	140,446(p.129)
Methyldiethylbenzene	207	140,446(p.129)
Ethylisopropylbenzene	213	140,446(p.130)
sec-Amylbenzene	210	140,446(p.120)
Triethylbenzene	219	140,446(p.133)
Diisopropylbenzene	219	140,446(p.130)
Methyldiisopropylbenzene	229	140,446(p.133)

TABLE I   **71**

	CST	References
DIETHYLENE GLYCOL (continued)		
Di-sec-butylbenzene	240	151
Di-sec-amylbenzene	262	140,446(p.130)
Hexaethylbenzene	258	140
Styrene	111	140,446(p.120)
Biphenyl	126	140,271,446(p.133)
Bibenzyl	160	140,446(p.134)
Naphthalene	85	140,271,446(p.139)
1-Methylnaphthalene	126	140,149,446(p.141)
2-Methylnaphthalene	125	140,267,271,446(p.142)
Isopropylnaphthalene	175	140,446(p.143)
sec-Amylnaphthalene	199	140,446(p.143)
Diisopropylnaphthalene	214	140,446(p.143)
Di-tert-butylnaphthalene	231	140
Di-sec-amylnaphthalene	262	140
Tetralin	132	140,446(p.45)
Isopropyltetralin	210	140,446(p.45)
Fluorene	138	140,446(p.144)
Acenaphthene	136	271
Phenanthrene	128	140,446(p.144)
Lubricating oil	>235	131,149
Anethole	108	271
n-Butylbenzoate	102	271
2,6-Di-tert-butyl-4-methyl-		
phenol	190.2	428
Ethyl salicylate	66.5	267,271
Isoamyl benzoate	116.5	271
Isobutyl benzoate	86	255,267,270,271
Isoafrole	84.2	271
p-Nitrochlorobenzene		
(m.p. 83)	<76	271,446(p.913)
o-Nitrophenol (m.p. 45)	<42	271
p-Nitrotoluene (m.p. 52)	<48.5	271
Phenyl ether	116	271
Safrole	84.5	271
Thymol (m.p. 51.5)	<33	271
Water	<20	284
DIETHYLENE GLYCOL MONOAMYL ETHER		
Water LCST, 30		449B
DIETHYLENE GLYCOL MONOETHYL		
ETHER (see CARBITOL, p. 51)		
(Tables VII,VIII)		121,211
DIETHYLENE GLYCOL MONOMETHYL		
ETHER (METHYL CARBITOL)		
n-Hexane	85	139
n-Heptane	104	130,139,149
2,2,4-Trimethylpentane	104	139
1-Heptene	57	139
Diisobutene	55	139
Cyclohexane	63	139
Methylcyclohexane	68	130,139
Paraffin wax	192	139
Paraffinic oil	200	139
Naphthenic oil	168	139
Water	<20	284

	CST	References
Four other ETHERS of DIETHYLENE GLYCOL (Table VIII)(see also WATER, p.182)		211
DIETHYLENE TRIAMINE (Table VIII)		211,284
n-Heptane	>110	149
Methylcyclohexane	98	149
Kerosene	150	149
Water	<20	284
DIETHYL ETHER (see ETHYL ETHER, p.90)		
DIETHYLFORMAMIDE (Table VIII)		
n-Heptane	70	149,151
Methylcyclohexane	45	151
Di-sec-butylbenzene	19	151
DI-(2-ETHYLHEXYL) AMINE (Table VIII)		211
DIETHYL KETONE (3-PENTANONE)		
2-Methylpentane	27.42	309
2,2-Dimethylbutane	26.73	309
2,3-Dimethylbutane	19.37	309
Water	>160	153,209,253,362, 392(p.298)
DIETHYL MALONATE		15
Camphene	55.4	260
Silicon tetrachloride	-32	152,462,466
3,5-DIETHYLPHENOL		
Water	248	119,152,433
DIETHYL PHTHALATE (see ETHYL PHTHALATE, p.93)		
DIFLUOROMETHANE (see METHYLENE FLUORIDE, p.120)		
DIGLYCOL (see DIETHYLENE GLYCOL, p.70)		
DIGLYCOLCHLOROHYDRIN		
Water	<20	284
2,4-DIHYDROXYBENZALDEHYDE(m.p.135)		
Glycerol	<135	153,328
o,o'-DIHYDROXYBIPHENYL (m.p.110)		
Water	186.3	152,433
DI(2-HYDROXYETHYL) ANILINE		
1-Methylnaphthalene	<20	149
2,2'-DIHYDROXYETHYL ETHER (see DIETHYLENE GLYCOL, p.70)		
2,3-DIHYDROXYQUINOXALINE		15
DIIODOMETHANE (see METHYLENE IODIDE, p. 121)		

TABLE I 73

	CST	References
DIISOAMYLAMINE		
2,2,4-Trimethylpentane	<0	149,311
DIISOBUTYL KETONE (Table VIII)		211
Polyisobutene		
(m.w. 22,700 to 6,000,000)	18-56	404A
DIISOPROPYLAMINE (Table VIII)		211
p-DIMETHOXYBENZENE		
(HYDROQUINONE DIMETHYL ETHER)		
n-Octadecane	47	145,151
Glycerol	>240	153,328
DIMETHOXYMETHANE (METHYLAL)		
n-Hexadecane (Cetane)(m.p. 18)	<10	149
Crystal oil (Nujol)	0	149
Magnesium bromide	>106	210(p.203),299,302, 391(p.939)
Water	160.3	26,153,209(p.393), 392(p.208),443
DIMETHOXYTETRAGLYCOL		
Water	<20	284
DIMETHOXYTETRAMETHYLENE GLYCOL		
Kerosene	35	149
N,N-DIMETHYLACETAMIDE		
(see ACETYLDIMETHYLAMINE, p.20)		
DIMETHYLAMINE (Table VII)		121
N,N-DIMETHYLAMINOAZOBENZENE		
(m.p. 117)		15
N,N-DIMETHYLAMINOBENZALDEHYDE		
(m.p. 74)		15
N,N-DIMETHYLAMINO-1,2-PROPANEDIOL		
n-Heptane	134	149
N,N-DIMETHYLANILINE (Table V)		15,106
Two lubricating oils	<0	131,139,149
Acetamide (m.p. 81)	120.5	255,256,268,270,271, 392(p.121),445(p.1101)
Acetic acid	ca 0	393(p.1076),489A
Ethanolamine	95	271
Ethylene glycol	171.4	255,256,268,271,272, 392(p.157)
Glycerol	287	153,209,328,392(p.615)
Sulfur (m.p. 113)	ca 88	393(p.1067),489
DIMETHYLDIHYDRORESORCINOL		
n-Heptane	205E	149
Decalin	<115	149
Paraffin wax	250	149
DIMETHYLFORMAMIDE		
Propane	>70	151
n-Butane	64.6	109
n-Pentane	63	151
Isopentane	>27.3	109
n-Hexane	68	151

	CST	References
DIMETHYLFORMAMIDE (continued)		
n-Heptane	73	151
Propylene	-27	151
1-Butene	-13.5	109,151
cis-2-Butene	-19.5	109
Isobutene	-26.7	109
1-Pentene, cis-2-Pentene,		
2-Methyl-2-butene, Isoprene		
and Cyclopentene	<20	109
Allene	<-78	151
1,3-Butadiene	<-50	109
Cyclopentane	>23	109
Cyclohexane	50	151
sec-Butylbenzene	<-57	151
Hydrogen cyanide	<25	151

DIMETHYLGLYOXIME (m.p. 234.5)   15

DIMETHYL OXALATE
(see METHYL OXALATE, p.123)

1,4-DIMETHYL-1-PENTANOL
  2,2'-Dichloroethyl ether (Chlorex) -4.0 446(p.416),455

DIMETHYLPHENOLS
(see XYLENOLS and WATER, pp.182,188)

Six DIMETHYLPYRIDINES
(see under DEUTERIUM OXIDE, p.64,
and WATER, p.182)

2,5-DIMETHYLPYRROLE		
n-Hexadecane (Cetane)	13	151
Lubricating oil	0	151
Crystal oil (Nujol)	21	151

2,6-DIMETHYLQUINOLINE   15

DIMETHYL SULFATE (see METHYL SULFATE,
p.124)

2,4-DIMETHYLTHIACYCLOPENTANE DIOXIDE		
n-Heptane	>45	130
Methylcyclohexane	>45	130

N,N-DIMETHYL-o-TOLUIDINE
  Acetamide   174   255,256,264,268,271,
                                              392(p.121),445(p.1109)

2,2'-DINAPHTHYLAMINE (m.p. 171)   15

2,4-DINITROANILINE (m.p. 176)   15

2,4-DINITROANISOLE (m.p. 95)		
Benzene	<45	88,392(p.534)
Acetone	<20	Ibid.
Chloroform	<50	Ibid.
Pyridine	<25	Ibid.

TABLE I   **75**

	CST	References
o-DINITROBENZENE (m.p. 118)		
Five Polycyclic hydrocarbons	<m.p.	149,210(p.176)
Urea (m.p. 132)	<130	210(p.100),246,459
m-DINITROBENZENE (m.p. 89.6)		15
n-Heptane	193E	149
1-Heptene	149	139
Diisobutene	115	139
Cyclohexane	143	139
Benzene	<35	90
Toluene	<45	90
Isopropylbenzene (Cumene)	<68	140
Diisopropylbenzene	<63	140
Di-sec-butylbenzene	85	151
Di-sec-amylbenzene	119	140
Di-sec-amylnaphthalene	<78	140,445(p.649)
Paraffin wax (m.p. 53)	238	139
Paraffinic oil	230	139,149
Naphthenic oil	169.	131,139,149
Five Polycyclic hydrocarbons	<m.p.	149,210(p.176)
Acetone	<20	90
Ethyl acetate	<45	90
Iodine (m.p. 114)	>109.2	210(p.34),322B
Pyridine	<25	86,90
Sulfur dioxide	<25	85
Urea (m.p. 132)	129	210(p.100),246,459
p-DINITROBENZENE (m.p. 173)		
Five Polycyclic hydrocarbons	<m.p.	149,210(p.176)
Urea (m.p. 132)	164	210(p.100),246,459
3,5-DINITROBENZOIC ACID (m.p. 205)		15
Water	123.8	136,153,209(pp.390, 393),253,392(p.471)
2,4-DINITROBENZOYL CHLORIDE (m.p. 69)		
n-Heptane	150E	149
All hydrocarbons	Above decomp.	139,149
4,4'-DINITROBIPHENYL (m.p. 232)		15
2,4-DINITROCHLOROBENZENE (m.p. 53)		
n-Hexane	199	139
n-Heptane	187	139,149
2,2,4-Trimethylpentane	190	139
1-Heptene	127	139
Diisobutene	128	139
Cyclohexane	124	139
Methylcyclohexane	132	139
Benzene	<10	89
Toluene	<16	89
Diisopropylbenzene	<25	140
Di-sec-butylbenzene	65	151
Di-sec-amylbenzene	101	140
Di-sec-amylnaphthalene	51	140,445(p.649)
Paraffin wax (m.p. 53)	218	139
Paraffinic oils	206	139
Naphthenic oils	151,177	131,139
Acetone	<0	89,392(p.322)
Chloroform	<16	Ibid.
Ethyl acetate	<16	Ibid.
Ethyl ether	<27	Ibid.

	CST	References
2,4-DINITRO-1-NAPHTHOL-7-SULFONIC ACID		15
2,4-DINITROPHENETOLE (m.p. 86)		
Benzene	<30	88,392(p.578)
Toluene	<35	Ibid.
Acetone	<15	Ibid.
Chloroform	<25	Ibid.
Ethyl acetate	<45	Ibid.
Pyridine	<20	Ibid.
2,3-DINITROPHENOL (m.p. 145)		
Water	122.5	153,209(p.388),392 (pp.350-1),405,416
2,4-DINITROPHENOL (m.p. 113)		15,405
Benzene	<35	392(p.351),405,416
Di-sec-amylbenzene	151	140,149,446(p.173)
Di-sec-amylnaphthalene	117	140,149,446(p.195)
Acetone	<51	92
Water	>200	115,153,209(pp.388) 392(p.350),393(p.648) 405,416
2,5-DINITROPHENOL (m.p. 105.6)		
Water	>200	153,209,392(pp.350-1) 405,416
2,6-DINITROPHENOL (m.p. 61.5)		
Benzene	<m.p.	392(p.351),405,416
Acetone	<16	92
Water	>200	392(p.350),393(p.648) 405,416
3,5-DINITROPHENOL		
Water	125	153,209,392(pp.350-1) 405,416
Other DINITROPHENOLS		
Benzene	<m.p.	153,392(p.351)405,416
Water (see WATER, p.182)	<m.p.	115,153,209(pp.388-9) 392(pp.350-1),393 (p.848),405,416
2,4-DINITRORESORCINOL (m.p. 148)		
Water	167	115,393(p.649)
2,4-DINITROTOLUENE (m.p. 70)		15
Acetone	<20	90
Urea (m.p. 132)	>130.5	353
DI-n-OCTADECYLAMINE (m.p. 72.3) (Table III)		
Propane (crit. temp. 95.6)		
LCST, 94.2		22,153
Acetone	High	196
Acetonitrile	High	196
n-Butyl alcohol	<63	196
Ethyl acetate	<60	196
Methanol	High	196
Nine other solvents	<m.p	196

TABLE I   77

	CST	References
DI-n-OCTYLAMINE (m.p. 14.6)		
Acetone	16	196
Acetonitrile	High	196
Twelve other solvents	<m.p.	196
p-DIOXANE (m.p. 11.7)		
n-Hexane	-13e	139
n-Heptane	-4e	139,149
2,2,4-Trimethylpentane	-7e	139
Cyclohexane	-17e	139
Methylcyclohexane	-14e	139
Paraffin wax (m.p. 53)	45	139
Paraffinic oil	45	139
Naphthenic oil	14	139
Benzaldehyde	<25	393(p.992),418A
Hydrogen cyanide	<25	148
Water	<-15	151,162A,200A,392
Water with 0.21% K_2CO_3 25 to 40		234A,393(p.272)
DI-n-PENTADECYLAMINE (m.p. 63.3)		
Acetone	54	196
Acetonitrile	High	196
Methanol	90e	196
Eleven other solvents	<m.p.	196
DIPHENYLAMINE (m.p. 53)		15
Isopentane	44.9	51,149,209
n-Hexane	23e	139
n-Heptane	26e	139
2,2,4-Trimethylpentane	43	139
n-Octadecane	50	151
Cyclohexane	31.3	47
Benzene	<0	94,392(p.703)
Toluene	<5	94,392(p.703)
m-Xylene	<20	94,392(p.703)
Di-sec-butylbenzene	<25	145
Paraffin wax (m.p. 53)	67	139
Paraffinic oil	64	139
Naphthenic oil	10e	139
Acetone	<0	94,392(p.703)
Carbon dioxide (crit.temp., upper layer, 38.8)		46
Carbon disulfide	<0	94,392(pp.703-4)
Carbon tetrachloride	<28	Ibid.
Chloroform	<5	Ibid.
Ethyl acetate	<0	94,392(p.703)
Ethyl alcohol	<40	278A,392(p.703),452
Ethyl ether	<0	51,94,392(p.703)
Formic acid	>25	13,393(p.575)
Methanol	<25	94,278A,392(p.703), 452
n-Propyl alcohol	<50	392(p.703),452
Pyridine	<0	86,94,392(p.703)
Resorcinol (m.p. 110)	<92	207,393(p.1075)
Urea (m.p. 132)	>132	207,393(p.1075)
Water	304	52,153,209(p.392),253 392(p.702)

	CST	References
DIPHENYLBENZAMIDE		15
DIPHENYL DISULFIDE		
Paraffinic oil	0	139,149
DIPHENYL ETHER (or OXIDE)		
(see PHENYL ETHER, p.150)		
DIPHENYLETHYLENEDIAMINE (m.p. 65)		
n-Hexane	109	139
n-Heptane	103	139,149
2,2,4-Trimethylpentane	118	139
1-Heptene	52	139
Diisobutene	62	139
Cyclohexane	33e	139
Methylcyclohexane	48	139
Di-sec-butylbenzene	<25	145
Paraffin wax (m.p. 53)	139	139
Paraffinic oil	134	139
Naphthenic oil	85	139
DIPHENYLGUANIDINE (m.p. 147.5)		15
DIPHENYLKETOXIME		15
DIPHENYLSULFONE (m.p. 125)		15
DIPHENYLUREA (CARBANILIDE)		
(m.p. 238)		15
DI-n-PROPYLAMINE (Table III)		
Water LCST, -4.9		193,295(pp.415-6)
Miscibilities with 52		
substances		15,296(pp.464-10)
DI-n-PROPYLANILINE (Tables V and VIII)		106,211
DIPROPYLENE GLYCOL (Table VIII)		211,284
n-Heptane	120	149
Cyclohexane	72	149
Methylcyclohexane	84	149
Benzene	-3	151
Di-sec-butylbenzene	19	151
Octyltoluene	105	151
1-Methylnaphthalene	<-40	149
Water	<20	284
DI-n-PROPYLKETOXIME		
2,2,4-Trimethylpentane	<0	149,311
DI-n-TETRADECYLAMINE (m.p. 60.6)		
Acetone	<52	196
Acetonitrile	High	196
Ethyl acetate	<49	196
Methanol	90	196
Ten other solvents	m.p.	196

TABLE I   79

	CST	References
2,2-DITHIODIGLYCOL		
n-Heptane	400E	149
Benzene	>80	151
Naphthalene	180	149
DI-p-TOLYLSELENIDE	15	
DITOLYTHIOUREA		
n-Heptane	<-78	149
DI-n-TRIDECYLAMINE (m.p. 56.5)		
Acetone	<48	196
Acetonitrile	High	196
Ethyl acetate	<44	196
Methanol	79	196
Ten other solvents	<m.p.	196
n-DODECYLALCOHOL (m.p. 24)		
(LAURYL ALCOHOL)(Table VI)		372
All hydrocarbons	<m.p.	151
Acetonitrile	35.2	146,152,196A
Adiponitrile	>100	151
Ethylene glycol	135	146,152
Nitroethane	28	146,152,196A
Nitromethane	63	146,152
Hydrogen cyanide	>25	148
Propylene glycol	<15	151
Trimethylene glycol	<15	151
EOSIN	15	
EPICHLOROHYDRIN		
Lubricating oil	53.2	131,149
Water	>80	274,392(p.169)

ETHANE (crit.temp.32)(Table III)

	CST	References
n-Octadecane (m.p. 28)	<m.p.	145

	LCST*	References
5-n-Butyleicosane	27.7	366
11-n-Decyldocosane	10.6	366
18-Ethylpentatriacontane	<15	366
n-Octadecylcyclohexane	<17	366
11-(Cyclohexylmethyl)-heneicosane (crit.temp., upper layer, 33)	13.4	365,366
Squalene ($C_{36}H_{62}$)	22.6	366
Squalene ($C_{30}H_{50}$)	3.7	366
Di-sec-butylbenzene	<20	151
Naphthalene (m.p. 80) (crit.temp., upper layer, 39.4)	37.4	342A,445(p.41)
1-Methylnaphthalene	<20	151
Polyisobutene	0	155
Four oils	<20	151
Amyl alcohol	43.15	250,446(p.2)
Amyl stearate	19ı	149,191
n-Butyl alcohol (crit.temp., upper layer, 39.8)	38.1	149,248,250,446(p.2)
Carbon tetrafluoride	-122	390

(*) Liquid ethane is miscible below this temperature but not above.

	CST	References

ETHANE (continued)

LCST*

p-Chlorobromobenzene (m.p. 65)(crit.temp., upper layer, 47.2)	40m	381,445(p.179)
p-Chloroiodobenzene (m.p. 57)(crit.temp., upper layer, 38.5)	34.4m	381,445(p.179)
p-Dichlorobenzene (m.p. 53)	<m.p.	381
Ethyl alcohol (crit.temp.,upper layer, 40.7)	31.9 <-78	149,155,248,250 446(p.1)
Fluoroform	-86.9	365,439
Hexafluoroethane	<-97	365
Isopropyl alcohol (crit. temp.,upper layer, 44)		149,220,250
Methanol (crit.temp.,upper layer, 35.37)(incomplete mixing at all temperatures)	None None	149,248,250,446(p.1)
Methylene fluoride	ca-76	365,439
o-Nitrochlorobenzene (m.p. 32)	22.0	380
m-Nitrochlorobenzene (m.p. 44)	32.0	149,380
o-Nitrophenol (m.p. 45)	34.5	380
n-Propyl alcohol (crit. temp.,upper layer, 41.7)	38.67	46,149,248,250, 446(p.2)
A Silicone	-1	155
p-Toluidine (m.p. 45)	32.6	380
1,3,5-Trichlorobenzene (m.p. 63)(crit.temp., upper layer, 46.8)	40.3	365,381,445(p.180)
3,4-Xylidine (m.p. 48.5)	28.0m	378,380

ETHANOL (see ETHYL ALCOHOL, p.82)

ETHANOLAMINE (2-AMINOETHANOL)		284
Benzene	103	140
Toluene	137	140
Ethylbenzene	150	140
Di-sec-butylbenzene	>217	151
Styrene (Phenylethylene)	115	140,446(p.45)
Biphenyl	133	140,446(p.133)
Bibenzyl	168	140,446(p.134)
Naphthalene	97	140,446(p.140)
1-Methylnaphthalene	134	140,446(p.141)
2-Methylnaphthalene	134	140,446(p.142)
Isopropylnaphthalene	168	140,446(p.143)
Tetralin	139	140,446(p.45)
Fluorene	145	140,446(p.45)
Phenanthrene	139	140,446(p.144)
Anisole	76	271
Bromobenzene	59.5	271
Carbon tetrachloride (Iso-optic)	220	17,151
Chlorobenzene	120	271
Cineole	150.4	267,271

(*) Liquid ethane is miscible below this temperature but not above.

TABLE I   81

	CST	References
ETHANOLAMINE (continued)		
p-Dichlorobenzene	104.5	267,271
N,N-Dimethylaniline	95	271
Ethyl ether	>25	393(p.1085),418A
Glycerol	<20	153,284,328
Pyridine	<25	393(p.1085),418A
Water	<20	153,284,328
ETHER (see ETHYL ETHER, p.90)		
2-ETHOXYETHANOL (see CELLOSOLVE, p.55)		
ETHYL ABIETATE		
Paraffinic oil	<0	139,149
N-ETHYLACETANILIDE (m.p. 54)		
n-Heptane	<30	151
2,2,4-Trimethylpentane	<33	149
n-Hexadecane (Cetane)	43	149
Paraffin wax (m.p. 53)	69	149
Octyltoluene	38	151
ETHYL ACETATE (Tables VI and VII)		121,372
n-Heptane	<-78	139,147,149
n-Octane	<-60	346
n-Decane	<0	147
n-Dodecane (m.p. -12)	<-13	346
n-Hexadecane and n-Heptadecane	<15	346
n-Dotriacontane (m.p. 70)	<60	346
Paraffin waxes	12e,68	139,149,340
Paraffinic oils	10.5,68	131,139,340
Naphthenic oils	-17	Ibid.
Five higher Alcohols	<m.p.	196A
Fourteen Amides	<m.p.	348
Five secondary Amines	<m.p.	196
m-Aminobenzoic acid (m.p. 174)	<145	259,392(p.541)
p-Aminobenzoic acid (m.p. 187)	<145	Ibid.
Anthranilic acid (m.p. 147)	<98	259,392(p.540)
Diethyldiphenylurea (m.p. 71)	<50	93
m-Dinitrobenzene (m.p. 89.5)	<45	90
2,4-Dinitrochlorobenzene(m.p.53)	<16	89,392(p.322)
2,4-Dinitrophenetole (m.p. 86)	<45	88,392(p.578)
Diphenylamine (m.p. 53)	<0	94,392(p.703)
Eight Esters	<m.p.	390A
Ethylene glycol	56.5	146,152,256,319,392
		(p.157),446(p.582)
Furfural	<25	278,392(p.248),
		393(p.986)
Four 1-Haloalkanes	<m.p.	194A
Five Nitriles	<m.p.	194
o-Nitroaniline (m.p. 71)	<32	69,392(p.402)
m-Nitroaniline (m.p. 114)	<73	69,392(p.403)
p-Nitroaniline (m.p. 147.5)	<105	Ibid.
o-Nitrobenzyl chloride (m.p. 49)	<30	285,392(p.345)
m-Nitrobenzyl chloride (m.p. 47)	<30	Ibid.
p-Nitrochlorobenzene (m.p. 83)	<25	89,392(p.345)
o-Nitrophenol (m.p. 45)	<15.5	92,392(p.364)
p-Nitrophenol (m.p. 114)	<14	Ibid.
p-Nitrotoluene (m.p. 52)	<17	90,392(p.537)
Perfluorodimethylcyclohexane	>27	389
Perfluoromethylcyclohexane(C_7F_{14})	>27	389

	CST	References
ETHYL ACETATE (continued)		
Tri-n-decylamine	<9.8	347
2,4,6-Trinitroanisole (m.p. 68)	<15	88
2,4,6-Trinitrochlorobenzene (Picryl chloride, m.p. 83)	<18	89
2,4,6-Trinitrophenetole (m.p. 78)	<35	88
Trinitrophenylethylnitroamine (m.p. 95.7)	<50	91
Tri-n-octadecylamine	46	347
Tri-n-octylamine	-22.5	347
ETHYL ACETOACETATE		15
Propane	32	149
n-Butane	25	149
Isobutane	37.7	149
n-Pentane	27.7	151
n-Hexane	32	139
n-Heptane	43	139,149
2,2,4-Trimethylpentane	35	139,149,311
1-Heptene	-2	139
Diisobutene	-2	139
Cyclohexane	24	139
Methylcyclohexane	26	139,145
Petroleum ether (42-62°)	29	149,343
Petroleum ether (80-100°)	28.5	149,343
Paraffin wax (m.p. 53)	125	139
Paraffinic oil	130	139,149
Naphthenic oils	101	131,139,149
Hexachloroethane (m.p. 187)	<86	260,271
ETHYL ACETYLGLYCOLATE		
n-Heptane	60E	149
2,2,4-Trimethylpentane	67.5	149,311
ETHYL ALCOHOL (Tables III,IV,V,VII,VIII)		17,106,121,211
Ethane (Crit.temp.,upper layer, 40.67) LCST, 31.9	<-78	149,155,248,250, 446(p.1)
n-Butane (EtOH perhaps not anhydrous) LCST, 37.5?	<-78	149,209,249,446(p.3)
n-Pentane	<-78	149,249
Isopentane	<-30	249,446(p.5)
n-Hexane	-65	139,149,248,446(p.8)
n-Heptane	-60	139,147,149
2,2,4-Trimethylpentane	-70	139
n-Decane	-15	17,446(p.27)
n-Dodecane	12	151
n-Tetradecane	31	151
n-Hexadecane (Cetane)	55	151
2,13-Dimethyltetradecane	38.7	149,446(p.28),487
1-Octadecene	47	151
Cyclohexane	-16	151
Toluene	<0	147
Tetralin	<25	178
Turpentine	108.2	209
Petroleum ether	-10	29
Paraffin waxes	75 to 112	17,139
Paraffinic oils	33 to 128	79,139,149,201,340, 446(p.30)
Naphthenic oils	70,108	139,149,340
Acetanilide (m.p. 114)	<55	425

TABLE I   **83**

	CST	References
ETHYL ALCOHOL (continued)		
Thirteen fatty Acids	<m.p.	345
Fourteen Amides (in 95% EtOH)	<m.p.	348
m-Aminobenzoic acid (m.p. 174)	<118	259,392(p.541)
p-Aminobenzoic acid (m.p. 187)	<105	Ibid.
Anisic acid (m.p. 184.2)	<8	392(p.591),452
Anthranilic acid (m.p. 147)	<75	259,392(p.540)
Benzamide (m.p. 130)	<72	338,392(p.536)
1-Bromotetradecane		
(with 95% EtOH)	75	194A
Camphor (m.p. 176)	<25	166,392(p.678),426
Camphoric acid (m.p. 187)	<15	392(p.681)
Carbon dioxide (miscible)	None	45(p.677),145
Carbon disulfide	-24.4	17,153,169,209,223,
		247B,254,256,288
		294A,386,391(p.240)
		446(p.388),464
Carbon tetrachloride (m.p. -23)	<-39	391(p.217),392
		446(p.282),464
Catechol (m.p. 104)	<20	392(p.391),471
Chloral hydrate (m.p. 52)	<0	392(p.92),425
1-Chlorododecane (with 95% EtOH)	38	194A
Cottonseed oil	60	152,350
2,2'-Dichloroethyl ether (Chlorex)	-32.1	455,456
2,2'-Dichloroethyl sulfide	15.6	153,209,392(p.242),
(Mustard gas)		435,436
Diethyldiphenylurea (m.p. 71)	<50	93
Diphenylamine (m.p. 53)	<40	278A,392(p.703),452
2-Heptadecylbenzothiazole	80	108A
Nine higher Esters (in 95% EtOH)	<m.p.	390A
Ethyl vinyl ether	<25	393(p.910),418A
Hydrogen bromide (forms		
crystalline complex)	<-28.5	147,283A
Hydroquinone (m.p. 170.5)	<72	392(p.396),471
o-Hydroxybenzoic acid (m.p. 159)	<65	410
(Salicylic acid)		
m-Hydroxybenzoic acid (m.p. 201)	<100	410
p-Hydroxybenzoic acid (m.p. 214)	<100	410
1-Iodododecane (with 95% EtOH)	58	194A
1-Iodohexadecane (with 95% EtOH)	High	194A
Mandelic acid (m.p. 118)	<8	452
Methylene iodide	93.8	153,209(p.397),443,
		446(p.260)
Five Nitriles	<m.p.	194
o-Nitroaniline (m.p. 71)	<48	69,392(p.402)
m-Nitroaniline (m.p. 111.8)	<80	69,392(p.403)
p-Nitroaniline (m.p. 147.5)	<100	Ibid.
1-Nitronaphthalene (m.p. 58)	44.1	80,392(p.647)
(in 95% EtOH)		
o-Nitrophenol (m.p. 45)	<27	55,392(pp.364-366)
m-Nitrophenol (m.p. 97)	<1	Ibid.
p-Nitrophenol (m.p. 114)	<0	55,92,108A,
		392(pp.364-6)
Nitrous oxide (crit.temp., 32)	<20	70A(p.611)
Olive oil	145?52	17,151,393(p.1081)
Peanut oil	65	152,350
Phenylacetic acid (m.p. 76.7)	<0	392(p.581),452
2-Phenylpropionic acid		
(m.p. 48.6)	<-16	392(p.634),452
Pyridine zincichloride	32.9	133

	CST	References
ETHYL ALCOHOL (continued)		
Pyrogallol (m.p. 134)	<25	234A,392(p.404)
Resorcinol (m.p. 110)	<0	392(pp.393-4),425, 442,452,471
Rhamnose (m.p. 126)	<59	392(p.448),458
Saccharin (m.p. 228)	<25	15
Salicylic acid (m.p. 159)	<65	410
Sesame oil	62	152,350
Soybean oil	65	152,350
Succinonitrile (m.p. 54.5)	28	153,209(pp.395,397), 253,330,387A,443, 446(p.694)
Tetryl (Trinitrophenylmethylene-tetramine)(95% Ethanol)	105	1(p.147),80,81,153, 209(p.395),210 (p.147),392(p.496)
p-Toluidine (m.p. 45)	<8	392(p.560),425
Trimethylamine	<25	170
2,4,6-Trinitrotoluene (m.p. 81)	96.5	1(p.147),80,153, 209(p.395)
Triolein	145	17,446(p.595)
2-Undecylbenzothiazole (m.p. 44)	<10	108A
Urethane (m.p. 50)	<0	392(p.202),425
Miscibilities with 213 substances		15
N-ETHYLANILINE		
n-Hexane	-47.8	149,392(p.615),435, 445(p.524)
2-Methylpentane	-40.8	149,392(p.615),435
2,2-Dimethylbutane	-33.7	149,392(p.615),435, 445(p.524)
Crystal oil (Nujol)	-5	151
Ethylene glycol	126.5	255,256,266,268,271 272,392(p.157)
Glycerol	273	153,328
ETHYL ANTHRANILATE		
n-Hexadecane (Cetane)	27.5	151
ETHYL BENZOATE (Tables V,VII,VIII)		106,121,211
Paraffinic oil	<0	139,149
Acetamide (m.p. 81)	<70.8	255,270,271,392 (p.121),445(p.1049)
p-Chlorophenol (m.p. 43)	<-8	270,271
Ethylene glycol	136	255,256,268,270,271 319,392(p.157)
o-Nitrobenzyl chloride (m.p. 49)	<30	285,392(p.500)
m-Nitrobenzyl chloride (m.p. 47)	<30	Ibid.
Propionamide (m.p. 79)	<65	255,270,271,392 (p.198),445(p.1049)
ETHYLBENZYLAMINE		
Glycerol LCST,50	281	153,209(p.396) 328,392(p.642)
N-ETHYL-N-BENZYANILINE		
n-Hexadecane (Cetane)(m.p. 18)	<13	151
Crystal oil (Nujol)	<0	151
ETHYL BROMIDE		
Isopentane	<-160	373,149
Paraffin wax (m.p. 50)	<31	341
Two lubricating oils	<10	341

TABLE I **85**

	CST	References
ETHYL BROMOACETATE		
Ethylene glycol	75	271
ETHYL CAPROATE		
Urethane (Ethyl carbamate)(m.p.50)	<22	271,445(p.1043)
ETHYL CARBAMATE (see URETHANE, p.**178**)		
ETHYL CARBONATE		15
Kerosene	<0	149
Paraffin wax (m.p. 50)	<40	341
Three lubricating oils	<10	131,149,341
ETHYL CHLOROACETATE (Table VIII)		211
n-Dodecane	15	151
n-Tetradecane	26	151
n-Hexadecane	34	151
Naphthenic oil	26	151
Crystal oil (Nujol)	64	151
ETHYL CHLOROCARBONATE (**ETHYL CHLOROFORMATE**)		
Paraffin wax (m.p. 50)	<10	341
Two lubricating oils	<10	149,341
Crystal oil (Nujol)	<0	151
ETHYL CINNAMATE (Table VIII)		211
Acetamide	75	271
ETHYL CYANOACETATE		15
2,2,4-Trimethylpentane	>93	149,311
ETHYLDIETHANOLAMINE		
n-Heptane	135	149
ETHYLENE (critical temp. 9.6) (Table III)		
p-Dichlorobenzene (m.p. 53) LCST, 26		96,365
Menthol (m.p. 35) LCST, −9		96
Sixteen other crystalline substances		342A,365(p.234)
ETHYLENE BROMIDE		15
All hydrocarbons	<m.p.	131,145,256,268,341
Ethylene glycol	102	256,268,271, 392(p.157)
Formic acid	71.8	153,256(p.679),260, 268,271,392(p.32)
Iodine	78.4	321A,391(p.673)
o-Nitrophenol (m.p. 45)	<21	392(p.365),414
p-Nitrophenol (m.p. 114)	<80	Ibid.
Yellow phosphorus	ca 165	153,182,184,188, 209(p.394)
ETHYLENE CARBONATE (m.p. 36)		
Benzene and Toluene	<25	151
Xylene	72	151
sec-Butylbenzene	133	151

	CST	References
ETHYLENE CHLORIDE (Table VI)		15,131,284,372
Carbon disulfide	-33	153,174,255,256
Paraffin wax (m.p. 50)	<29	341
Lube oil	<10	341
Water	High	284

ETHYLENE CHLOROHYDRIN
(see 2-CHLOROETHANOL, p.58)

ETHYLENE CYANIDE
(see SUCCINONITRILE, p.165)

ETHYLENE CYANOHYDRIN
(see 2-HYDROXYPROPIONITRILE, p.108)

	CST	References
ETHYLENE DIACETATE (Table VIII)		211,284
n-Hexane	47	149
n-Heptane	58	149
2,2,4-Trimethylpentane	57	149,311
1-Heptene	11	149
Cyclohexane	18	140
Methylcyclohexane	29	140,445(p.419)
Decalin	53	140,445(p.419)
sec-Butylbenzene	<-78	140
Methylethylbenzene	-42	140
Ethylisopropylbenzene	-50	140
sec-Amylbenzene	-41	140
Diisopropylbenzene	-33	140
Triethylbenzene	-26	140
Methyldiisopropylbenzene	-14	140
Di-sec-amylbenzene	31	140
sec-Amylnaphthalene	-60	140
Diisopropylnaphthalene	-30	140
Di-sec-amylnaphthalene	32	140
Isopropyltetralin	-21	140,445(p.424)
Paraffin wax (m.p. 53)	137	149
Water	>20	284

	CST	References
ETHYLENE DIAMINE		284
n-Heptane	108	73,149,256
2,2,4-Trimethylpentane	112	73,149,256
Lubricating oil	<0?	131,149
Ethyl ether	-8	73,153
Isopropyl ether	36	73,153,256(p.678), 392(p.66)
Tetrachloroethylene	15.8	Ibid.
Water	<20	284,483A
Miscibilities with 33 substances		296(p.400),483A

ETHYLENE DICHLORIDE
(see ETHYLENE CHLORIDE, this page)

	CST	References
ETHYLENE DIFORMATE		
(CST in ref. 140 reduced 25°, cf. ref. 149)(p.304)		
n-Heptane	190E	149
Benzene (m.p. 5.5)	<-5	140
Toluene	-10	140
Ethylbenzene	21	140
m-Xylene	19	140
Methylethylbenzene	41	140
Cumene (Isopropylbenzene)	43	140

TABLE I   **87**

	CST	References
ETHYLENE DIFORMATE (continued)		
Pseudocumene	57	140
tert-Butylbenzene	58	140
sec-Butylbenzene	66	140
Diethylbenzene	64	140
Cymene (p-Isopropyltoluene)	64	140
Methyldiethylbenzene	76	140
Ethylisopropylbenzene	79	140
sec-Amylbenzene	87	140
Triethylbenzene	91	140
Diisopropylbenzene	97	140
Methyldiisopropylbenzene	106	140
Di-sec-butylbenzene	129	151
Di-sec-amylbenzene	147	140
Hexaethylbenzene	134	140
Styrene	-33	140
1-Methylnaphthalene	0	140
2-Methylnaphthalene	6	140
Isopropylnaphthalene	51	140
sec-Amylnaphthalene	85	140
Diisopropylnaphthalene	93	140
Di-tert-butylnaphthalene	125	140
Di-sec-amylnaphthalene	156	140
Tetralin	17	140
Isopropyltetralin	87	140
Phenylcyclohexane	106	151
Indene (m.p. -2)	<-8	151
ETHYLENE GLYCOL (Tables V to VIII)		106,121,211,284,372
(m.p. -12.6)		
n-Heptane (probably iso-optic), not CST)	80?	271(p.98)
Benzene	180	140
Toluene	210	140,446(p.113)
Biphenyl	<65?217	140,271,446(p.133)
Camphene	>152.51	260
Naphthalene	195	140,446(p.139)
1-Methylnaphthalene	217	140,446(p.141)
2-Methylnaphthalene	216	140
Tetralin	213	140,446(p.45)
Fluorene	220	140,446(p.144)
Anthracene	217	140,446(p.144)
Phenanthrene	225	140,446(p.144)
Lubricating oil	>190	131
33 Hydrocarbons mostly cyclic with CST above azeotropic boiling point		271(pp.98-9)
Acetone	<22	393(pp.1082-3),453A
Acetonitrile	-13.5	146,152
Acetonylacetone	>180.5	271
Acetophenone	114.5	256,268,271, 392(p.157)
Adiponitrile	27	146,152
Anisole	134.5	255,256,268,271,272 392(p.157)
Benzaldehyde	20	151
Benzonitrile	73	151
Benzyl acetate	100	256,268,271, 392(p.157)
Benzyl formate	107.5	271
Borneol (m.p. 208)	<99	260,271

	CST	References
ETHYLENE GLYCOL (continued)		
Bornyl acetate	110	256,268,271,392(p.157)
Bromobenzene	>150.2	271
Bromoform	142	255,256,262,268,271, 392(p.157)
1-Bromonaphthalene	>195	260,271
o-,m-,and p-Bromotoluene	>168	260,271
n-Butyl benzoate	178	255,263,271,392(p.157)
Camphor (m.p. 176)	<117	271
Carvone	97.8	256,268,271,392(p.157)
Chlorobenzene	>130.8	271
p-Chlorobromobenzene	>173.8	271
1-Chloronapthalene	>193.1	271
o-Chlorotoluene	>152.5	271
p-Chlorotoluene	>154.8	271
Cineole	>164.7	260,271
Citronellal	165	255,256,268,270,271, 392(p.157)
o-Cresol (m.p. 30)	<4.5	255,270,271
p-Cresol methyl ether	156	255,256,266,268,271,272 392(p.157)
n-Decyl alcohol (Iso-optic)	60,105?	146,152,255,262, 392(p.157).
p-Dibromobenzene	>183.9	271
1,3-Dibromopropane	85.7	271
o-Dichlorobenzene	>165.8	271
p-Dichlorobenzene	>163	271
2,2'-Dichloroethyl ether (Chlorex)	115	267,271,446(p.416),455
N,N-Diethylaniline	>183.4	271
N,N-Dimethylaniline	171.4	255,256,268,271,272, 392(p.157)
n-Dodecyl alcohol (Lauryl alcohol)	135	146,152
Ethyl acetate	56.5	146,152,256,319, 392(p.157),446(p.582)
N-Ethylaniline	126.5	255,256,266,268,271,272 392(p.157)
Ethyl benzoate	136	255,256,268,270,271,319 392(p.157)
Ethyl bromoacetate	75	271
Ethylene bromide	102	256,268,271,392(p.157)
Ethyl ether	>60	151
Ethyl fumarate	79.5	267,271
2-Ethylhexanol	<-5	151
Ethylidine diacetate	32.8	271
Ethyl maleate	79	271
Ethyl valerate	30	271
Eugenol methyl ether	144	255,256,268,270,271, 392(p.157)
2-Heptanone	>25	393(p.942)
n-Heptyl alcohol	<0	151
n-Hexyl bromide	>150.5	271
Hydrogen bromide (forms crystalline complex)	<45	147
Hydrogen cyanide	<25	148
Iodobenzene	>170.2	271
p-Iodotoluene	>181.5	271

TABLE I 89

	CST	References
ETHYLENE GLYCOL (continued)		
Isoamyl acetate	26	271
Isoamyl benzoate	182	255,256,268,270,271, 392(p.157)
Isoamyl carbonate	>188.5	271
Isobutyl benzoate	172	255,270,271,392(p.157)
β-Isosafrole	172	255,256,268,271, 392(p.157)
Menthol (Hexahydrothymol) (m.p. 35)	<17.6	271
Methanethiol (Iso-optic at 13.5)	>13.5	143
Methyl acetate	26.8	271,319,392(p.157), 446(p.577)
p-Methylacetophenone	77.5	255,256,268,270,271, 319,392(p.157)
N-Methylaniline	70	255,256,266,268,271, 272,392(p.157)
Methyl benzoate	107.5	256,271,319,392(p.157)
Methyl cinnamate	101.5	255,256,268,270,271, 392(p.157)
Methylene bromide (Dibromomethane)	>168.6	271
Methylene iodide (Diiodomethane)	>168.7	271
2-Methylheptanol	<0	151
Methyl heptenone	65	151,256,268,271, 392(p.157)
Methyl maleate	47.8	271
Methyl salicylate	143	255,256,266,268,270,271 392(p.157)
Nitrobenzene	120.2	255,256,260,268,271,272 392(p.157),446(p.903)
p-Nitrochlorobenzene	136.5	255,256,264,268,270,271 392(p.157),446(p.913)
Nitroethane	68	146,152
Nitromethane	39.7	146,152
o-Nitrophenol	>189.3	271
o-Nitrotoluene	142	255,256,264,266,268,271 272,392(p.157)
p-Nitrotoluene	141.5	Ibid.
2-Octanone(Methyl hexyl ketone)	66	255,256,266,268,269,271 392(p.157)
n-Octyl alcohol	<0	151
Pentachloroethane	>154.5	260,271
Phenyl acetate	67.7	256,268,271,392(p.157)
Propyl benzoate	164	255,256,268,270,271, 392(p.157)
Safrole	187.5	Ibid.
1,1,2,2-Tetrachloroethane	88.5	255,256,268,271, 392(p.157)
o-Toluidine (m.p. -24)	-55	151,255,256,262,268,271 272,392(p.157)
1,3,5-Trichlorobenzene	>181	256,271
1,2,3-Trichloropropane	>152.5	271
Vinyl bromide(Iso-optic at 15.7)	>15.7	143
Water	<20	284

	CST	References

ETHYLENE GLYCOL ETHERS (see BUTYL
CELLOSOLVE, p.48; CELLOSOLVE,
p.55; METHOXYETHANOL, p.117
PHENYL CELLOSOLVE, p. 149
WATER, p.183; Tables III,VIII)

ETHYLENE OXIDE
  Bromine $<$-50   283
  Chlorine $<$-80   283
  Perfluoromethyldecalin   11   151
  Perfluorononyldecalin
    (Iso-optic at 110e)   104   143
  Water $<$2   151,283,392(p.101)

ETHYL ETHER (crit.temp. 194)
(Tables III to VIII)   17,106,121,211,372
  All hydrocarbons $<$m.p.   131,145
  Chrysene (m.p. 254) LCST, 213   1,45,140,149,209(p.396)
                                                                   445(p.513)
  Bromine $<$20   70A(p.120)
  Camphor (m.p. 176) $<$25   166,392(p.678),426
  Camphoric acid (m.p. 187) $<$30   392(p.681)
  Catechol (m.p. 104) $<$38   392(p.391),471
  Chloral hydrate (m.p. 52) $<$25   392(p.93),426
  Diethyldiphenylurea (m.p. 71) $<$50   93
  2,4-Dinitrochlorobenzene
    (m.p. 53) $<$27   89,392(p.322)
  Diphenylamine $<$0   51,94,392(p.703)
  Ethanolamine $>$25   393(p.1085),418A
  Ethylenediamine   -8   73,153
  Ethylene glycol $>$60   151
  Hydrogen disulfide $<$20   19A,70A(p.384)
  Hydroquinone (m.p. 170.5) $<$122   392(p.396),471

  Magnesium bromide $>$23 and $>$158   210(p.203),253,299,
    (in two ranges of composition,   300,364,391(p.937)
    involving molecular compounds)
  Magnesium iodide (m.p. $>$700d)   38.5   153,209,210(p.204),
                                                                   253,297,391(p.973)
  Five Nitriles $<$m.p.   194
  o-Nitroaniline (m.p. 71) $<$43   69,392(p.402-3)
  m-Nitroaniline (m.p. 111.8) $<$89   Ibid.
  p-Nitroaniline (m.p. 147.5) $<$122   Ibid.
  o-Nitrobenzoic acid (m.p. 147) $<$75   70,392(p.488)
  m-Nitrobenzoic acid (m.p. 141) $<$80   70,392(p.489)
  p-Nitrobenzoic acid (m.p. 242) $>$170   70,392(p.490)
    (explodes)
  p-Nitrochlorobenzene (m.p. 83) $<$50   89,392(p.345)
  o-Nitrophenol (m.p. 45) $<$17   55,92,392(pp.364-366)
  m-Nitrophenol (m.p. 97) $<$0   Ibid.
  p-Nitrophenol (m.p. 114) $<$0   Ibid.
  p-Nitrotoluene (m.p. 52) $<$20   90,255,256,268,271,272,
                                                                   328,392(p.537)
  Nitrous oxide (crit.temp., 32) $<$20   70A(p.611)
  Perfluorodimethylcyclohexane $<$27   389
  Perfluoromethylcyclohexane $<$27   389
  Pyrogallol (m.p. 134) $<$25   234A,392(p.404)
  Saccharin (m.p. 228) $<$25   15
  Sulfuric acid (94.6%) $<$16   393(p.1065),439A
  Water (crit.temp.,upper layer,
    202.2) LCST, -70e   None   168A,250,377
  Miscibilities with 173 substances   15,347

TABLE I 91

	CST	References
ETHYL FORMATE (Table VII)		
n-Hexane	−40	139
n-Heptane	−34	139,149
n-Dodecane	<25	145
2,2,4-Trimethylpentane	−42	139
Diisobutene	−82e	139
Cyclohexane	−48e	139
Methylcyclohexane	−36	139
Paraffin waxes	65	139,346
Paraffinic oils	71	139,149,341
Naphthenic oils	41	Ibid.
ETHYL FUMARATE		
Naphthalene (m.p. 80)	<40	271
Ethylene glycol	79.5	267,271
Thymol (m.p. 51.5)	<35.5	271
ETHYL FUROATE		
n-Hexane	16	139
n-Heptane	20	139,149
2,2,4-Trimethylpentane	20	139
Diisobutene	−30e	139
Cyclohexane	−1e	139
Methylcyclohexane	−1e	139
Paraffin wax (m.p. 53)	85	139
Paraffinic oil	85	139
Naphthenic oil	49	139
ETHYL GLYCOLATE		
n-Heptane	80E	149
2,2,4-Trimethylpentane	>91	149,311
2-ETHYLHEXANOL (Table V)	106	
Crystal oil (Nujol)	<0	151
Ethylene glycol	<−5	151
Glycerol	>150	151
Nitromethane	36.4	151
Propylene glycol	<0	151
Trimethylene glycol	<0	151
ETHYLIDINE DIACETATE		
Ethylene glycol	32.8	271
ETHYL IODIDE	15	
ETHYL ISOTHIOCYANATE (Table V)	106	
Lubricating oil	<0	131,149
ETHYL LACTATE		
n-Hexane	8	139
n-Heptane	21	139,149
2,2,4-Trimethylpentane	−25	139
1-Heptene	17	139,149
Cyclohexane	−2	139
Methylcyclohexane	−1	139
Diisobutene	−30	139
Camphene (m.p. 50)	<16.4	271
Paraffin wax (m.p. 53)	115	139
Paraffinic oil	121	139
Naphthenic oil	94	139
Pinene	19.15	149,256,268,392(p.677)
Water	<25	296(p.737)

	CST	References
ETHYL MALEATE		
n-Heptane	32	151
n-Dodecane	57	151
Methylcyclohexane	<25	145
Naphthalene (m.p. 80)	<67	271
Paraffinic oil	61	151
Acetamide (m.p. 81)	<63	271,445(p.1046)
Ethylene glycol	79	271
ETHYL MALONATE		15
Camphene	55.4	260
Silicon tetrachloride	-32	152,462,466
ETHYL METHYL CARBAMATE		
n-Heptane	45E	149
2,2,4-Trimethylpentane	52	149,311
ETHYL METHYL KETONE		
(see 2-BUTANONE, p.47)		
ETHYL METHYL XANTHATE		
n-Heptane	<-30	149
ETHYL OXALATE		15
n-Hexane	15	139
n-Heptane	23.5	139,149
2,2,4-Trimethylpentane	21	139
1-Heptene	-26	139
Diisobutene	-30	139
Cyclohexane	5	139
Methylcyclohexane	5	139
Camphene (m.p. 50)	<23.8	255,270,271
Paraffin wax	114	139
Paraffinic oil	120	139
Naphthenic oil	85	139
Acetamide (m.p. 81)	<31.5	255,270,271,392(p.121), 445(p.1045)
Hexachloroethane (m.p. 187)	<105	255,270,271,392(p.66)
Urethane (m.p. 50)	<19	271,445(p.1045)
p-ETHYLPHENOL (m.p. 46)		
n-Octadecane (m.p. 28)	<30	151
Water	185	119,152,433
OTHER ETHYLPHENOLS (see		
WATER, p.183)		
ETHYL PHENYLACETATE (Table VIII)		211
n-Hexadecane (Cetane, m.p. 18)	<15	151
Acetamide (m.p. 81)	<60.5	271,445(p.1050)
Glycerol	81?>193	151,153,256,268,271, 392(p.210)
ETHYL PHENYLETHANOLAMINE		271
n-Heptane	84	149
2,2,4-Trimethylpentane	88	149
Di-sec-amylbenzene	<27	140,149,446(p.130)
Water	>20	284

TABLE I   **93**

	CST	References
ETHYL-2-PHENYL GLYCOLATE		
Petroleum ether (42–62°)	>b.p.	149,343
Petroleum ether (80–100°)	60	149,343
ETHYL PHTHALATE		
Propane (lower phase point, 100.5)		149,192
n-Hexane	24.95	310
2-Methylpentane	27.42	310
3-Methylpentane	20.59	310
2,2-Dimethylbutane	26.73	310
2,3-Dimethylbutane	19.37	310
n-Heptane	28.2	309
2-Methylhexane	30.05	309
2,2-Dimethylpentane	31.1	309
2,3-Dimethylpentane	18.85	309
2,4-Dimethylpentane	32.4	309
2,2,3-Trimethylbutane	16.9	309
Methylcyclohexane	<25	145
Petroleum ether (42–62°)	20.5	149,343
Petroleum ether (80–100°)	8	149,343
Carbon dioxide (Table III) LCST, 25		145
1-ETHYLPIPERIDINE (Table III)		
Water (LCST 7.45)		134,153,209(p.391),253
ETHYL PROPIONATE		
Paraffin wax (m.p. 50)	<33	341
Two lubricating oils	<10,>45?	149,341
Three **ETHYLPYRIDINES** (Table III)		
(see WATER, p.183)		
ETHYL SALICYLATE		
Paraffinic oil	<0	139,149
Acetamide	103.5	256,268,271,392(p.121)
Benzoic acid (m.p. 122)	<25.5	271
Diethylene glycol	66.5	267,271
Glycerol	>226	153,256,268,271, 392(p.210)
ETHYL STEARATE (m.p. 31.36)		
Benzene	<15	390A
Acetone	<25	390A
Acetonitrile	65.5	390A
Ethyl acetate	<22	390A
95% Ethyl alcohol	<30	390A
ETHYL SUCCINATE		
n-Heptane	29	151
n-Dodecane	54	151
Paraffinic oil	69	151
Methylcyclohexane	<25	145
ETHYL SULFATE		
n-Hexane	69	321
n-Heptane	75	149,150
2,2-Dimethylpentane	65	149,150
2,3-Dimethylpentane	61	149,150
2,4-Dimethylpentane	65	149,150
2,2,3-Trimethylbutane (Triptane)	56	149,150

	CST	References
ETHYL SULFATE (continued)		
n-Octane	79	321
2,2,4-Trimethylpentane	73	321,445(p.401)
2,7-Dimethyloctane	90	321,445(p.402)
"Amylene"	<20	321
1-Hexene	<20	321
4-Methyl-2-pentene	22	321
5-Methyl-1-hexene	16	321
4-Methyl-1-hexene	<20	321
1-Heptene	<20	321
2-Heptene	14	321
1-Octene	<-10	321
2-Octene	12	321
4-Methyl-2-heptene	37	321
Diisobutene	>25	321
1-Nonene	38	321
4-Methyl-2-octene	48	321
4,5-Dimethyl-2-heptene	46	321
4,6-Dimethyl-2-heptene	48	321
4,5,5-Trimethyl-2-hexene	41	321
1-Decene	>40	321
4-Butyl-2-octene	70	321
Hexadecene (Cetene)	>100	321
2-Methylnonadecene	111	321
Cyclohexane	>20	321
Decalin	>30	321
3-Cyclohexyl-1-propene	16	321,445(p.420)
4-Cyclohexyl-2-pentene	57	321,445(p.420)
1,3-Pentadiene	<-10	321
2,4-Heptadiene	<-10	321
4-Methyl-1,5-heptadiene	-5	321
5,5-Dimethylhexadiene	<-10	321
2,4-Octadiene	<-10	321
4,5-Dimethyl-2,6-octadiene	31	321
4-Propylheptadiene	26	321
4-n-Butyl-1,5-heptadiene	34	321
4,5-Dibutyl-2,6-octadiene	78	321
1-Octyne	<-10	321
1-α-Pinene	<-15	321
Lubricating oil	136	131,149
Hydrogen sulfide (Iso-optic at -47)	>25	143
ETHYL TARTRATE		
n-Heptane	125	149
Cyclohexane	82	149
Methylcyclohexane	92	149
ETHYL THIOCYANATE (Table V)		106
n-Heptane	-7	149
Lubricating oils	30.4	131,149
ETHYL VALERATE		
Ethylene glycol	30	271
ETHYL VINYL ETHER		
Ethyl alcohol	<25	393(p.910),418A
Water	>25	Ibid.

TABLE I   95

	CST	References
EUGENOL (2-METHOXY-4-ALLYLPHENOL)		
n-Butane	23	141,149
Isobutane	43	141,149
2,2,4-Trimethylpentane	24.5,11	139,149,311
n-Hexane	0	139
n-Heptane	3	139
n-Dodecane	18	151
n-Tetradecane	22	151
n-Hexadecane (Cetane)	26.5	151
1-Heptene	-44	139
Diisobutene	-42	139
Cyclohexane	-38e	139
Methylcyclohexane	-30	139
Paraffin wax (m.p. 53)	64	139
Paraffinic oil	63	139,149
Naphthenic oils	21 to 44.4	131,139,149
Acetamide (m.p. 81)	<59.5	255,270,271,392(p.121)
Glycerol	166	153,256,268,271,
		392(p.210)
EUGENOL METHYL ETHER		
Acetamide (m.p. 81)	<61.5	255,260,270,271,
		392(p.121),445(p.1000)
Benzoic acid (m.p. 122)	<117	271
Ethylene glycol	144	255,256,268,270,271,
		392(p.157)
Propionamide (m.p. 79)	<55	255,264,270,271,
		392(p.198)
FLUORESCEIN		15
FLUOROBENZENE		
Water (Isopycnic at 48)	High	140A
FLUOROFORM		
Ethane	-86.9	365,439
Methane	>-174	439
Carbon tetrafluoride	-142.7	365,390,438
Hexafluoroethane	<-87	365,390,438,439
Methylene fluoride	<-97	365,439
Xenon	-87	365,439
Other FLUORINE Compounds (see		
PERFLUORO-, p.143,HYDROPERFLUORO-,		
p.106,METHYLPERFLUORO-, p.123)		
FORMAMIDE (Tables V,VII)		106,121
Propane (crit.temp.,upper		
layer, 98)		22
n-Hexane (crit.temp.,upper		
layer, 250)		149,215
Benzene	>202	341B,445(p.608)
Naphthalene	>203	140,149
Chloroform (Iso-optic)	High	144
Hydrogen cyanide	<-44	331,332
Nitrobenzene	108.2	215,226,393(p.1070),
		445(p.1145)

	CST	References

FORMANILIDE (m.p. 49)

n-Heptane	228	149
Methylcyclohexane	150	149
Benzene	<1	151
Di-sec-butylbenzene	81	151
Lubricating oils	>100	131,149

FORMIC ACID (Table IV)   17

n-Pentane, (Lecat's observation, 28? probably an iso-optic, not a CST)		256,268,271(p.18), 392(p.32)
n-Pentane	>180	144,151
n-Hexane	>130	17,149
n-Heptane	185E	149
n-Decane	200	17,149
Benzene	74	10,127,149,209,253,254, 255,392(p.27), 393(p.1069),442,443, 446(p.219),446B,469
Xylene	>100	151,352
Paraffin wax (m.p. 53)	200	17,149
Allyl isothiocyanate	39.8	153,209,226,260, **392(p.32)**
Bromodichloromethane	61.3	153,**256**,268,271, **392(p.16)**
Bromoform	>70	10,**165,392**(pp.12,25), 393(p.1069)
Carbon disulfide	>42.5	165,271
Carbon tetrachloride	220	17,446(p.359)
Chlorobenzene	106.6	17,209,443,446(p.374)
Diphenylamine (m.p. 53)	>25	13,393(p.575)
Ethylene bromide	71.8	153,256(p.679),260, 268,271,392(p.32)
Hydrogen cyanide	<-32	331,332
Triethylamine	>25	226,392(p.32)
Water	<-48	129
22 Hydrocarbons and 15 halogenated hydrocarbons, CST above azeotropic b.p.		135,271(pp.12,18)

FREON 12 (CCl_2F_2)

Phenanthrene (m.p. 100)	<m.p.	151
Butylanthracene	<m.p.	151
Nitromethane	>52	151

FREON 21 ($CHCl_2F$)

| Water (Iso-optic at 71) | >71 | 143 |

FREON 22 ($CHClF_2$)

| Nitromethane | <0 | 151 |

FREON 114 ($CClF_2)_2$

1-Methylnaphthalene	12	151
Phenanthrene	High	151
Nitromethane	>50	151
Snow (iso-optic at -2)		143
Nonaromatic oil	-20	151

TABLE I   97

	CST	References
Other FREONS		
Most hydrocarbons	<m.p.	151
Solubilities in many solvents		296(p.376)
FURFURAL (Tables II and VI)		372,383
n-Hexane	92	139,152,333
2-Methylpentane	88e	152,333
2,2-Dimethylbutane	93e	152,333
2,3-Dimethylbutane	79e	152,333
n-Heptane	93.7	130,139,152,333
2,4-Dimethylpentane	96e	149,152,333
2,2,3-Trimethylbutane	90	149
2,2,4-Trimethylpentane	101	139,152,333
2,2,5-Trimethylhexane	104.4	152,333
n-Docosane	144.3	34,149
Isobutene	>-6.7	393(p.1091),423A
1-Heptene	56	139
Diisobutene	62	139
Butadiene	>-6.7	393(p.1091),423A
Cyclopentane	48e	152,333
Methylcyclopentane	67.3	78,152,333
Cyclohexane	66.3	139,140,152,333,
		445(p.412)
Methylcyclohexane	73.2	130,139,140,152,
		333,445(p.418)
Decalin	81	151
Camphene	48	149,260,271
Dipentene	20.1	271
α-Pinene	62.4	149,260,271
Toluene	<-60.7	140,149,354
m-Xylene	-55	Ibid.
Methyldiisopropylbenzene	-18	140
Di-sec-butylbenzene	20	151
Di-sec-amylbenzene	47	140
Di-sec-amylnaphthalene	23	140
Diphenylhexane (m.p. 137)	<45	34,393(p.1092)
Paraffin waxes	159	139,340
Paraffinic oils	165	131,139,340,354
Naphthenic oils	122 to 140	Ibid.
Furfural points of about		
261 other pure hydrocarbons		
are listed in Table II		382,383
Six fatty acids	<m.p.	198
p-Dichlorobenzene (m.p. 53)	<19.4	271
Dichlorohexafluorocyclobutane	29.5	151
Ethyl acetate	<25	278,392(p.248),
		393(p.986)
Hydrogen cyanide	<25	148
Oleic acid	26.2	195,446(p.546)
Stearic acid	<62	198
Sulfur (m.p. 113)	>130	151
Water	122	82B,125,153,167A,
		209(p.388),253,278,
		330,362,392(p.281),
		393(pp.636-7),442,486
Miscibilities with 24 organic		
acids		198,296(p.576)

	CST	References
FURFURYL ALCOHOL (Tables V,VI and VII)		
n-Hexane	115	139
n-Heptane	115	139,149
2,2,4-Trimethylpentane	122	139
1-Heptene	76	139
Diisobutene	79	139
Cyclohexane	78	139,140,446(p.40)
Methylcyclohexane	93	139,140
Decalin	88	140,149
Cumene (Isopropylbenzene)	-50	140,446(pp.117-8)
Pseudocumene	-11	140
sec-Butylbenzene	-22	140,446(p.119)
tert-Butylbenzene	-32	140,446(p.119)
Diethylbenzene	-16	140,446(p.128)
p-Cymene (p-Isopropyltoluene)	-19	140
Methyldiethylbenzene	2	140,446(p.129)
sec-Amylbenzene	11	140,446(p.120)
Ethylisopropylbenzene	2	140,446(p.130)
Triethylbenzene	16	140,446(p.133)
Diisopropylbenzene	20	140,446(p.130)
Methyldiisopropylbenzene	32	140,446(p.133)
Di-sec-butylbenzene	58	151
Di-sec-amylbenzene	82	140,446(p.130)
sec-Amylnaphthalene	0	140,446(p.143)
Diisopropylnaphthalene	18	140,446(p.143)
Di-sec-amylnaphthalene	88	140
Isopropyltetralin	32	140,446(p.45)
Phenylcyclohexane	16	151
Paraffin wax (m.p. 53)	180	139
Paraffinic oil	183	139,149
Naphthenic oils	148,154	131,139,149
Water	<25	296(p.43),362
FUROIC ACID (m.p. 131)		
n-Hexane	166	139
n-Heptane	168	139,149
2,2,4-Trimethylpentane	184	139
Diisobutene	107	149
Cyclohexane	98e	139
Methylcyclohexane	112e	139
Paraffin wax (m.p. 53)	267e	139
Paraffinic oil	250	139
Naphthenic oil	214	139
GALACTOSE and GALLEIN		15
GALLIC ACID (3,4,5-TRIHYDROXYBENZOIC ACID)		15
GELATIN		15
GERANIOL (3,7-DIMETHYL-2,6-OCTADIEN-1-OL)		
Acetamide (m.p. 81)	<58.6	255,270,271,392(p.121)
Propionamide (m.p. 79)	<55	255,264,271,392(p.198)
GERMANIUM TETRACHLORIDE		
Sulfur dioxide	-4.7	24,25,153,188,256(p.676)
GLUCOSE		15

TABLE I   **99**

	CST	References
β-GLUCOSE PENTAACETATE		15

GLUTARIC DINITRILE
| Water | 68.3 | 153,256(p.669), 392(p.290),395 |

GLYCEROL (Tables III to VIII)
		15,17,106,121,211,372
Naphthalene	>250	140,149,446(p.139)
Lubricating oil	>200	131
All other hydrocarbons	High	145
Acetic acid	<25	393(p.1075),418A
Acetic anhydride	High	339A,393(p.1086)
Acetone	95.7	153,209(p.395),286, 328,330,341B,392(p.180) 446(p.484)
Acetonitrile	90	146,153
Acetophenone	185.5	153,209(p.396),286,328, 330,392(p.579)
m-and p-Aminophenols	<m.p.	153,328
n-Amyl alcohol	61.1	341B,446(p.1128)
Aniline	<0	153,328
o-Anisidine	145	153,209(p.396),328, 392(p.560),399
p-Anisidine (m.p. 58)	<57.1	153,328
Anisole	275.5	153,209(p.395),286,328, 392(p.546)
Benzaldehyde	160.7	17,153,209(p.395),286, 328,330,392(p.497), 446(p.467)
Benzylamine	<20	153,328
N-Benzylaniline	High	153,328
Benzylethylamine LCST, 50	281	153,209(p.396),328, 392(p.642)
Benzylmethylamine	<20	153,328
Bornyl acetate	200	153,256,268,270,271, 392(p.210)
o-,m-,and p-Bromotoluenes	>168	271
2-Butanone(Methyl ethyl ketone)	164.5	153,209(p.395),253,286, 328,330,362,365, 392(p.244),418,443,446 (p.488),486
n-Butylamine	<20	153,328
n-Butyl benzoate	243	153,256,268,271, 392(p.210)
Butylchloral hydrate	<15	166,392(p.218)
Carbon disulfide (Isopycnic at 20)	High	140A,151
Carbon tetrachloride	270	17
Carvacrol (2-p-Cymenol)	>200	153,328
Catechol (m.p. 104)	<100	153,209,286,328
Catechol diethyl ether	>240	153,328
Catechol dimethyl ether (Veratrole)	>240	153,328
Catechol monoethyl ether	192.9	153,209(p.396),328, 392(p.209)
Chloral hydrate (m.p. 52)	<25	392(p.93),426
Chlorobenzene	>200	17
o-,m-,and p-Cresols	<m.p.	153,328
2,2'-Dichloroethyl ether (Chlorex)	>178	455
N,N-Diethylaniline	>300	153,328

	CST	References

GLYCEROL (continued)

2,4-Dihydroxybenzaldehyde		
(m.p. 135)	<135	153,328
p-Dimethoxybenzene	>240	153,328
N,N-Dimethylaniline	287	153,209(p.396),328, 392(p.615)
Ethanolamine	<20	153,284,328
N-Ethylaniline	273	153,328
Ethylbenzylamine LCST, 50	281	328,392(p.642),153,209
2-Ethylhexanol	>150	151
Ethyl phenylacetate 81?,>193		151,153,256,268,271, 392(p.210)
Ethyl salicylate	>226	153,256,268,271,392(p.210)
Eugenol (4-Allylguaiacol)	166	Ibid.
Guaiacol (o-Methoxyphenol)		
(Table III) LCST, 39.5	83.5	153,209(p.395),287,328, 341A,392(p.209),444
Hydroquinone dimethyl ether	>240	153,328
Isoamyl alcohol	74.2	17,153,209(p.395),287,328 330,392(p.314),446(p.1128)
Isobutylamine	<20	153,328
Isobutyl benzoate	230	153,256,268,271,392(p.210)
N-Methylaniline	224.5	153,209(p.395),328, 392(p.553)
N-Methyl-N-benzylaniline	High	153,328
Methyl salicylate	170	256,268,271,392(p.210)
o-,m-,and p-Methyl tolyl		
ethers	High	153,328,392(p.210)
p-Nitrochlorobenzene		
(m.p. 83)	215	271,446(p.913)
Nitromethane	>120	151
o-Nitrotoluene	193	153,255,256,268,271,272, 392(p.210)
p-Nitrotoluene (m.p. 52)	220	153,255,256,268,271,272, 328,392(p.210)
Orcinol (m.p. 108)	<107	153,328
Orcinol dimethyl ether	>240	153,328
Orcinol monomethyl ether		
(m.p. 44)	<44	153,328
Phenol	<0	153,166,328,392(p.379)
o-,m-,and p-Phenylenediamines <m.p.		153,328
2-Phenylethanol	4.5,59?	153,328
3-Phenylpropanol	>100	153,328
α-Picoline (2-Methylpyridine)	<20	153,328
Piperidine	<20	153,328
Piperonal	159	153,328
Propionitrile	140	17,446(p.191)
Protocatachualdehyde (m.p.153)	<153	153,328
Pyridine	<20	106,153,328
Pyrogallol trimethyl ether	230.5	153,328
Quinol diethyl ether	>240	153,328
Quinol dimethyl ether	>240	153,328
Quinol monoethyl ether		
(m.p. 66)	<66	153,328
Quinol monomethyl ether		
(m.p. 53)	<53	153,328
Quinoline	<20	153,328
Resorcinol diethyl ether	>240	153,328
Resorcinol dimethyl ether	>240	153,328
Resorcinol monoethyl ether	<20	153,328
Resorcinol monomethyl ether	<20	153,328

TABLE I 101

	CST	References

GLYCEROL (continued)

Salicyl alcohol (Saligenin)		
(m.p. 86)	<86	153,328
Salicylaldehyde	176.6	153,209(p.395),287,328, 392(p.210)
Sulfur dioxide (no complete mixing)	None	151
Thymol	218.5	153,209,220,287,328
o-Toluidine	154.4	153,209(p.395),328, 330,392(p.210)
m-Toluidine (LCST, 6.7) (Figure 2)	120.5	153,209(p.396),272,328, 330,392(p.210)
p-Toluidine (m.p. 45)	<42.8	153,286,328
2,4-Toluylene diamine (m.p.99)	<99	153,328
3,4-Toluylene diamine (m.p.89)	<88.5	153,328
Vanillin (m.p. 81-2)	<80	153,286,328
Water	<-23	256A,392(p.209)
m-Xylenol (2,4-Xylenol-1) (m.p. 26)	<20	153,328
p-Xylenol (2,5-Xylenol-1) (m.p. 74.5)	<74.5	153,286,328
m-Xylidine (2,4-Xylidine-1)	196.5	153,328
Miscibilities with 30 substances		296(p.565)

GLYCEROL DICHLOROHYDRIN

		15
n-Heptane	20E	149
Pinene	43.3	149,256,268,392(p.677)

GLYCEROL-1-ISOAMYL ETHER

n-Heptane	-45E	149
Kerosene	<-25	149

GLYCEROL-1-METHYL ETHER

n-Heptane	220E	149
Benzene	<1	149
1- and 2-Methylnaphthalenes	57	149

GLYCEROL MONOACETATE
(see MONOACETIN, p.125)

GLYCEROL-1-MONOCHLOROHYDRIN

n-Heptane	352E	149
Naphthalene	132	140,446(p.140)
1-Methylnaphthalene	153	140,446(p.141)
2-Methylnaphthalene	155	140,446(p.142)
Phenanthrene	174	140,446(p.144)
Bibenzyl	178	140,446(p.134)
Lubricating oil	>100	131,149

GLYCEROL-1-PHENYL ETHER

n-Heptane	100E	149
Methylcyclohexane	>100	149

GLYCERYL FURFURAL

n-Heptane	215E	149
Benzene	<-5	149

GLYCERYL OLEATE

n-Heptane	-18E	149
2,2,4-Trimethylpentane	-18	149
Paraffinic oil	<0	149

	CST	References
GLYCOL (see ETHYLENE GLYCOL, p. 87)		
GLYCOL DERIVATIVES (see WATER, pp.181,183)		284
GLYCOLIC ACID (m.p. 63)		
n-Heptane	320E	149
Benzene	>90	149
GUAIACOL (o-METHOXYPHENOL) (m.p. 28.2)(Table III)		15
Acetamide (m.p. 81)	<20.5	255,270,271,392(p.121)
Citronellal	<18	255,270,271,392(p.551)
Glycerol LCST, 39.5	83.5	153,209(p.395),287, 328,341A,392(p.209)444
GUANIDINE NITRATE		15
GUM ARABIC		15
H ACID		15
HALOHEPTANE (see PERFLUORO-, p.143)		
HEMOGLOBIN		15
HENDEC- (see UNDEC-,p. 178)		
n-HENDECYLIC ACID		
Fifteen Organic solvents	<m.p.	197,345,392(pp.735-6)
16-HENTRIACONTANONE (PALMITONE, m.p. 83.7)		
Acetonitrile	High	158,393(pp.805-6)
Twelve other solvents	<m.p.	158,393(pp.805-6)
14-HEPTACOSANONE (MYRISTONE) (m.p. 17.2)		
Acetonitrile	>82	153,158,393(p.804)
Twelve other solvents	<m.p.	158,393(pp.803-4)
n-HEPTADECYL ALCOHOL (Table VIII)		211
2-HEPTADECYLBENZOTHIAZOLE (m.p. 39.6)		
Acetonitrile, 95% Ethyl alcohol	>80	108A
Methanol	>65	108A
Seven solvents	<m.p.	108A
n-HEPTADECYLIC ACID		
Five solvents	<m.p.	197,345
1-HEPTALDEHYDE		
n-Octadecane	21	151
HEPTAFLUOROBUTYRIC ACID		
Propane (Iso-optic at O)	>O	143
1,7-HEPTANEDIOL		
2,2'-Dichloroethyl ether (Chlorex)	60.5	446(p.416),455

TABLE I 103

	CST	References
3-HEPTANOL (Table VIII)		211
2-HEPTANONE		
Ethylene glycol	>25	393(p.942)
n-Heptyl acetate (Table VIII)		211
n-HEPTYL ALCOHOL		
All hydrocarbons	<m.p.	145
2,2'-Dichloroethyl ether		
(Chlorex)	-3	455,456
Ethylene glycol	<0	151
Nitromethane	36.5	151
Urethane (Ethyl carbamate)	<20.5	271,446(p.876)
(m.p. 50)		
Water	248.5	118,152,153
HEXACHLOROBENZENE (m.p. 229)		
Lubricating oil	<216	131
HEXACHLOROETHANE (m.p. 187)		
Aniline	<101	260,271
o-Cresol	<122	260,271
Ethyl acetoacetate	<86	260,271
Ethyl oxalate	<105	255,270,271,392(p.66)
Isovaleric acid	<104	271
Phenol	<124	255,270,271,392(p.66)
HEXACHLOROPHENOL (m.p. 106)		
n-Heptane	<55	149
Paraffin wax (m.p. 53)	<100	149
n-HEXADECYL ALCOHOL		
(CETYL ALCOHOL)(m.p. 49.6)		
Acetonitrile	58	196A
Nitroethane (Figure 4)	<45	196A
Pyridine zincichloride	241	133
Sulfur dioxide	<25	210(p.188),392(p.767), 396
n-HEXADECYLAMINE (m.p. 46.77)		
Propane	None	22
Acetone	<36	349
Acetonitrile	<42	349
HEXAFLUOROETHANE		
Ethane	<-97	365
Fluoroform	<-87	365,390,439
Methylene fluoride	>-68	365,439
HEXAMETHYLENEIMINE (Table III)		
Water LCST, 66.9	228	152,494
HEXAMETHYLENETETRAMINE		15
Water	<20	392(p.434),458A
n-HEXANE (Table IV)		17
64 pure substances	<m.p.	194B
2,5-HEXANEDIOL		
Benzene	34.2	218

	CST	References

2,5-HEXANEDIONE
  (see ACETONYL ACETONE, p.19)

2-HEXANONE
  Water   >90   271

n-HEXYL ALCOHOL
  All hydrocarbons   <m.p.   145
  2,2'-Dichloroethyl ether
    (Chlorex)   -12   455,456
  Water   222.2   118,152

n-HEXYLBROMIDE
  Ethylene glycol   >150.5   271
  Urethane (m.p. 50)   <32   271

n-HEXYL ETHER (Table VIII)   211

HIPPURIC ACID and HYDRAZINE SULFATE   15

HYDRAZOBENZENE (m.p. 123)
  n-Heptane   150E   149

HYDROCINNAMALDEHYDE
  n-Heptane   21.1   151
  n-Dodecane   34   151
  n-Tetradecane   40   151
  n-Hexadecane (Cetane)   43   151
  Naphthenic lubricating oil   25.5   151

**HYDROCINNAMIC ACID (see
2-PHENYLPROPIONIC ACID p. 152)**

HYDROGEN BROMIDE (crit.temp., 90)
  n-Heptane   <-78   149
  Practically all organic
    liquids   <m.p.   147
  Carbon dioxide   <0   147
  Ethyl alcohol (forms
    crystalline complex)   <-28.5   147,283A
  Ethylene glycol (ibid)   <45   147
  Hydrogen cyanide   <-78   148
  Methanol (forms crystalline
    (complex)   <-12   147,283A
  Water (incomplete mixing)   None   56B, 70A(p.114),147,359

HYDROGEN CHLORIDE (crit.t., 51.4)
  Ethane   <-134.5   210(p.212)
  Propane   <50   149,163A
  n-Butane   <21   149,325A
  n-Heptane   <-91   147,149
  Practically all organic
    liquids   <m.p.   147,210
  Aniline LCST, 10.5   210(p.186),275
  Carbon dioxide   <0   70A(p.219),147
  Hydrogen cyanide   <-78   148
  Hydrogen sulfide   <20   70A(p.219),147
  Krypton   <-30   163A
  Water (incomplete mixing)   None   147,368

TABLE I   **105**

	CST	References
HYDROGEN CYANIDE (b.p. 26)		
Propane, n-Hexane, Cyclohexane	>25	148
Propylene	<-78	148,151
Benzene, Xylenes	<25	148
1-Hexene, 1-Octene, Decalin	>25	148
Tetralin, sec-Butylbenzene	>25	148
1-Methylnaphthalene	>25	148
Acetonitrile, Aniline	<25	148
Benzaldehyde	<-65	332
n-Butyl alcohol	<25	148
Carbon disulfide	>25	148
Carbon tetrachloride	>25	148
Chlorex	<25	148
2-Chloroethanol, Chloroform	<25	148
m-Cresol, n-Decyl alcohol	<25	148
Dimethylformamide	<25	151
Dioxane, Ethylene glycol	<25	148
Formamide	<-44	331,332
Formic acid	<-32	148,331,332
Furfural	<25	148
Hydrogen bromide and chloride	<-78	151
Lauryl alcohol	>25	148
Methanol	<25	148
Nitrobenzene, Nitromethane	<25	148
Perfluorodimethylcyclohexane	>25	148
Sulfur dioxide	<-78	151
Water	<-24m	68,332
HYDROGEN DISULFIDE		
Benzene, Carbon disulfide	<20	19A,70A(p.384)
Ethyl ether	<20	Ibid.
HYDROGEN FLUORIDE (b.p. 19.4)		
Methane (crit.temp.,upper layer, -73.4)		236
Benzene (and most hydrocarbons)	>15	149,233
Mercaptans, organic sulfides, and disulfides	<25	277A,393(p.1064)
Uranium hexafluoride	100.5	152,369
HYDROGEN SULFIDE (crit.temp., 100.4)		
Methane	-77	236,365
Practically all hydrocarbons	<m.p.	145,149
Ethyl sulfate (Iso-optic at -47)	>25	143
Hydrogen chloride	<20	70A(p.219)
Nitromethane (m.p. -29)	<m.p.	151
Pentaerithritolperfluoro- tetrabutyrate	-16	151
Perfluoromethyldecalin ($C_{11}F_{20}$)	62	151
Perfluorononyldecalin ($C_{19}F_{36}$) (Iso-optic at 63.4)	76	143
Sulfur dioxide (reacts vigorously)	<-78	151
Water (Iso-optic at 47.6)	>47.6	143,393A

	CST	References
HYDROPERFLUOROHEPTANE ($C_7F_{15}H$)		
n-Heptane	32	252
Methylcyclohexane	52	252
Toluene	36	252
HYDROQUINONE (QUINOL)(m.p. 170.5)		15
Benzene	>157.1	392(p.396),471
Diisopropylbenzene	>237	140,446(p.173)
Di-sec-amylbenzene	>256	Ibid.
Bibenzyl	171	140,446(p.181)
Diphenylmethane	<160	149,210(p.140),245
Triphenylmethane	177	Ibid.
Naphthalene	<154	Ibid.
Isopropylnaphthalene	198	140,446(p.195)
sec-Amylnaphthalene	229	Ibid.
Diisopropylnaphthalene	233	Ibid.
Di-tert-butylnaphthalene	257	Ibid.
Isopropyltetralin	235	Ibid.
Phenanthrene	<164	16,149
Acetone	<65	392(p.396),471
Carbon tetrachloride	163.2	Ibid.
Ethyl alcohol	<72	Ibid.
Ethyl ether	<122	Ibid.
Water	<90	Ibid.
HYDROQUINONE DIMETHYL ETHER (m.p. 56)		
n-Octadecane	<47	131,139
Glycerol	>240	153,328
Three HYDROXYBENZALDEHYDES (see WATER, p.184 and SALICYLALDEHYDE, p.162)		
Benzene	<m.p.	406
o-HYDROXYBENZOIC ACID (SALICYLIC ACID)(m.p. 159)		
n-Heptane	90e	410
Benzene	17e	410
Paraffin wax (m.p. 53)	140	149
n-Butyl alcohol	<86	410
Ethyl alcohol	<65	410
Water	90	1,11,27,136,153,209 (p.391),253,392 (pp.518-19),410,486
m-HYDROXYBENZOIC ACID (m.p. 201.3)		
n-Heptane	Very high	410
Benzene	119e	410
n-Butyl alcohol	<133	410
Ethyl alcohol	<100	410
Water	122e	153,406,410
p-HYDROXYBENZOIC ACID (m.p. 215)		
n-Heptane	Very high	410
Benzene	150e	410
n-Butyl alcohol	<140	410
Ethyl alcohol	<100	410
Methanol	<15	374,392(p.530),410
Water	<110	153,406

TABLE I 107

	CST	References

o-HYDROXYBENZYL ALCOHOL
  (see SALICYL ALCOHOL, p.162)

o-HYDROXYBIPHENYL (o-PHENYLPHENOL)
  (m.p. 56)

	CST	References
n-Heptane	28e	139,149
2,2,4-Trimethylpentane	49	139
Methylcyclohexane	<25	145
Paraffin wax (m.p. 53)	77	139
Paraffinic oil	69	139
Naphthenic oil	18	139
Water	258	152,433

m-HYDROXYBIPHENYL (m-PHENYLPHENOL)
  (m.p. 78)

	CST	References
n-Hexane	134	139
n-Heptane	121	139,149
2,2,4-Trimethylpentane	138	139
1-Heptene	<56	139
Diisobutene	67	139
Methylcyclohexane	60	139
Paraffin wax (m.p. 53)	162	139
Paraffinic oil	156	139
Naphthenic oil	100	139

p-HYDROXYBIPHENYL (p-PHENYLPHENOL)
  (m.p. 165)

	CST	References
n-Heptane	120	149
Paraffin wax (m.p. 53)	165	149
Paraffinic oil	165	139(p.766),149

2-HYDROXYETHYL ACETATE
  (CELLOSOLVE ACETATE)

	CST	References
Benzene	<25	145
Toluene	32	151
sec-Butylbenzene	95	151
Di-sec-butylbenzene	138	151
Water	<25	296(p.720)

2-HYDROXYETHYLANILINE
  (see PHENYLETHANOLAMINE, p.150)

HYDROXYETHYLETHYLENEDIAMINE (Table V)		106,284
n-Heptane	280E	149
Benzene (Iso-optic)	60	149
Di-sec-butylbenzene	201	151
1-Methylnaphthalene	73	151
Water	<20	284

5-HYDROXYHYDRINDINE

	CST	References
Water	200.8	152,433

HYDROXYLAMINE HYDROCHLORIDE		15

2-HYDROXY-3-METHOXYBEZALDEHYDE

	CST	References
n-Heptane	113	149

4-HYDROXY-4-METHYL-2-PENTANONE
  (see DIACETONE ALCOHOL, p.64)

	CST	References

2-HYDROXYPROPIONITRILE
  (ETHYLENE CYANOHYDRIN)

	CST	References
Benzene	91	151
Di-<u>sec</u>-butylbenzene	257	151
Naphthalene	98	151
1-Methylnaphthalene	128	151

Three HYDROXYTOLUALDEHYDES
(see under WATER, p.134)

	CST	References
Benzene	<m.p.	406

Five HYDROXYTOLUIC ACIDS
(-COOH=1, -OH, -Me)

Isomer	Heptane	Benzene	Water	References
1,2,3-	84E	-33E	153.5	153,209(p.392), 392(p.598),410
1,2,4-	111E	-16E	145.2	Ibid.
1,2,5-	107E	-47E	142.8	Ibid.
1,3,4-	High	+117E	+9E	209(p.392), 392(p.598),410
1,4,3-	High	98E	17E	Ibid.

2,2'-IMINODIETHANOL
  (see DIETHANOLAMINE, p.59)

IODINE (m.p. 114)

	CST	References
Arsenic (m.p. 814)	>135	210(p.24)
Benzoic acid (m.p. 122)	>111.5	210(p.34),322B
Benzoic anhydride (m.p. 42)	>110.2	Ibid.
Bismuth (m.p. 271)	>340	210(p.24)
Carbon tetrachloride	160.5	181,277B(p.1275)
<u>m</u>-Dinitrobenzene (m.p. 89.6)	>109.2	210(p.34),322B
Ethylene bromide	<78.4	321A,391(p.673)
Water	ca 300	153,240,256(p.670), 391(p.655)

IODINE MONOCHLORIDE

	CST	References
Carbon tetrachloride	14m	73A

IODOBENZENE

	CST	References
Ethylene glycol	>170.2	271

p-IODOBENZOIC ACID (m.p. 270)

	CST	References
Water	175m	136,153,392(p.477)

1-IODODODECANE

	CST	References
Acetonitrile and Methanol	High	194A,445(p.741)
Five other solvents	<m.p.	Ibid.

IODOFORM (m.p. 119)

	CST	References
Pyridine	<20	86

1-IODOHEXADECANE

	CST	References
95% Ethyl alcohol	High	194A

p-IODOTOLUENE (m.p. 35)

	CST	References
Acetamide (m.p. 81)	175	255,263,271,392(p.121) 445(p.800)
Ethylene glycol	>181.5	271

IRON (m.p. 1535)

	CST	References
Sulfur	1970	322A

TABLE I   109

	CST	References
ISATIN (m.p. 201)		15
ISOAMYL ACETATE (Table VIII)		211
Lubricating oil	<0	131
Ethylene glycol	26	271
ISOAMYL ALCOHOL		
(Tables IV,V,VII)		15,17,106,121
n-Heptane	<-78	139
Paraffin wax	12e	139,341
Paraffinic oils	18,33	139,341
Naphthenic oils	-15	139,341
Carbon dioxide	-24	446(p.381)
2,2'-Dichloroethyl ether		
(Chlorex)	12.9	446(p.416),455
Glycerol	74.2	17,153,209,287,328,330,
		392(p.314),446(p.1128)
Nitromethane	13.5	153,256,268,392(p.36)
Piridine zincichloride	62.9	133
Sulfur	220	17
Water	187.5	38,137,153,209(p.388),
		253,330,392(p.313)
ISOAMYLAMINE (miscibilities		
with 175 substances)		15
Paraffinic oil	-6	139
ISOAMYL BENZOATE		
Acetamide	140	255,256,268,270,271,
		392(p.121),445(p.1050)
Diethylene glycol	116.5	271
Ethylene glycol	182	255,256,268,270,271,
		392(p.157)
Methyl cinnamate (m.p. 36)	<15.8	255,270,271,392(p.667)
Phenylacetic acid (m.p. 77)	<30	255,264,271,392(p.584)
Phenyl ether (m.p. 28)	<23.5	255,270,271,392(p.700)
ISOAMYL BUTYRATE		
Acetamide	126.8	256,268,271,392(p.121),
		445(p.1041)
Phenol (m.p. 41)	<-7	255,269,271,392(p.389)
Urethane (m.p. 50)	<29.5	271,445(p.1041)
ISOAMYL CARBONATE		
Acetamide	186.5	271,445(p.1044)
Ethylene glycol	>188.5	271
ISOAMYL ETHER		
Acetamide (m.p. 81)	<71	271
Methyl fumarate (m.p. 102)	<72	271
Methyl oxalate (m.p. 52)	<51.5	271
Urethane (m.p. 50)	<44	271
ISOAMYL ISOBUTYRATE		
Acetamide	100	271,445(p.1042)

	CST	References
ISOAMYL ISOVALERATE		
Acetamide	163	256,268,271,392(p.121), 445(p.1043)
Chloroacetic acid (m.p. 62)	<44	271
Methyl fumarate (m.p. 102)	<83	271
Propionamide (m.p. 79)	<70	255,263,271,392(p.198), 445(p.1043)
Urethane (m.p. 50)	<36	271,445(p.1043)
ISOAMYL NITRITE		
Paraffinic oil	<0	139,149
ISOAMYL OXALATE		
Acetamide	113	255,265,271,392(p.121), 445(p.1045)
Phenylacetic acid (m.p. 77)	<46	255,264,271,392(p.584)
ISOAMYL PHTHALATE		
2,2,4-Trimethylpentane	<-40	149
Decalin	<-35	149
ISOAMYL SULFIDE (Table V)		106
ISOBUTANE (Table III)		
Phenanthrene (m.p. 101)		
LCST, <100		358
Cottonseed oil		
lower phase pt.,126		149,191
Polyisobutene LCST, 114		155
A Silicone	Miscible	155
ISOBUTYL ALCOHOL (Table V)		106
n-Heptane	<-78	139,149
Paraffin waxes	38e	139,149,341
Paraffinic oils	40,50,80	131,139,149,341
Naphthenic oils	<10,14,28	Ibid.
1-Bromonaphthalene	8.6	153,209(p.397),443, 446(p.341)
Carbon dioxide	-22	45(p.677),145,446(p.381)
2,2'-Dichloroethyl ether (Chlorex)	-12.3	446(p.416),455,455A
1,1'-Dichloromethyl ether (M-Chlorex)(m.p. -41.5)	-30.5	455A
3,3'-Dichloro-n-propyl ether (P-Chlorex)(m.p. <-80)	-62	455B
Methylene iodide	77.5	153,209(p.397),266,443, 446(p.363)
Nitromethane	17	153,256(p.680),266,270, 271,392(p.36)
2-Phenylpropionic acid (m.p. 48.6)	<10	392(p.634),452
Pyridine zincichloride	54.6	133
Succinonitrile	67	153,209(p.397),256,443, 446(p.695)
Water	129	1,38,153,209(pp.388,393) 214,253,256,271,304,325, 330,365,392(pp.268-9), 443,446A,463,486
ISOBUTYLAMINE		
Glycerol	<20	153,328

	CST	References
ISOBUTYL BENZOATE		
Acetamide	126	255,256,268,270,271, 392(p.121)
Benzoic acid (m.p. 122)	<48.5	271
Diethylene glycol	86	255,267,270,271
Ethylene glycol	172	255,270,271,392(p.157)
Glycerol	230	153,256,268,271, 392(p.210)
ISOBUTYL CARBONATE		
Acetamide	120	271,445(p.1044)
ISOBUTYL ISOBUTYRATE (Table IV)		17
ISOBUTYL ISOVALERATE		
Acetamide	119	255,256,264,268,271, 392(p.121),445(p.1042)
Urethane (m.p. 50)	<24	271,445(p.1042)
ISOBUTYL MERCAPTAN (Table V)		106
ISOBUTYL VALERATE		
Acetamide	163	255,264,392(p.121)
ISOBUTYRIC ACID (Table IV)		17
Deuterium oxide	41.4	331,392(p.251)
Methylene iodide	15	17
Water	22	1,17,56,105,128,152,153, 157,201,209(pp.388,393), 246A,253,255,256,264,271 331,344,362,362B, 392(pp.250-1),422,442, 442A,443,445,446A
ISOCAPROIC ACID		
All hydrocarbons	<m.p.	145
ISOEUGENOL METHYL ETHER		
Acetamide (m.p. 81)	<74	255,270,271,392(p.121), 445(p.1000)
Phenylacetic acid (m.p. 77)	<48.5	255,264,271,392(p.584)
ISOPROPANOLAMINE (1-AMINO-2-PROPANOL)(Table VIII)		
Water	<20	284
ISOPROPYL ACETATE		
Sulfuric acid	<25	149,393(p.1065)
ISOPROPYL ALCOHOL (Tables VI,VII)		121,372
Ethane (crit.temp.,upper layer,44)		149,220,250
n-Heptane	<-78	139,147,149
n-Octane (m.p. -56.5)	<-57	346
n-Dodecane (m.p. -12)	<-12	346
n-Hexadecane (Cetane)	17	346
n-Heptadecane	<20	346
n-Octadecane (m.p. 28)	<24	151,346
n-Dotriacontane (m.p. 70.16)	82.3	149,346,446(p.29)
1-Decene	<0	147
Cyclohexane	<0	147
m-Xylene	<0	147
Paraffin waxes	68,75	139,149,340

	CST	References
ISOPROPYL ALCOHOL (continued)		
Paraffinic oils	80,83	131,139,149,340
Naphthenic oils 40.8,60,70		131,139,340
"Paraffin oil" (d.0.8723)	39.7	149,487
Fourteen amides	<m.p.	348
2,2'-Dichloroethyl ether		
(Chlorex)	-16.8	446(p.416),455,455A
1,1'-Dichloromethyl ether		
(M-Chlorex)	-37.3	455A
3,3'-Dichloro-n-propyl		
ether (P-Chlorex)	-59.4	455B
Methylene iodide	93.2	153,209(p.397),443,
		446(p.260)
Tri-n-decylamine	41.1	347
Tri-n-octadecylamine	144e	347
Tri-n-octylamine (m.p. -34.6)<-36		347
2-Undecylbenzothiazole		
(m.p. 44)	<10	108A
Water	<-23	296(p.470)
ISOPROPYLBENZALDEHYDE		
2,2,4-Trimethylpentane	<0	149,311
ISOPROPYL CELLOSOLVE		
Water	<25	296(p.44)
ISOPROPYL ETHER		
All hydrocarbons	<m.p.	131,145
Ethylenediamine	36	73,153,256(p.678)
ISOPROPYL LACTATE		
Water	<25	296(p.44)
o-**ISOPROPYLPHENOL**		
Water	239.8	152,433
p-**ISOPROPYLPHENOL**		
Water	196	152,433
ISOQUINOLINE		15
β-**ISOSAFROLE**		
Acetamide	128.5	255,256,268,270,271,
		392(p.121),445(p.1000)
Benzoic acid (m.p. 122)	<89	271
Diethylene glycol	84.2	271
Ethylene glycol	172	255,256,268,270,271,
		392(p.157)
ISOVALERIC ACID		
Hexachloroethane (m.p. 187)	<104	271
p-Dichlorobenzene	<40	271
Water	95	153,209(p.393),443
KRYPTON		
Hydrogen chloride	<-30	163A

TABLE I   **113**

	CST	References
LACTIC ACID		
n-Heptane	286E	149
Diisobutene	160	149
Benzene	66	140,149,446(p.235)
Toluene	100	140,149,446(p.244)
m-Xylene	124	140,149,446(p.248)
Di-sec-butylbenzene	237	151
1-Methylnaphthalene	128	151
LACTOSE, and LANOLIN		15
LAURIC ACID (m.p. 48)(Table III)		
Propane (Lower phase point,111)		149,191,192
All hydrocarbons	<m.p.	145
Nitromethane	72,78.9	34A,198,446(p.1005)
15 Organic solvents	<m.p.	197,345,390A
LAURONITRILE (UNDECYL CYANIDE)		
16 Organic solvents	<m.p.	194
LAURYL ALCOHOL (see n-DODECYL ALCOHOL, p.79)		
LEAD (m.p. 327)		
Selenium (m.p. 218)	>673	210(p.27)
LIMONENE (DIPENTENE)		
Lubricating oil	95?	131,149
LINOLEIC ACID (Table III)		
Propane Lower phase point,79.8		149,191
Benzene	3	342
Acetonitrile	39.5	195,446(p.1007)
Nitroethane	1.5	Ibid.
Twelve other liquids	<m.p.	195
LINSEED OIL		15
Sulfur dioxide	0.5	475
LITHIUM		
Ammonia	-35	167,367
LUTIDINE (2,6-DIMETHYLPYRIDINE)		
Deuterium oxide LCST, 28.7	228	76,78
Water LCST, 34.06	230.7	2,76,77,78,133,135,152, 153,209,444
LYSOL		15
MAGNESIUM BROMIDE		
Ethyl ether	>23 and >158		210(p.203),253,299,300, 364,391(p.937)
(in two ranges of composition, involving molecular compounds)		
Methylal (Dimethoxymethane)	>106	210(p.203),299,302, 391(p.939)
MAGNESIUM IODIDE (m.p. >700d)		
Acetal	>77	210(p.204),301,391(p.974)
Ethyl ether	38.5	153,209,210(p.204) 253,299,391(p.973)
Methyl acetate	>103	210(p.204),302,391 (p.974)

	CST	References
MALEIC ACID (m.p. 130.5)		
n-Heptane	250E	139,149
MALEIC ANHYDRIDE (m.p. 54)		
n-Heptane	200E	149
Decalin	211	140,149,445(p.422)
m-Xylene	15	140,445(p.494)
Methylethylbenzene	31	140
Cumene (Isopropylbenzene)	55	140,445(p.490)
Pseudocumene	70	140
tert-Butylbenzene	71	140
sec-Butylbenzene	87	140
Diethylbenzene	73	140
Cymene (p-Isopropyltoluene)	73	140
Methyldiethylbenzene	79	140
Ethylisopropylbenzene	101	140
sec-Amylbenzene	123	140
Triethylbenzene	112	140
Diisopropylbenzene	130	140
Methyldiisopropylbenzene	139	140
Di-sec-butylbenzene	169	151
Di-sec-amylbenzene	191	140
1-Methylnaphthalene	<12	151
Isopropylnaphthalene	40	140
sec-Amylnaphthalene	90	140
Diisopropylnaphthalene	91	140
Di-sec-amylnaphthalene	184	140
Isopropyltetralin	110	140
Hexaethylbenzene	176	140
Lubricating oil	100	131,149
MALONIC ACID (m.p. 132)		15
Water	<0	392(p.166)
MALTOSE (m.p. 166)		
Pyridine	<25	86
Water	<25	86
MANDELIC ACID (m.p. 118)		
Ethyl alcohol	<8	452
Methanol	<0	452
n-Propyl alcohol	<30	452
MANNITE (m.p. 166)		15
d-MENTHOL (m.p. 35)(HEXAHYDROTHYMOL)		15
Ethylene LCST, -9		96
Naphthalene (m.p. 80)	<42	96,271
Acetamide (m.p. 81)	<45	255,263,271,392(p.121)
p-Dibromobenzene (m.p. 87)	<55	255,270,271,392(p.341)
Ethylene glycol	<17.6	271
Nitrobenzene	<20	271,446(p.903)
o-Nitrophenol	<35	271
o-Nitrotoluene	<26	271
Phenylethanol	<35	271
Propionamide (m.p. 79)	<36	271
MERCURIC ACETATE, CYANIDE		15
MERCURIC BROMIDE (m.p. 236)		
Selenium (m.p. 218)	>227.4	210(p.31)

TABLE I 115

	CST	References
MERCURIC CHLORIDE (m.p. 282)		
All hydrocarbons	High	145
MERCURY (Table IV)		17
(Miscible only with certain metals)		
MERCURY DIPHENYL, DI-p-TOLYL		15
MESITYL OXIDE (4-METHYL-3-PENTENE-2-ONE)		
Paraffin wax (m.p. 50)	<50	340
Paraffin oil	0	139,149
Two other lubricating oils	<10	149,340
METHANETHIOL (METHYL MERCAPTAN)		
Ethylene glycol (Iso-optic at 13.5)	>13.5	143
METHANOL (Tables IV,VI,VII)		17,121,372
Ethane (crit.temp.,upper layer, 35.37)	None	
(Incomplete mixing at all temperatures)		149,248,250,446(p.1)
Propane LCST, 21.15?	<-32	149,247A,371A,446(p.3)
(Methanol perhaps not anhydrous)		
n-Butane LCST, +17?(Ibid.)	-17	149,209,249,443,444,446(p.3)
Isobutane LCST, 20.1?(Ibid.)	-14.5	151,209,249,443,449A
n-Pentane	14.75	73,149,249,315,446(p.3),490
Isopentane	10.5	149,209,249,446(p.5)
n-Hexane	35	17,73,130B,139,152,154,201, 209,238,246A,253,256,344, 362,365,392(p.53),394,442, 443,446(p.7),486,490
3-Methylpentane	26.8	149
n-Heptane	51.0	73,130,139,149,150,218, 256,271
2,2-Dimethylpentane	40	149,150
2,3-Dimethylpentane	37	149,150
2,4-Dimethylpentane	40	149,150
2,2,3-Trimethylbutane (Triptane)	32	149,150
n-Octane	66.7	446(p.22),490
2,2,4-Trimethylpentane	42.5,54	73,139,149,311
n-Decane	76,91	17,446(p.27),490
2,7-Dimethyloctane	86.8	17,209,443,446(p.27)
n-Undecane	103	490
Propylene	<-78	149
1-Heptene	12	139,149
Diisobutene	0	139,149
Cyclopentane	15	149
Methylcyclopentane	30.4	149
Cyclohexane	45	73,78,111,113A,139,140,149, 152,207,222,253,256,266, 268,313,344,365,392(p.52), 442,442A,443
Methylcyclohexane	46	130,139,140,149,261,268A, 271,446(p.41)
Decalin	101	140,149,446(p.44)
Pinene	-64?48	149,151,268

	CST	References
METHANOL (continued)		
Limonene (Dipentene)	18	151
Indene	<-10	151
Benzene	29?<0	29,147,464
Toluene	<0	147
m-Xylene	<-78	140
Methylethylbenzene	<-78	140,446(p.128)
Pseudocumene	-26	140,393(p.716),446(p.129)
Cymene (p-Isopropyltoluene)	-33	140,393(p.724),446(p.128)
Diethylbenzene	-18	140,393(p.723),446(p.128)
Methyldiethylbenzene	10	140,393(p.735),446(p.129)
Ethylisopropylbenzene	-5	140,446(p.130)
Diisopropylbenzene	9	140,446(p.130)
sec-Amylbenzene	-6	140,446(p.120)
Triethylbenzene	19	140,446(p.133)
Methyldiisopropylbenzene	32	Ibid.
Di-sec-butylbenzene	26.5	151
Octyltoluene	68	151
Di-sec-amylbenzene	76	140,446(p.130)
Tetralin	-37,30?	149,151,178,264
Naphthalene	<60	392(p.651),429,472
1-Methylnaphthalene	<-78	140,147,446(p.141)
Isopropylnaphthalene	11	140,446(p.143)
sec-Amylnaphthalene	49	140,446(p.143)
Diisopropylnaphthalene	58	Ibid.
Isopropyltetralin	57	140,446(p.45)
Phenylcyclohexane	47	151
Paraffins (160-180°)	42	201
"Paraffin oil"	166	79,149
Diesel fuel	91.5	151
Paraffin wax (m.p. 53)	187	139
Paraffinic oils	204	139,149
Naphthenic oils	188	131,139,149
Acetanilide (m.p.114)	<42	425
Five higher alcohols	<m.p.	196
14 Amides	<m.p.	348
15 Amines	<m.p.	349
m-Aminobenzoic acid		
(m.p. 174)	<108	259,392(p.541)
p-Aminobenzoic acid		
(m.p. 187)	<90	Ibid.
Anisic acid (m.p. 184)	<0	392(p.591),452
Anthranilic acid (m.p. 147)	<65	259,392(p.540)
Benzoic acid (m.p. 122)	<50	392(p.513),452
1-Bromonaphthalene	62	153,209,238,443,446(p.341)
Bromosuccinic acid		
(m.p. 159)	<22	392(p.219),452
Camphoric acid (m.p. 187)	<0	392(p.681)
Carbon disulfide	36	(see CARBON DISULFIDE, p.53)
Chlorobenzene	<25	393(p.863),418A
2,2'-Dichloroethyl ether		
(Chlorex)	<-53	455,456
Di-n-dodecylamine	38	196
Diethyldiphenylurea (m.p. 71)	<50	93
Di-n-octadecylamine	High	196
Di-n-octylamine	<-8	196
Di-n-pentadecylamine	90e	196
Diphenylamine	<25	94,278A,392(p.703),452

TABLE I 117

	CST	References
METHANOL (continued)		
Di-<u>n</u>-tetradecylamine	90	196
Di-<u>n</u>-tridecylamine	79	196
2-Heptadecylbenzothiazole		
(m.p. 39.6)	>65	108A
Hydrogen bromide (forms		
crystalline complex)	<-12	147,283A
Hydrogen cyanide	<25	148
<u>p</u>-Hydroxybenzoic acid		
(m.p. 215)	<15	374,392(p.530),410
1-Iodododecane	High	194A,445(p.741)
Mandelic acid (m.p. 118)	<0	452
Methyl stearate	40.8	390A
Methyl esters of five		
fatty acids	<m.p.	390A
<u>o</u>-Nitrobenzoic acid (m.p.147)	<22	452
<u>o</u>-Nitrophenol (m.p. 45)	<27	271,392(p.362,364)
<u>p</u>-Nitrophenol (m.p. 114)	<14	92,271,392(p.364)
Phenylacetic acid (m.p. 76.7)	<-17	392(p.581),452
2-Phenylpropionic acid		
(m.p. 48)	<-20	392(p.634),452
Pyridine zincichloride	1.9	133
Resorcinol (m.p. 110)	<9	392(p.393),452,469
Rhamnose (m.p. 126)	<36	392(p.448),458
Silicon tetraethyl	77.6	18,153,256,392(p.53)
Tetrachloroethylene	-10	73,153,256,392(p.53)
Triisobutylamine (Miscible)	None	446(p.655)
Trimethylamine	<25	170,392(p.211)
2-Undecylbenzothiazole		
(m.p. 44)	56	108A
Urethane (m.p. 50)	<0	392(p.202),425
<u>p</u>-METHOXYBEZOIC ACID		
(ANISIC ACID, m.p. 184.2)		
Water	138.2m	136,153,209(p.392),253,
		392(p.591)
2-METHOXYBIPHENYL (m.p. 29)		
All hydrocarbons	<m.p.	131,145
2-METHOXYBUTYL ACETATE		
(BUTOXYL)		
<u>o</u>-Cresol	<12	271
2-METHOXYETHANOL (METHYL		
CELLOSOLVE)(Table VIII)		211,254,284
<u>n</u>-Hexane	28	139
<u>n</u>-Heptane	49	73,130,139,149,256
2,2,4-Trimethylpentane	46	73,139,149,256
1-Heptene	-10	139
Diisobutene	-2	139
Cyclohexane	25	139
Methylcyclohexane	26	130,139
Benzene	<0	147
Di-<u>sec</u>-butylbenzene	<25	145
Paraffin waxes	<50?115	139,340
Lubricating oils	92 to 123	131,139,149,340
Tetrachloroethylene	-25	73,153
Water	<20	284
METHOXYETHYL ACETATE		
Water	<20	284

	CST	References

1-METHOXYNAPHTHALENE
  All hydrocarbons   <m.p.   145

o-METHOXYPHENOL
  (see GUAICOL, p.102)

N-METHYLACETANILIDE (m.p. 101)
  Acetic acid   <0e   30,392(p.636)

METHYL ACETATE
n-Heptane	<15	149
2,2,4-Trimethylpentane	<15	149
n-Octadecane (m.p. 28)	<20	151
Paraffin waxes	>50	149,341
Three lubricating oils	13-70	131,149,151,341
Ethylene glycol	26.8	271,319,392(p.157), 446(p.577)
Magnesium iodide (m.p. 700d)	>103	210(p.204),302, 391(p.974)
Water	108	153,209(p.387)

METHYL ACETOACETATE
  Water   >25   296(p.44)

p-METHYLACETOPHENONE
Acetamide (m.p. 81)	<54.4	255,256,270,271, 392(p.121),445(p.1021)
p-Chlorophenol (m.p. 43)	<-12	270,271
Ethylene glycol	77.5	255,256,268,270,271, 319,392(p.157)
Propionamide (m.p. 79)	<50	255,263,271,392(p.198) 445(p.1021)
Thymol (m.p. 51.5)	<7.7	271

meso-METHYLACRIDINE   15

METHYLAL (see DIMETHOXYMETHANE,
p.73)

METHYL ALCOHOL (see METHANOL, p.115)

METHYL ALKYL KETONES
  Twelve organic solvents   <m.p.   197A

METHYLAMINE
  Miscibilities with 68 substances   15

1-METHYL-2-AMINOETHANOL
  (1-AMINO-2-PROPANOL)(Table VIII)   211

METHYL-n-AMYL KETONE (2-HEPTANONE)
  Ethylene glycol   >25   393(p.942)

TABLE I **119**

	CST	References
N-METHYLANILINE		
n-Hexane	-18.6	149,209,392(p.553), 435,445(p.522)
2-Methylpentane	-14	149,209,435
3-Methylpentane	-17.25	149,209,435,445(p.524)
2,2-Dimethylbutane	-7.65	Ibid.
n-Heptane	0	139
2,2,4-Trimethylpentane	7.5	139,149,311
n-Hexadecane	18	151
n-Octadecane	25	151
Methylcyclopentane	-47.4	149,209,435
Ethylcyclopentane	-49.4	149,209,435,445(p533)
n-Propylcyclopentane	-43.0	Ibid.
Paraffin wax (m.p. 53)	46	149
Lubricating oils	12 to 46	131,139,149
Crystal oil (Nujol)	31	151
Acetamide (m.p. 81)	<45.5	260,271,445(p.1100)
Acetic acid	ca 0	393(p.1076),152,153, 489A
Ethylene glycol	70	255,256,266,268,271, 272,392(p.157)
Glycerol	224.5	153,209,328,392(p533)
Sulfur (m.p. 113)	ca 110	393(p.1067),489
Water (Isopycnic at 2°)	High	140A
METHYL ANTHRANILATE		
n-Hexane	47	139
n-Heptane	46	139
2,2,4-Trimethylpentane	58	139
1-Heptene	-13	139
Diisobutene	3	139
Cyclohexane	16	139
Methylcyclohexane	15	139
Paraffin wax (m.p. 53)	101	139
Paraffinic oil	99	139
Naphthenic oils	55	131,139
Petroleum ether (42-62°)	2	149,343
Petroleum ether (80-100°)	<-20	149,343
METHYLANTHRANILIC ACID (m.p. 170)		
n-Heptane	<100	149
Paraffinic lubricating oil	<170	139,149
METHYL BENZOATE		
n-Octadecane (m.p. 28)	<20	151
Naphthenic lubricating oil	ca -6	151
Acetamide (m.p. 81)	<61.7	255,270,271,392(p.121) 445(p.1048)
p-Chlorophenol (m.p. 43)	<17.5	271
Ethylene glycol	107.5	256,271,319,392(p157)
Propionamide (m.p. 79)	<43	263,271,445(p.1048)
Urethane (m.p. 50)	<36	271,445(p.1048)
α-METHYLBENZYLAMINE (Table VIII)		211
N-METHYL-N-BENZYLANILINE (Table VIII)		211
Glycerol	High	153,328
α-METHYLBENZYLDIETHANOLAMINE (Table VIII)		211

	CST	References
α-METHYLBENZYLDIMETHYLAMINE (Table VIII)		211
α-METHYLBENZYLETHANOLAMINE (Table VIII)		211
2-METHYL-1-BUTANOL 2,2'-Dichloroethyl ether (Chlorex)	-9.4	446(p.416),455
3-METHYL-2-BUTANONE (METHYL ISOPROPYL KETONE) Water	>79	271

METHYL CAPRYLATE (m.p. -33.8)

Acetamide (m.p. 81)	155	271,445(p.1043)
Acetonitrile and Methanol	<-40	390A
Urethane (Ethyl carbamate) (m.p. 50)	<37	271,445(p.1043)
Nine other solvents	<m.p.	390A

METHYL CARBITOL (see DIETHYLENE
GLYCOL MONOMETHYL ETHER, p.71)

METHYL CELLOXOLVE
(see 2-METHOXYETHANOL, p.117)

| METHYL CELLOXOLVE ACETATE
  (2-METHOXYETHYLACETATE)
  Water | <20 | 284 |

| METHYL CHLORIDE
  Perfluorononyldecalin (Iso-optic
  at 49) | >49 | 143 |
| Water (Iso-optic at 26) | >26 | 143 |

METHYL CINNAMATE (m.p. 36)

Acetamide (m.p. 81)	<60.8	255,270,271,392(p.121) 445(p.1050)
Ethylene glycol	101.5	255,256,268,270,271, 392(p.157)
Isoamyl benzoate	<15.8	255,270,271,392(p.667)

| p-METHYLCYCLOHEXANOL
  Paraffinic lubricating oil | -16 | 139,145,149 |

| METHYLDIETHYLAMINE (Table III)
  Water LCST, 49.42 | | 71,78,152,344 |

| METHYL DISULFIDE (Table V) | | 106 |

| METHYLENE AMINOACETONITRILE | | 15 |

| METHYLENE BROMIDE
  Ethylene glycol | >168.6 | 271 |

| METHYLENE DIANILINE | | 15 |

METHYLENE FLUORIDE

Ethane	ca -76	365,439
Carbon tetrafluoride	>-118	365,439
Fluoroform	<-97	365,438
Hexafluoroethane	>-68	365,439

	CST	References
METHYLENE IODIDE (DIIODOMETHANE)		17
(Table IV)		
n-Pentane	>100	149
n-Hexane	102	17,149,209(p.397),443
2,2-Dimethylbutane	>100	149
n-Heptane	97	149
2,2,3-Trimethylbutane (Triptane)	100	149
n-Octane	96	149
2-Methylheptane	96	149
2,2,4-Trimethylpentane	112	149
n-Decane	90	17
2,7-Dimethyloctane	119.5	149,209(p.397),443
Cyclopentane	30.5	149
Methylcyclopentane	44	149
Cyclohexane	31	149,209(p.397),443
Methylcyclohexane	45	149
Di-sec-butylbenzene	13	151
Parattin wax	128	17,149
Lubricating oils	105,127	151
Acetic acid	45?94.8	17,446(p.355)
Ethyl alcohol	93.8	153,209(p.397),443, 446(p.260)
Ethylene glycol	>168.7	271
Isobutyl alcohol	77.5	153,209(p.397),443, 446(p.263)
Isobutyric acid	15	17
Isopropyl alcohol	93.2	153,209(p.397),443, 446(p.260)
Oleic acid	90	17
Propionic acid	52	17
n-Propyl alcohol	75.5	153,209(p.397),443, 446(p.260)
Resorcinol	180	17,446(p.342)
Sulfur (m.p. 113)	<100	70A(p.898)151,182,188
Urethane	82	271
Valeric acid	73	17

METHYL ETHYL KETONE
(see 2-BUTANONE, p. 47)

Six **METHYLETHYLPHENOLS**
(see under WATER, p. 185)   152,433

2-METHYL-5-ETHYLPYRIDINE (Table VIII)   211

METHYLFORMAMIDE		
Toluene	-12	151
p-Xylene	45	151
sec-Butylbenzene	92	151

METHYL FORMATE (Table IV)		17
n-Hexane	-5	151
n-Heptane	6	149
2,2,4-Trimethylpentane	-3.5	151
n-Decane	21.7	151
n-Dodecane	32	151
1-Decene	-12	151
1-Octadecene	36	151
Cyclohexane	-0.5	151
Methylcyclohexane	-1.0	151
Di-sec-butylbenzene	-38	151
Water (Isopycnic at 2.7)	70E	137A,209(p.387)

	CST	References
METHYL FUMARATE (m.p. 102)		
Cineole	<70	271
Isoamyl ether	<72	271
Isoamyl isovalerate	<83	271
METHYL FUROATE		
n-Hexane	50	139
n-Heptane	57	139,149
2,2,4-Trimethylpentane	61	139
Diisobutene	14	139
Cyclohexane	34	139
Methylcyclohexane	36	139
Paraffin wax (m.p. 53)	114	139
Paraffinic oil	113	139
Naphthenic oil	78	139
β-METHYLGLYCEROL-α-MONOCHLOROHYDRIN		
Benzene	12	151
1-Methylnaphthalene	32	151
2-METHYLHEPTANOL		
Ethylene glycol	<0	151
Nitromethane	31	151
METHYL HEPTENONE		
Ethylene glycol	65	151,256,268,271, 392(p.157)
METHYLHEXYL CARBINOL		
Pyridine zincichloride	97	133
METHYL HEXYL KETONE (2-OCTANONE)		
Ethylene glycol	66	255,256,266,268,269, 271,392(p.157)
METHYL HYDROGEN ADIPATE		
n-Heptane	127	149
METHYL IODIDE (Table III)		
Pyridine (reacts)	<0	152(p.449)
Methyl iodide-Pyridine complex		
(m.p. about 90) LCST, 78.4		7,209,253,330
METHYL ISOBUTYL KETONE (Table V)		
(4-METHYL-2-PENTANONE)		106
METHYL ISOPROPYL CARBINOL		
Water	>91	271(p.55)
METHYL ISOPROPYL KETONE (Table VIII)		211
METHYL ISOTHIOCYANATE (m.p. 35)		
Lubricating oil	<29.2	131,149
METHYL LAURATE (m.p. 5.08)		
Acetonitrile and Methanol	<0	390A
Nine other solvents	<m.p.	390A

TABLE I   **123**

	CST	References
METHYL MALEATE		
Naphthalene (m.p. 80)	<22	271
Acetamide (m.p. 81)	<42	271,445(p.1046)
Borneol (m.p. 208)	<62.5	271
p-Cresol (m.p. 36)	<15	271
Ethylene glycol	47.8	271
METHYL MALONATE		
n-Heptane	70E	149
Dipentene	34.5	271
α-Pinene	54.5	149,256,268,271, 392(p.677)
Camphene	55.4	149,256,260,268,271, 435
METHYL MYRISTATE (m.p. 18.39)		
Acetonitrile and Methanol	<11	390A
Nine other solvents	<m.p.	390A
METHYL NITRATE		
n-Heptane	5E	149
Lubricating oil	49.5	131
2-METHYL-2-NITROPROPANEDIOL		
Benzene	123	151
METHYL ORANGE		15
METHYL OXALATE (m.p. 54)		
n-Heptane	75E	149
Camphene	62.6	149,256,260,268,271, 392(p.224),435
Dipentene	100	260,268,271,435
α-Pinene	130	271
Indene	<46	271
Cineole	<46.8	271
p-Dichlorobenzene (m.p. 53)	<43	271
Isoamyl ether	<51.5	271
Pinacol	<48.5	271
Water	>96	153,231,392(pp.223-4) 421A
METHYL PALMITATE (m.p. 28.9)		
Acetonitrile	31.0	390A
Methanol	<24	390A
Eight other solvents	<m.p.	390A
2-METHYL-2,4-PENTANEDIOL		296(pp.557-8)
n-Pentane	7	149
Benzene (m.p. 5.5)	<5	218
2-METHYL-1-PENTANOL		
2,2'-Dichloroethyl ether (Chlorex)	-6.7	446(p.416),455
4-METHYL-2-PENTANONE (METHYL ISOBUTYL KETONE)		106
METHYL PERFLUOROÖCTANOATE(C_7F_{15}COOMe)		
n-Heptane	33	252
Methylcyclohexane	45	252
Toluene	6	252

	CST	References
METHYL PHTHALATE		
Propane (immiscible)	None	192
n-Heptane	89	149
Methylcyclohexane	56	151
Di-sec-butylbenzene	-13	151
Tri-sec-butylbenzene	33	151
Four **METHYLPIPERIDINES** (see WATER, p.185)(Table III)		
2-METHYLPYRIDINE (α-PICOLINE) (Table III)		
Lubricating oil	30?	131,145,149
Deuterium oxide, LCST, 93.8	111.8	76,341A
Glycerol	<20	2,133,153,328
Water (miscible)		133
Water with 0.56% KCI	108	133
3-METHYLPYRIDINE (β-PICOLINE) (Table III)		
Deuterium oxide LCST, 38.5	117	76,78,152
Water LCST, 49.4	152.5	2,19,71,76,78,133, 153,209(p.389),253,
Water (miscible)	None	2,133
4-METHYLPYRIDINE (γ-PICOLINE)		
Water (miscible)	None	2,133
METHYL RICINOLEATE (Table III)		
Propane (Lower phase point, 91.3)		149,191
METHYL SALICYLATE		
n-Heptane	-20	151
n-Hexadecane (Cetane)	<15	151
Crystal oil (Nujol)	9	151
Acetamide (m.p. 81)	80.0	256,268,271,392(p.121)
p-Dibromobenzene (m.p. 87)	<69	255,270,392(p.341)
Ethylene glycol	143	255,256,266,268,270, 271,392(p.157)
Glycerol	170	256,268,271,392(p.210)
Propionamide (m.p. 79)	<60.2	271
METHYL STEARATE (m.p. 37.85)		
Acetonitrile	53.1	390A
Methanol	40.8	390A
Nine other solvents	<m.p.	390A
METHYL SULFATE		
n-Heptane (Iso-optic)	154	149
Propylene	None	151
Cyclohexane	100	140,445(p.413)
Methylcyclohexane	124	140,445(p.420)
Decalin	146	140,445(p.423)
Cumene	<-50	140,445(p.421)
Pseudocumene	3	140
sec-Butylbenzene	-22	140
tert-Butylbenzene	-45	140
Diethylbenzene	-13	140
Cymene	-17	140

	CST	References
METHYL SULFATE (continued)		
Methylethylbenzene	13	140
Ethylisopropylbenzene	7	140
sec-Amylbenzene	28	140
Triethylbenzene	41	140
Diisopropylbenzene	32	140
Methyldiisopropylbenzene	49	140
Di-sec-butylbenzene	93	151
Di-sec-amylbenzene	114	140
1-Methylnaphthalene	<-40	151
sec-Amylnaphthalene	5	140
Diisopropylnaphthalene	19	140
Di-sec-amylnaphthalene	111	140
Isopropyltetralin	57	140,445(p.424)
Limonene (Dipentene)	70	151
Turpentine	108.2	108,149,209,253, 392(p.159)
Lubricating oils	>160	131,139
METHYL THIOCYANATE		
n-Heptane	44	149
Lubricating oil	77.8	131,149
METHYL ISOTHIOCYANATE (m.p. 35)		
Lubricating oil	<29.2	131,149
o-,m-, and p-METHYL TOLYL ETHERS		
Glycerol	High	153,328
METHYL-o-TOLYL KETONE		
2,2,4-Trimethylpentane	<0	149,311
METHYL TRIDECANOATE (m.p. 6.52)		
Acetonitrile and Methanol	<0	390A
n-Butyl and 95% Ethyl alcohol	<m.p.	390A
4-METHYL-n-VALERIC ACID (Table VIII)		211
METHYL VINYL ETHER		
Water (Iso-optic at 66.3)	>66.3	143
MICHLER'S KETONE (p,p'-BISDIMETHYLAMINOBENZOPHENONE)		
n-Heptane	>100	139,149
MONOACETIN (GLYCEROL MONOACETATE)		
Benzene	93	140,446(p.99)
Di-sec-butylbenzene	>283	151
Biphenyl	140	140
Bibenzyl	140	446(p.134)
Naphthalene	78	140,446(p.139)
1-Methylnaphthalene	124	140,446(p.141)
Phenanthrene	130	140,446(p.144)
MORPHOLINE (TETRAHYDRO-1,4,2-OXAZINE)		
n-Heptane	5.3	149,311
2-Methylhexane	5.1	149,311
2,2-Dimethylpentane	6.1	149,311
2,3-Dimethylpentane	0.1	149,311
2,4-Dimethylpentane	6.3	149,311

	CST	References

MORPHOLINE (continued)
2,2,3-Trimethylbutane (Triptane)	0	149,311
2,2,4-Trimethylpentane	13,29	149,311
n-Dodecane	>25	145
Paraffin wax (m.p. 53)	79	149
Miscibilities with 33 substances		296(p.400),483A

MORPHOLINE ETHANOL and
MORPHOLINE ETHYL ETHER
Miscibilities with 33 substances		Ibid.

MORPHOLINE VINYL ETHER
Water LCST, 70		483A

MUSTARD GAS (see DICHLOROETHYL
SULFIDE, p.68)

MYRISTIC ACID ($C_{14}H_{28}O_2$)(Table III)
Propane (Lower phase point, 104.5)		149,191,192
Nitromethane	87.8	198
Fifteen solvents	<m.p.	197,345

MYRISTONITRILE
Sixteen organic solvents	<m.p.	194

NAPHTHALENE (m.p. 80)
Eight alcohols	<60	429
Eleven solvents	<50	472
Miscibilities with about 100 other substances		392(pp.648-57)

NAPHTHIONIC ACID
		15

1-NAPHTHOL (m.p. 96)
		15
Water	209	152,433

2-NAPHTHOL (m.p. 122)
		15
n-Hexane	145	139
n-Heptane	130	139,149
2,2,4-Trimethylpentane	150	139
Diisobutene	73e	139
Methylcyclohexane	58e	139
Paraffin wax (m.p. 53)	159	139
Paraffinic oil	152	139
Naphthenic oil	92e	139
Sulfur	164	182,391(p.1452),423
Water	192.6	152,433

1-and 2-NAPHTHONITRILES

	1-	2-	
Melting point	33.5	66.5	
n-Hexane	73	79	139
n-Heptane	67	74	139,149
1-Heptene	5		139
2,2,4-Trimethylpentane	85	93	139
Diisobutene	26	29	139
Cyclohexane	25	30	139
Methylcyclohexane	33	35	139
Paraffin wax (m.p. 53)	92	98	139
Paraffinic oil	91	95	139,149
Naphthenic oil	42	45	131,139,149
Another lubricating oil	52.2		131,139

TABLE I   127

	CST		References
1- and 2-NAPHTHYLAMINES	1-	2-	
Melting point	50	110	
n-Hexane	117	143	139
n-Heptane	113	131	139,149
2,2,4-Trimethylpentane	130	147	139
n-Dodecane	104		151
Hexadecane	118	189	151
1-Heptene	58		139
Diisobutene	74	88e	139
1-Octadecene	92		151
Cyclohexane	57	65e	139
Di-sec-butylbenzene	<25		145
Methylcyclohexane	65	79e	139
Paraffin wax (m.p. 53)	145	160	139
Paraffinic oil	141	155	139
Naphthenic oil	87	98e	139
Resorcinol (m.p. 110)	<m.p.		207
Sulfur	113		207,393(p.1067)
NICOTINE (Table III)			
Deuterium oxide LCST, 54			171,451
Water (Isopycnic at 96)		210	4A,140A,153,171,182,
LCST, 61			208A,209(pp.392-3)
			253,256,315,392(p.672)
			394,443,451,454
NITRIC ACID			
Nitrogen dioxide		61	72A,210(p.44),233A
			277B(p.1131),379A
NITRIC OXIDE			
Nitrogen dioxide		-103	210(p.44)
Ten NITRILES			
n-Heptane		High	393(pp.1095-6)
Cyclohexane		High	393(pp.1095-6)
Benzene		<20	393(pp.1095-6)
Three NITROACETANILIDES			
(see also WATER, p.185)			15
Benzene		<m.p.	413,392(p.597)
m-NITROACETOPHENONE (m.p. 81)			
n-Heptane		178	149
n-Hexadecane (Cetane)		189	151
Methylcyclohexane		110	140,149
Decalin		106	140,149
Octyltoluene		52	151
Di-sec-amylbenzene		93	140,149
Di-sec-amylnaphthalene		56	140,149
3,4-NITROAMINOTOLUENE (m.p. 115)			
n-Hexane		181	139
n-Heptane		173	139,149
2,2,4-Trimethylpentane		190	139
1-Heptene		114	139
Diisobutene		118	139
Cyclohexane		107	139
Methylcyclohexane		113	139
Paraffin wax (m.p. 53)		191	139
Paraffinic oil		187	139
Naphthenic oil		129	139

	CST	References
o-NITROANILINE (m.p. 71)		
n-Hexane	233	139
n-Heptane	206	139,149
2,2,4-Trimethylpentane	222	139
Diisobutene	151	139
Cyclohexane	133	139
Methylcyclohexane	147	139
Paraffin wax (m.p. 53)	227	139
Paraffinic oil	216	139
Naphthenic oil	163	139
Benzene	<45	69,392(p.402),413
Di-sec-butylbenzene	67	151
Acetone	<25	69,392(p.402)
Carbon tetrachloride	<55	Ibid.
Chloroform	<43	Ibid.
Dibromoacetylene	<50	Ibid.
Ethyl acetate	<32	Ibid.
Ethyl alcohol	<48	Ibid.
Ethyl ether	<43	Ibid.
Nitrobenzene	<43	Ibid.
Water	211	153,209(p.389), 392(p.401),413
m-NITROANILINE (m.p. 111.8)		15
Benzene	<87	69,392(p.403)
Acetone	<75	Ibid.
Carbon tetrachloride	<95	Ibid.
Chloroform	<88	Ibid.
Dibromoacetylene	<95	Ibid.
Ethyl acetate	<73	Ibid.
Ethyl alcohol	<80	Ibid.
Ethyl ether	<89	Ibid.
Nitrobenzene	<80	Ibid.
Water	187.5	153,209(p.389), 392(p.401),413
p-NITROANILINE (m.p. 147.5)		
Decalin	239	140,149
Benzene	<118	69,392(p.401-3)
sec-Butylbenzene	139	140
Diethylbenzene	139	140
Cymene	139	140
Methyldiethylbenzene	139	140
sec-Amylbenzene	171	140
Ethylisopropylbenzene	150	140
Triethylbenzene	159	140
Diisopropylbenzene	172	140
Methyldiisopropylbenzene	190	140
Hexaethylbenzene	221	140
sec-Amylnaphthalene	<135	140
Diisopropylnaphthalene	<132	140
Di-sec-amylnaphthalene	220	140
Isopropyltetralin	<140	140
Acetone	<70	69,392(p.403)
Chloroform	<115	Ibid.
Dibromoacetylene	<125	Ibid.
Ethyl acetate, Ethyl alcohol	<105	Ibid.
Ethyl ether	<122	Ibid.
Nitrobenzene	<110	Ibid.
Water	172.5	153,209(p.389), 392(p.401),413

TABLE I   **129**

	CST	References
p-NITROANILINE RED		15
o-NITROANISOLE (m.p. 10)		
n-Heptane	115	151
Cyclohexane	70	151
Methylcyclohexane .	77	151
Di-sec-Butylbenzene	<-5	151
Lubricating oils	>100	131,149
Three NITROBENZALDEHYDES		15
(see also WATER, p.185)		
Benzene	<m.p.	392(p.479),409
NITROBENZENE (m.p. 5.7)		
(Tables III and IV)		15,17
Propane (no complete mixing)	None	141,149
n-Butane	28.3,40	141,149,188,209,443,
		445(p.586),485
Isobutane	61	141,149,485
n-Pentane	24.5	31,97,120,141,149,188,
		442,444,448,485
Isopentane	30.5	31,97,120,141,152,209,
		238,253,344,442,443,444
		445(p.587),447,449A,450
		452,485
Neopentane	54E	141,149
n-Hexane	20.29	1A,17,31,87,97,120,139,
		141,149,175,188,209,215
		238,246A,253,290,310,
		315,316,337A,362A,362B,
		365,384,392(pp.358-9),
		430A,442,442A,443,444,
		445(pp.588-90),446B,447
		448,449,450A,453,485
2-Methylpentane	25.19	120,149,188,290,310,485
3-Methylpentane	20.69	149,188,290,310,485
2,2-Dimethylbutane	32.60	141,188,149,290,310,485
2,3-Dimethylbutane	23.38	149,188,290,310,485
n-Heptane	18.15	31,97,120,139,141,149,
		188,309,485
2-Methylhexane	22.35	97,120,149,309,485
2-2-Dimethylpentane	26.8	141,309
2,3-Dimethylpentane	16.05	309
2,4-Dimethylpentane	26.55	309
2,2,3-Trimethylbutane		
(Triptane)	20.9	188,309,485
n-Octane	20.1	31,97,149,188,291,442,
		447,448,449,450,450A,
		485
2-Methylheptane	23.6	97,149,291
3-Methylheptane	21.2	149,291
4-Methylheptane	20.5	149,291
3-Ethylhexane	18.9	149,291
2,3-Dimethylhexane	19	149,291
2,4-Dimethylhexane	22.8	149,291
2,5-Dimethylhexane	28	97,149,291,442,446B,447,
		485
3,4-Dimethylhexane	16.7	149,291

	CST	References
NITROBENZENE (continued)		
2-Methyl 3-ethylpentane	17.2	149,291
2,2,4-Trimethylpentane	29	139,149,309,311,485
n-Nonane	21.78	149,188,293,485
2-Methyloctane	19.4	97,149
n-Decane	23.6	17,149,188,293,341B, 445(pp.598-9)
2,7-Dimethyloctane	28.37	31,97,149,209,256,443, 445(p.599),447,449A
n-Hendecane	24.9	293
n-Dodecane	27.0	97,149,293
n-Tetradecane	25.2,32.2	97,149,151,293
n-Hexadecane (Cetane)	36.1	97,149,151,188,485
n-Octadecane	39	151
n-Dotriacontane	66.95	341B,445(p.599)
1-Octene	<-3	151
1-Octadecene	<13	151
Diisobutene	-25e	139,149
1-Methyl-2-propylcyclo- propane	-10	277
Cyclohexane	-4	139,149,365
Methylcyclohexane	-3	139,149
sec-Butylcyclohexane	5.5	86A,445(p.605)
Decalin	-2	151
Petroleum ether (42-62°)	20.5	149,343
Petroleum ether (80-100°)	5	149,343
Paraffin wax (m.p. 53)	54	139,149
Paraffinic oils	53	139,149
Naphthenic oils 14 to 34		131,139,149,326,443
Acetamide (m.p. 81)	<54.6	260,271
Six fatty Acids	<m.p.	198
Benzoic acid (m.p. 122)	<90	318,392(p.514)
Borneol (m.p. 208)	<82	256,266,271,446(p.903)
Carbon dioxide (Table III and IV) LCST 30	-53	17,45,237,365,445(p.941)
Ethylene glycol	120.2	255,256,260,268,271,272, 392(p.157),446(p.903)
Formamide	108.2	215,226,393(p.1070), 445(p.1145)
Hydrogen cyanide	<25	148
Menthol (m.p. 35)	<20	271,445(p.903)
o-Nitroaniline (m.p. 71)	<43	69,392(p.402)
m-Nitroaniline (m.p. 111.8)	<80	69,392(p.403)
p-Nitroaniline (m.p. 147.5)	<110	Ibid.
o-Nitrobenzyl chloride (m.p. 49)	<30	285,392(p.500)
m-Nitrobenzyl chloride (m.p. 47)	<30	Ibid.
Phosgene	<17	8
Propionamide (m.p. 79)	<51	271,445(p.1147)
Pyridine (listing in ref. 86 should be for pyridine- nitrophenols)		
Resorcinol (m.p. 110)	<78	318,392(p.394)
Sulfur dioxide	<25	85
Urea (m.p. 132)	130.6	459
Urethane (m.p. 50)	<42.5	271,445(p.1162)
Water	240	28,52,79,153,209(p.389) 253,330,392(p.356)

TABLE I   **131**

	CST	References
NITROBENZENESULFONAMIDE		15
o-NITROBENZOIC ACID (m.p. 147)		15
n-Heptane	248E	149,410
Decalin	218	140,149,446(p.216)
Benzene	-21e	70,404,410
Triethylbenzene	<136	140,446(p.251)
Diisopropylbenzene	149	140,446(p.251)
Methyldiisopropylbenzene	168	140,446(p.251)
Di-sec-amylbenzene	250	140
Hexaethylbenzene (m.p. 128)	211	140,446(p.251)
Isopropyltetralin	<132	140,446(p.216)
Di-tert-butylnaphthalene	<135	140,446(p.257)
Di-sec-amylnaphthalene	200	140,446(p.251)
Acetone	<30	70,392(p.488)
Carbon tetrachloride	>127.2	70
Chloroform	<110	Ibid.
Ethyl ether	<75	Ibid.
Methanol	<22	452
Water	52e	136,153,209(p.391), 253,392(p.481)
m-NITROBENZOIC ACID (m.p. 141.4)		
n-Heptane	High	410
Benzene	-9e	70,404,410
Acetone	<35	70,392(p.489)
Carbon tetrachloride	<119	Ibid.
Chloroform	<100	Ibid.
Ethyl ether	<80	Ibid.
Water	108	1,136,153,209 (pp.391,393),253, 392(p.481),410,443, 486
p-NITROBENZOIC ACID (m.p. 242.4)		15
n-Heptane	High	410
Benzene	84E?210	70,404,410
Acetone	<160	70,392(p.490)
Carbon tetrachloride (explodes)	>170	Ibid.
Chloroform and Ethyl ether (explodes)	>170	Ibid.
Water	118e	136,153,392(p.481),410
o-NITROBENZYL CHLORIDE (m.p. 48)		
Benzene	<30	285,392(p.500)
Acetone and Ethyl acetate	<30	Ibid.
Ethyl benzoate and Nitrobenzene	<30	Ibid.
m-NITROBENZYL CHLORIDE (m.p. 47)		
Acetone and Ethyl acetate	<30	Ibid.
Ethyl benzoate and Nitrobenzene	<30	Ibid.

	CST	References

p-NITROBENZYL CHLORIDE (m.p. 71)
n-Hexane	104	139
n-Heptane	103	139,149
2,2,4-Trimethylpentane	111	139
1-Heptene	47	139
Diisobutene	55	139
Cyclohexane	56	139
Methylcyclohexane	63	139
Paraffin wax (m.p. 53)	139	139
Paraffinic oil	134	139
Naphthenic oil	80	139
Acetone and Acetonitrile	<25	170,285,392(pp.499-500)

o-NITROBIPHENYL (m.p. 37)
2-Methylpentane	88	151
n-Heptane	79	151
2,2,4-Trimethylpentane	94	151
n-Dodecane	85	151
n-Tetradecane	89	151
n-Hexadecane	92	151
n-Octadecane	102	151
1-Octene	25	151
1-Octadecene	71	151
Cyclohexane	28	151
Methylcyclohexane	34	151
Di-sec-butylbenzene	-34e	151
Paraffinic oil	108	151
Naphthenic oil	76	151

o-NITROBROMOBENZENE
| Carbon dioxide LCST, 0 | | 45(p.683)145,445(p.944) |

p-NITROBROMOBENZENE (m.p. 127) | | 15 |

3-NITROCATECHOL
| Water | 105.3 | 115,153,393(p.654) |

o-NITROCHLOROBENZENE (m.p. 32)
(Table II)
Ethane (crit.temp. 32) LCST, 22		380
n-Hexane	41	139
n-Heptane	41	139,149
2,2,4-Trimethylpentane	49	139
Diisobutene	-4e	139
Cyclohexane	0e	139
Methylcyclohexane	12e	139
Paraffin wax (m.p. 53)	78	139
Paraffinic oil	73	139
Naphthenic oil	28	139
Aniline	<-2.5	242A,392(p.346)
Carbon dioxide (crit.temp., upper layer, 34.5) LCST, 3m		45(p.682),379,445(p.942)

m-NITROCHLOROBENZENE (m.p. 45)
(Table III)
Ethane LCST 32		149,380
n-Heptane	40E	149
Lubricating oil	32	131,151
Aniline	<10	242A,392(p.346), 445(p.942)
Carbon dioxide (crit.temp., upper layer, 37.5) LCST, 8.5		45,379,445

TABLE I   **133**

	CST	References
p-NITROCHLOROBENZENE (m.p. 83)		
n-Heptane	<70E	149
2,2,4-Trimethylpentane	<74	149
Benzene	<20	89,392(p.345)
Toluene	<25	89,392(p.345)
Paraffinic oil	<70	139
Another lubricating oil	<79.8	131
(listed in ref. 131 under		
meta isomer)		
Acetamide (m.p. 81)	<73.2	255,264,271,392(p.121)
Acetone	<17	89,392(p.345)
Aniline	<30	242A,392(p.346)
Benzoic acid (m.p. 122)	<86	255,264,271,392(p.346),
		446(p.1013)
Carbon dioxide (crit.temp.,		
upper layer, 37.5)		45(p.682),379,445(p.942)
Carbon disulfide	<50	89,392(p.345)
Carbon tetrachloride	<50	Ibid.
Chloroform	<30	Ibid.
Diethylene glycol	76	271,446(p.913)
Ethyl acetate	<25	89,392(p.345)
Ethylene glycol	136.5	255,256,264,268,270,
		271,392(p.157),
		446(p.913)
Ethyl ether	<50	89,392(p.345)
Glycerol	215	271,446(p.913)
Propionamide (m.p. 79)	66.5	255,264,271,392(p.198)
Pyridine	<18	86,89,392(p.345)
Sulfur dioxide	>25	85
Six NITRODICHLOROBENZENES		
(m.p. 33 to 72)		
Carbon dioxide LCST, <0		45(p.684),445(p.943)
2-NITRODIPHENYLAMINE (m.p. 76)		
n-Heptane	84	149
NITROETHANE (Table VI)		372
n-Hexane	27	151
n-Heptane	34.5	151
2,2,4-Trimethylpentane	29	151,152,468
n-Decane	50	151
n-Dodecane	61	151
n-Tetradecane	70	151
n-Hexadecane	75	151
n-Octadecane	83	151
1-Decene	-1	151
Cyclohexane	21.3	151
Methylcyclohexane	21.3	151
Decalin	41	151
Di-sec-butylbenzene	<-40	151
Paraffinic oil	104	151
Naphthenic oil	78	151
Aromatic oil	10	151
Fourteen amides	<m.p.	348
n-Decyl alcohol (m.p. 7)	19	146,152,196A

	CST	References
NITROETHANE (continued)		
n-Dodecyl alcohol		
(Lauryl alcohol)(m.p. 24)	28	146,152,196A
Ethylene glycol	68	146,152
n-Hexadecyl alcohol (m.p.49.6)	<45	196A
(Figure 4)		
Linoleic acid	1.5	195,446(p.1007)
Five nitriles	<m.p.	194,348
n-Octadecyl alcohol (m.p.58.5)	<53	196A
Oleic acid	31.7	195,446(p.1007)
n-Tetradecyl alcohol (m.p.38.3)	35	196A
Trimethylene glycol	56.5	151
Water (Isopycnic at 60)		140A
NITROGEN		
Oxygen	<-191.5	70A(p.608),117A

NITROGEN DIOXIDE (NO_2 or N_2O_4)

Bromine	<20	70A(p.120),153A
Nitric acid (anhydrous)	61	72A,210(p.44),233A, 277B,(p.1131),329A
Nitric acid (21N)	43	233A,277B(p.1131)
Nitric oxide	-103	210(p.44)
Water (Isopycnic at 60)	67	280
NITROHYDROQUINONE		
Water	120.2	115,153,393(p.654)
NITROMETHANE (Tables V,VI,VII)		106,121,372
n-Butane	100	151
n-Hexane	60?106	149,193,267,271,321, 445(p.588)
n-Heptane (Iso-optic at 95)	115	144,149,321
n-Octane	>20	321
2,2,4-Trimethylpentane	107	149,321
n-Nonane	>85	321
n-Decane	>30	321
2,7-Dimethyloctane	>30	321
n-Tetradecane	>30	321
Propylene	21	151
1-Butene	33	151
2-Butene	27.5	151
1-Pentene	>40	321
2-Pentene	>40	321
"Amylene"	18	321
1-Hexene	>70	321
2-Hexene	65	321
4-Methyl-1-pentene	>25	321
4-Methyl-2-pentene	>75	320,321
2,3-Dimethyl-1-butene	>60	321
2,3-Dimethyl-2-butene	51	321
1-Heptene	>70	321
2-Heptene	67	320,321
3-Heptene	65	320,321
4-Methyl-1-hexene	>25	321
5-Methyl-1-hexene	>25	321
2,4-Dimethyl-2-pentene	65	320,321
2-Octene	>25	321
4-Methyl-2-heptene	81	321
Diisobutene	>25	321
1-Nonene	84	320,321

TABLE I   135

	CST	References
NITROMETHANE (continued)		
4-Nonene	84	320,321
4-Methyl-2-octene	101	320,321
4,5-Dimethyl-2-heptene	>100	321
4,6-Dimethyl-2-heptene	98	320,321
4,5,5-Trimethyl-2-hexene	88	320,321
1-Decene	>100	321
4-Butyl-2-octene	>107	321
Triisobutene	>110	321
1-Hexadecene (Cetene)	>120	321
1-Octadecene	56	151
Docosene	>125	321
Dotriacontene	>125	321
1,3-Pentadiene	<-10	321
1,5-Hexadiene	5	321
2,4-Hexadiene	-9	321
4-Methyl-1,3-pentadiene	-2	321
2,4-Heptadiene	17	320,321
2,4-Octadiene	36	320,321
4-Methyl-1,5-heptadiene	53	320,321
5,5-Dimethyl-2,3-hexadiene	20	320,321
4,5-Dimethyl-2,6-octadiene	78	320,321
4-Propyl-1,5-heptadiene	77	320,321
4-Butyl-1,5-heptadiene	82	320,321
4,5-Dibutyl-2,6-octadiene	>100	321
1-Pentyne	<-10	321
1-Heptyne	<10	321
3-Heptyne	24	320,321
1-Octyne	<-10	321
2-Octyne	-3	321
4-Nonyne	45	320,321
1-Hexadecyne	92	320,321
Cyclohexane	79,93.6	140,149,321,341B, 445(p.603)
Methylcyclohexane	90	140,149,260,321
Dimethylcyclohexane	107	320,321
tert-Amylcyclohexane	73	320,321,445(p.605)
Cyclohexene	>20	321
1-Methylcyclohexene	>25	321
1-Cyclohexyl-2-propene	75	320,321
4-Cyclohexyl-2-pentene	>106	321
4-Cyclohexyl-2-heptene	>100	321
Dicyclopentadiene (m.p. 32)	60	320,321
Camphene (m.p. 50)	77	320,321
Caryophyllene	85	320,321,445(p.608)
Cedrene	>105	321
Hydrindine	<-10	321
d-Limonene	50	320,321,445(p.607)
p-Menthane	>20	321
d-Menthene	79	320,321
Phellandrene	37	320,321,445(p.608)
Pinene (Dipentene)	>20	321
d-α-Pinene	78	320,321,445(p.607)
l-α-Pinene	68	Ibid.
l-β-Pinene	70	320,321
Sabinene	52	320,321,445(pp.607-8)
Decalin	116	140,149,321

	CST	References
NITROMETHANE (continued)		
Benzene	10.8?	271,445(p.617)
Benzene, Toluene, o-,m-,p-Xylenes	<-10	321
Ethylbenzene	<-31	140,321,445(p.633)
Methylethylbenzene	-25	140,445(p.636)
n-Propylbenzene	<-10	321
Cumene (Isopropylbenzene)	-28	140
Mesitylene	<20	321
Pseudocumene	1	140,321,445(p.638)
n-Butylbenzene	4	320,321
sec-Butylbenzene	-1	140,320,321,445(p.634)
tert-Butylbenzene	-19	140,321,445(p.634)
p-Cymene (Methylisopropyl-benzene)	-4	140,320,321
m-Diethylbenzene	-3	140,320,321,445(p.637)
p-Diethylbenzene	-5	320,321,445(p.637)
Durene (1,2,4,5-Tetramethyl-benzene)(m.p. 77)	<100	321
sec-Amylbenzene	25	140
tert-Amylbenzene	14	320,321,445(p.634)
Methyldiethylbenzene	11	140,445(p.638)
Ethylisopropylbenzene	9	140,445(p.637)
Hexamethylbenzene (m.p. 165)	<10?	321
Triethylbenzene	26	140,445(p.639)
Diisopropylbenzene	22	140,445(p.637)
Methyldiisopropylbenzene	34	140,445(p.639)
Di-sec-butylbenzene	56	151
Di-sec-amylbenzene	85	140,445(p.637)
Hexaethylbenzene (m.p. 128)	<83	321
Styrene (Vinylbenzene)	<-10	321
1-Phenyl-1-pentene	<-10	321
4-Benzylideneheptane	<-10	321
2-Phenyl-3-isopropyl-4-methyl-2-pentene	49	320,321,445(p.639)
2,4-Dimethyl-3-benzylidene-pentane	34	320,321
Phenylacetylene	<10	321
Phenylcyclohexane	24	320,321,445(p.639)
Tetralin	-16	320,321,445(p.606)
Isopropyltetralin	34	140,445(p.606)
Bibenzyl (m.p. 50)	<50	321
Diphenylmethane (m.p. 26)	<-10	321
Biphenyl (m.p. 69)	<30	321
p,p'-Bitolyl (m.p. 121)	<69	321
bis (1-Phenyl-1,3-butadiene)	27	321
1,1,2-Triphenylethylene (m.p. 67)	<21	321
1,1-Diphenyl-1-propene	<-10	321
Tetraphenylethylene (m.p.223)	<100	321
Naphthalene (m.p. 80)	<45	321
1-Methylnaphthalene	<-31	151,321
2-Methylnaphthalene (m.p. 32)	<-10	321
1,6-Dimethylnaphthalene	<-10	321
2,6-Dimethylnaphthalene (m.p. 110)	<62	321
Isopropylnaphthalene	-2	140
sec-Amylnaphthalene	27	140

	CST	References
NITROMETHANE (continued)		
Diisopropylnaphthalene	35	140,445(p.649)
Di-sec-amylnaphthalene	95	140,445(p.649)
Dihydronaphthalene	<-10	321
Anthracene (m.p. 216)	<100	321
9-Isoamylanthracene (m.p.58)	<20	321
Octahydroanthracene (m.p.71)	76	321,445(p.608)
Lubricating oils	>100	131,149
Allyl iodide	-50	271,445(p.795)
$\underline{n}$-Amyl alcohol	21	151
$\underline{tert}$-Amyl alcohol	3	153,256(p.680),260,266, 268,271,392(p.36)
Capric acid (m.p. 31.5)	54.8	198,446(p.1005)
Caproic acid	-3.40	Ibid.
Caprylic acid	34.85	Ibid.
Carbon disulfide	63.4	144,146,152,153,209,226 256,341B,344,392(p.10), 444,445(p.946),447
Carbon tetrachloride	2	341B,445(p.785)
$\underline{n}$-Decyl alcohol	56.3	146,152
$\underline{n}$-Dodecyl alcohol (Lauryl alcohol)	63	146,152
Ethylene glycol	39.7	146,152
2-Ethylhexanol	36.4	151
Freon 12 (CCl_2F_2)	>52	151
Freon 22 ($CHClF_2$)	<0	151
Freon 114 ($CClF_2)_2$	>50	151
Glycerol	>120	151
$\underline{n}$-Heptyl alcohol	36.5	151
Hydrogen cyanide	<25	148
Hydrogen sulfide	<-29	151
Isoamyl alcohol	13.5	153,256,268,392(p.36)
Isobutyl alcohol	17	153,256(p.680),266,271, 392(p.36)
Lauric acid	72,78.9	35A,198,445(p.1005)
2-Methylheptanol	31	151
Myristic acid ($C_{14}H_{28}O_2$)	87.8	198
$\underline{n}$-Octyl alcohol	40.2	151
Oleic acid	94.5	195
Palmitic acid	104.55	35A,198,446(p.1006)
Pelargonic acid	48.6	Ibid.
Propylene glycol	15.5	151
Stearic acid	114	35A,198,446(p.1006)
Tetrachloroethylene	41	73,153,256(p.678), 392(pp.36,66)
Trimethylene glycol	41	151
Water	103.3	153,209(pp.387,393), 443,444
2-NITRO-4-METHYLPHENOL (m.p. 36.5)		
$\underline{n}$-Hexane	18	139
$\underline{n}$-Heptane	18	139,149
2,2,4-Trimethylpentane	25	139
Diisobutene	-22e	139
Paraffin wax (m.p. 53)	56	139
Paraffinic oil	54	139
Naphthenic oil	12e	139

	CST	References
1-NITRONAPHTHALENE (m.p. 57)		
n-Heptane	79	151
n-Octadecane	93	151
Methylcyclohexane	40	151
Di-sec-butylbenzene	<25	145
Paraffin waxes	103	52,149,209,253
Paraffinic oil	94.5	151
Naphthenic oil	64	151
95% Ethyl alcohol	44.1	80,392(p.647)
o-NITROPHENOL (m.p. 45)		
Ethane (Table III) LCST, 34.5		380
n-Hexane	41	139
n-Heptane	43	139,149
2,2,4-Trimethylpentane	48	139
Diisobutene	-3e	139
Cyclohexane	25e	139
Methylcyclohexane	24e	139
Benzene	<0	55,92,392(pp.364-5),405
Toluene	<17	392(p.365),414
Naphthalene (m.p. 80)	<42.5	253,264,271,392(p.367)
Paraffin wax	81	139
Paraffinic oil	69,76	139
Naphthenic oil	32,45.5	139
Acetamide (m.p. 81)	<43	255,256,271,392(p.121)
Acetone	<0	55,392(pp.364-5)
Borneol (m.p. 208)	<123	271
Bromobenzene	<21	392(p.365),414
Carbon dioxide LCST, 25.9		
(crit.temp.,upper layer,39)		45(p.685),153,209,365,
		379,392(p.364),443,
		445(p.942)
Chloroform	<16	69,92,392(p.364)
p-Dibromobenzene (m.p. 87)	<46	271
Diethylene glycol	<42	271
Ethyl acetate	<15.5	92,392(p.364)
Ethyl alcohol	<27	55,85,392(pp.364-6)
Ethylene bromide	<21	392(p.365),414
Ethylene glycol	>189.35	271
Ethyl ether	<17	55,92,392(pp.364-366)
Menthol	<35	271
Methanol	<27	271,392(pp.362,364)
Pyridine	<15	86,92,392(p.364)
Propionamide (m.p. 79)	<45	271
α-Terpineol	<30	271
Water	>200	153,209(p.389),
		392(p.361),405,414
m-NITROPHENOL (m.p. 97)		
n-Heptane	100E	149
Benzene	<72	55,392(p.365),405
Toluene	<75	392(p.365),414
Methyldiisopropylbenzene	115	140
Acetone	<0	55,92,392(p.365)
Ethyl alcohol	<1	55,392(p.366)
Ethyl ether	<0	55,92,392(p.366)
Pyridine	>25	86
Water	98.7	153,209(p.389),
		392(p.361),405,414

TABLE I   **139**

	CST	References
p-NITROPHENOL (m.p. 114)		15
n-Heptane	100E	149
Benzene and Toluene	<89	55,392(p.365),405,414
Acetone	<0	55,92,392(pp.364-5)
Bromobenzene	<86	392(p.365),414
Ethyl acetate	<14	92,392(p.364)
Ethyl alcohol	<0	55,92,392(pp.364,366)
Ethylene bromide	<80	392(p.365),414
Ethyl ether	<1	55,92,392(pp.364,366)
Methanol	<14	92,271,392(p.364)
Pyridine	<20	86,92,392(p.364)
Water	93	155,209,253,392(p.361), 405,414,443,444
p-NITROPHENYLHYDRAZINE		15
1-NITROPROPANE (Table VI)		372
n-Heptane	<0	151
n-Tetradecane	25.5	151
Naphthenic lubricating oil	29	151
Two NITRORESORCINOLS (see WATER p.186)		115,153,393(p.653)
NITROSO-2-NAPHTHOL (m.p. 110)		
n-Heptane	100e	149
NITROSOPIPERIDINE		
Water	150.3	133,153,209(p.388)
o-NITROTOLUENE (m.p. -3)		15
Propane	65	141,149
n-Butane	12.5	141,149
Isobutane	32.8	141,149
n-Pentane	2	141,149
Isopentane	9	141,149,176,256,435, 442A,443
Neopentane	30E	176,256
n-Hexane	0	87,139,141,149
Neohexane (2,3-Dimethylbutane)	11E	141,149
n-Heptane	-1	139,141
2,2,3-Trimethylbutane	-1	149
2,2,4-Trimethylpentane	8	139
n-Hexadecane	18	151
Diisobutene	-46e	139
Cyclohexane	-28e	139
Methylcyclohexane	-20	139
Paraffin wax (m.p. 53)	39e	139
Paraffinic oil	35	139,149
Naphthenic oil	-4	139,149
Two other lubricating oils	8,10.5	131,149
Crystal oil (Nujol)	29	151
Acetamide (m.p. 81)	<70.5	271
p-Dibromobenzene (m.p. 87)	<64.5	271,445(p.798)
Ethylene glycol	142	255,256,264,266,268, 271,272,392(p.151)
Glycerol	193	153,255,256,268,271, 272,392(p.210)
Menthol (m.p. 35)	<26	271
Water	263.5	52,153,209(p.391),253, 330,392(p.537)

	CST	References
m-NITROTOLUENE (m.p. 16)		
Isopentane	7.05	149,176,256,442A
n-Hexane	-30E	87,149,253
p-NITROTOLUENE (m.p. 52)		15
n-Hexadecane (Cetane)	<40	151
Benzene	<15	90,392(p.537)
Toluene	<15	90,392(p.537)
Lubricating oil	<45	131,149
Acetamide (m.p. 81)	<60.8	271
Acetone	<15	90,392(p.537)
Benzoic acid (m.p. 122)	<47	271,446(p.1011)
Carbon dioxide LCST, 15		145,392(p.205)
Chloroform	<15	90,392(p.537)
Diethylene glycol	<48.5	271
Ethyl acetate	<17	90,392(p.537)
Ethyl ether	<20	90,255,256,266,268, 392(p.537)
Ethylene glycol	141.5	255,256,264,268,271, 272,392(p.157)
Glycerol	220	153,255,256,268,271, 272,328,392(p.210)
Pyridine	<18	86,90,392(p.537)
Quinoline	<50	271

	CST	References
3-NITRO-p-TOLUIDINE		15
NITROUREA		15
NITROUS ANHYDRIDE (N_2O_3)		
Water	55	280
NITROUS OXIDE (N_2O) (crit.temp. 32)		
n-Heptane	<-91	149
Carbon tetrachloride	<27	143
Ethyl alcohol	<20	70A(p.611)
Ethyl ether	<20	70A(p.611)
2-NONADECANONE (m.p. 55)		
Thirteen solvents	<m.p.	197A
10-NONADECANONE (CAPRINONE) (m.p. 57.8)		
Acetonitrile	70	153,158,393(p.792)
Twelve other solvents	<m.p.	158,393(p.792)
2-NONANONE		
Eleven solvents	<-20	197A
n-NONYL ALCOHOL		
Water	282e	118,152
n-NONYL CYANIDE (see CAPRINITRILE)		
n-NONYLIC ACID		
Fifteen solvents	<m.p.	197,345
NOVOCAINE SALTS (see WATER, p.186)		

TABLE I   141

	CST	References
n-OCTADECYL ALCOHOL (m.p. 58.5)		
Acetonitrile	63	196A
Nitroethane	<53	196A
n-OCTADECYLAMINE		
Propane (no complete mixing)	None	22
Acetone	88e	349
Acetonitrile	76	349
OCTADECYL STEARATE (Table III)		
Propane (lower phase point,94.9)		149,161,191
2-OCTANOL		
p-DICHLOROBENZENE (m.p. 53)	<45	271
Urethane (m.p. 50)	<30	271,446(p.876)
2-OCTANONE (METHYL-n-HEXYL KETONE)		
All hydrocarbons	<m.p.	145
Ethylene glycol	66	255,256,266,268,269,271
		392(p.157)
n-OCTYL ALCOHOL		
Acetamide (m.p. 81)	<21	271
2,2-Dichloroethyl ether		
(Chlorex)	-1.0	455,456
Ethylene glycol	<0	151
Nitromethane	40.2	151
Urethane (m.p. 50)	<39	271,446(p.876)
Water	265e	118,152
OCTYL PHTHALATE (Table III)		
Propane (Lower phase point,105e)		149,192
OLEIC ACID (Tables III,IV,VI)		17,372
Propane LCST, 91.1		22,149,191,192,
		393(p.1087)
Isobutane (Miscible at all		
temperatures)		191
Benzene	<0	17,342
Lubricating oils	<25,123?	131,145,149
Acetonitrile	61	195
Furfural	26.2	195,446(p.546)
Methylene iodide	90	17
Nitroethane	31.7	195,446(p.1007)
Nitromethane	94.5	195
Sulfur dioxide	24	17,475
Nineteen other liquids	<m.p.	195
OLEUM		
Aromatic hydrocarbons (react)	<25	145
OLIVE OIL (Table IV)		17
All hydrocarbons	<m.p.	1
Chloral hydrate (m.p. 52)	<25	392(p.93),426
Ethyl alcohol	52,145?	17,151
Phenol	ca 25	166,392(p.379)
Resorcinol	245	17
Sulfur	>130	70A(p.899)
Sulfur dioxide	28	17,475
ORANGE IV		15

	CST	References
ORCINOL (m.p. 108)		
Glycerol	<107	153,328
ORCINOL DIMETHYL ETHER		
Glycerol	>240	153,328
ORCINOL MONOMETHYL ETHER (m.p. 44)		
Glycerol	<44	153,328
OXALIC ACID		
Naphthalene	>200	149
OXALIC ACID HYDRATE and OXANILIDE		15
OXATHIANE (THIOXANE)		
All hydrocarbons	<m.p.	145
2,2'-OXYDIETHANOL (see DIETHYLENE GLYCOL, p.70)		
OXYGEN		
Nitrogen	<-191.5	70A(p.608),117A(p.393)
Ozone	179.9	36,153,209,217,356, 365,388A
PALMITAMIDE (m.p. 106)(Table III)		
Propane (crit.pt.,upper layer, 99) LCST, <92	None	22
PALMITONITRILE		
Propane	None	22
16 organic solvents	<m.p.	194
PALMITIC ACID ($C_{16}H_{32}O_2$)(m.p.64) (Table III)		
Propane (LCST, 96.9)		22,101,149
Benzene, Xylene, Petroleum ether	<m.p.	342
Aniline	<45	342
Nitromethane	104.55	35A,198,446(p.1006)
15 organic solvents	<m.p.	197,345
PARAFFIN (Table IV)		15,17
PARALDEHYDE		
n-Hexane	-61e	139
n-Heptane	-54e	139,149
2,2,4-Trimethylpentane	-60e	139
n-Dodecane	<25	145
Paraffin waxes	34e	139,341
Paraffinic oil	40	139,149,341
Naphthenic oils	12,14	131,139,149,341
Three other lubricating oils	<10	131,341
PEANUT OIL		
Ethyl alcohol	65	152,350
PELARGONIC ACID ($C_9H_{18}O_2$)		
Nitromethane	48.6	35A,198,446(p.1005)

TABLE I   **143**

	CST	References
PENTACHLOROETHANE		
Paraffin wax (m.p. 50)	<32	341
Two lubricating oils	10	341
Acetamide (m.p. 81)	95	255,256,268,270,271,
		392(pp.67,121)
Chloroacetic acid (m.p. 62)	43	271
Ethylene glycol	>154.5	260,271
Phenylacetic acid (m.p. 77)	<30	177,392(p.584)

PENTAERITHRITOL PERFLUORO-TETRABUTYRATE

Hydrogen sulfide	-16	151

n-PENTADECYLIC ACID

15 solvents	<m.p.	197,345

n-PENTANE (Table VI)

		372
High polymers LCST >100		365

1,5-PENTANEDIOL

Benzene	>80	218

2-PENTANONE

Water	>83	209,271,362,392(p.298)

3-PENTANONE (see DIETHYL KETONE, p.72)

18-PENTATRIACONTANONE (STEARONE) (m.p. 88.7)

Acetonitrile	High	158,393(p.808)
Eleven other solvents	<m.p.	158,393(p.808)

PENTFORANE
(see PERFLUORO-n-PENTANE, p.146)

PERFLUORINATED LUBE OIL STOCK

n-Pentane	23.6	151
n-Hexane	43.3	151

PERFLUORO-n-BUTANE

n-Butane	-41	78,152,390,420

PERFLUOROCHLOROHEPTANE
(Hooker's "Haloheptane", 90%F,10%Cl)

n-Hexane	-11	151
n-Heptane	7	151
2,2,4-Trimethylpentane	-22	151
n-Decane	48	151
n-Dodecane	74	151
n-Tetradecane	96	151
n-Hexadecane	120	151
Benzene	48	151
Toluene	45	151
Xylene	52	151
sec-Butylbenzene	68	151
1-Methylnaphthalene	>140	151
Acetone	<20	151
Acetonitrile, Methanol	>25	151

	CST	References
PERFLUOROCYCLIC OXIDE ($C_8F_{16}O$)		
n-Pentane	6	151
n-Hexane	26.5	151
n-Heptane	46	151,252
2,2,4-Trimethylpentane	20	151
n-Decane	95	151
Cyclohexane	71.5	151
Methylcyclohexane	65	252
Benzene	111	151
Toluene	108	151,252
m-Xylene	117	252
2-Butanone (Methyl ethyl ketone)	96	252
Carbon tetrachloride	48	252
PERFLUOROCYCLOBUTANE (C_4F_8)		
n-Heptane	-5.5	151
n-Decane	48	151
Methylcyclohexane	20	151
Benzene	68	151
PERFLUOROCYCLOHEXANE (m.p. 63)		
Cyclohexane	42.5	113
1,3,5-Trimethylcyclohexane	40e	113
PERFLUORODIMETHYLCYCLOHEXANE		
Propane	-40	151
n-Hexane	13	117,153
n-Heptane	31	117,153
2,2,4-Trimethylpentane	8	117,153
1-Hexene	16	117,153
Methylcyclohexane	48	117,153
Benzene	84	117,153
Acetone	>27	389
Carbon disulfide	High	151
Carbon tetrachloride	>27	389
Chloroform	>27	389
Ethyl acetate	>27	389
Ethyl ether	<27	389
Hydrogen cyanide	>25	148
Sulfur (m.p. 113)	High	151
PERFLUORO-n-HEPTANE (C_7F_{16})		
n-Hexane	29	117,152,153,179,390
3-Methylpentane	18.9	179,390
2,2-Dimethylbutane	-0.5	179,390
2,3-Dimethylbutane	9.5	179,390
n-Heptane	50	117,153,181A,186,252, 390
3-Methylpentane	18.9	152,179
2,2-Dimethylbutane	-0.5	152,179
2,3-Dimethylbutane	9.5	152,179
n-Octane	68	50,152,390
2,2,4-Trimethylpentane	23	117,152,153,181A,183, 186,390
1-Hexene	35	117,153
Methylcyclohexane	72	117,153
Benzene	113.5	117,153,181A,186,219A, 390
Carbon tetrachloride	58.7	50,152,153,181A,186,219A 252,390
Chloroform	78.5	153,181A,186,219A,390
Stannic chloride	97	50,152,390
$Me_8(SiO)_4$	69.97	219A,390

TABLE I 145

	CST	References
PERFLUORO-n-HEXANE (C_6F_{14})		
n-Hexane	23	389
"PERFLUOROKEROSENE" ($C_{12}F_{26}$)		
Nine liquids	>27	389
"PERFLUORO-LUBE OIL" ($C_{20}F_{42}$)		
Nine liquids	>27	389
PERFLUOROMETHYLCYCLOHEXANE (C_7F_{14})		
n-Pentane	-9.5	117,153
n-Hexane	9	117,153
n-Heptane	25	117,153
n-Octane	41	117,153
2,2,4-Trimethylpentane	2	117,153
1-Pentene	-5.5	117,153
2-Pentene	0	117,151,153
1-Hexene	11	117,153
1-Heptene	28	117,153
1-Octene	45	117,153
Cyclohexane	50	117,153
Methylcyclohexane	45.8	113,117,153
Benzene	84	78,117,153,185,188, 219A,390,393(p.657)
Toluene	89	117,153,185,390, 393(p.685)
o-Xylene	109	117,153
m-Xylene	96	117,153
p-Xylene	94	117,153
Acetone	>27	389
Carbon tetrachloride	>27	78,152,153,183,185,219A, 390,495
Chlorobenzene	126.8	153,185,390
Chloroform	50.3	153,185,219A,390
Ethyl acetate	>27	389
Ethyl ether	<27	389
Me(SiO)$_4$	43.86	219A,390
PERFLUOROMETHYLDECALIN ($C_{11}F_{20}$)		
Propane (Iso-optic at -42)	-29.5	143,151
Propylene	-22	151
n-Heptane	47	151
Benzene	100e	151
Ethylene oxide	11	151
Hydrogen sulfide	62	151
Sulfur dioxide	68	151

PERFLUORONONYLDECALIN ($C_{19}F_{36}$)

	Iso-optic	CST	References
Propylene	-22.5	-12	143
Isobutane	0e	-6	143
n-Pentane		27.8	151
n-Hexane		46.2	151
n-Heptane		67	151
2,2,4-Trimethylpentane		39.8	151
n-Decane		112	151
Cyclohexane		84	151
Methylcyclohexane		80	151

		CST	References
PERFLUORONONYLDECALIN (continued)			
Benzene		119	151
Toluene		116	151
m-Xylene		127	151
Iso-optic			
Ethylene oxide	110e	104	143
Hydrogen sulfide	63.4	76	143
Methyl chloride	49	49	143
Sulfur dioxide	74	75	143
PERFLUORO-n-PENTANE (n-PENTFORANE)			
n-Pentane		-7.7	390,419
n-Hexane		14.7	108B,390
2-Methylpentane		-0.29	108B,390
3-Methylpentane		5.30	108B,390
2,2-Dimethylpentane		-15.70	108B,390
2,3-Dimethylpentane		-4.29	108B,390
Silicon tetramethyl		-21.2	108C
PERFLUOROPROPIONIC ACID			
Propane		ca -40	151
PERFLUOROTRIBUTYLAMINE			
Propane		ca -40	151
n-Hexane		60.6	152,361,390
n-Heptane		82	252
2,2,4-Trimethylpentane		51	152,361,390,445(p.527), 468
Methylcyclohexane		98.4	152,361,390,445(p.541)
Toluene		142	252
PETROLEUM ETHER (Tables V and VII)			106,121
Two lubricating oils		<21	340
Twenty solvents			151,343
PHENACETIN (ACETYL-p-PHENETIDINE)			15
Urea		ca 163	206
o-PHENETIDINE (Table VIII)			211
n-Hexane		26	139
n-Heptane		28	139,149
2,2,4-Trimethylpentane		38	139
1-Heptene		-16	139
Diisobutene		-9	139
Cyclohexane		-2	4,139
Methylcyclohexane		-1	139
Decalin (cis)		-6.3	4,149
Decalin (trans)		-6.8	4,149
Paraffin wax (m.p. 53)		80	139
Paraffinic oil		76	139
Naphthenic oil		35	139
p-PHENETIDINE			
n-Hexane		81	139
n-Heptane		83	139
2,2,4-Trimethylpentane		92	4,139,149,393(p.1103)
1-Heptene		41	139
Diisobutene		48	139
Cyclohexane		46	4,139,149,393(p.1103)
Methylcyclohexane		54	Ibid.
Di-sec-butylbenzene		<25	145
Decalin (cis)		47.3	4,149

TABLE I 147

	CST	References
p-PHENETIDINE (continued)		
Decalin (trans)	48.1	4,149
Paraffin wax (m.p. 53)	139	139
Paraffinic oil	131	139
Naphthenic oil	90	139
Nine aromatics	<20	3,4,4A,393(p.1102)
Catechol (m.p. 104)	<38.5	271
PHENETOLE		
Acetamide	108.5	255,256,268,270,271, 392(p.121)
PHENOL (m.p. 41)(Table IV)		15,17
Propane (immiscible)	None	192
Isobutane	121	149
n-Pentane	56.6	149,467
Isopentane	66	52,149,209,253,467
n-Hexane	51	52,139,149,209,246B, 253,446(p.147),467
2-Methylpentane	57.2	149,467
n-Heptane	23.5?52.9	52,139,149,152,209,246B, 253,344,446(p.147),467
n-Octane	49.5	52,149,209,253
2,2,4-Trimethylpentane	66	139,149
1-Pentene	<20	149
Diisobutene	0e	139,149
1-Methyl-2-propylcyclopropane	13	277
Methylcyclohexane	14	139,149,467
Camphene (m.p. 50)	<29	271
Paraffin wax (m.p. 53)	117	139,149
Paraffinic oils	112	139,149
Three naphthenic oils	74 to 83	78,131,139
Petroleum fraction (240-5, d 0.822)	54.3	149,467
Acetanilide (m.p. 114)	<40	318,392(p.603)
Benzoic acid (m.p. 122)	<80	318,392(p.514)
Camphor (m.p. 176)	<-12	142,168B,446,484A
Deuterium oxide	78.7	171,341A,451
p-Dibromobenzene (m.p. 87)	<40	318,392(p.341)
p-Dichlorobenzene (m.p. 53)	<42.4	271
Glycerol	<0	153,166,328,392(p.379)
Hexachloroethane (m.p. 187)	<124	255,270,271
Isoamyl butyrate	<-7	255,269,271,392(p.389)
Olive oil	ca 25	166,392(p.379)
Sulfur (m.p. 113)	>175	423
Sulfur dioxide	<25	85
Urethane (m.p. 50)	<6.5	271,446(p.926)
Water	66	1,11,27,49B,56A,78,82A, 85,99,107,108B,119,130A, 153,157,171,190,202,209, (pp.389,393),213,238, 246A,253,254,255,256,273, 274,341A,344,364,375, 387B,C,392(pp.372-6),424, 432A,433,442,442A,443,444 449,451,457,486
PHENOLPHTHALEIN (m.p. 261)		15
Pyridine	<20	86

	CST	References

PHENOXYETHANOL
(see PHENYL CELLOSOLVE, p.149)

PHENYLACETALDEHYDE

	CST	References
n-Heptane	30E	149
Petroleum ether (42-62°)	17.5	149,343
Petroleum ether (80-100°)	6.5	149,343

PHENYL ACETATE

	CST	References
n-Heptane	7.45	149,309
2-Methylhexane	8.9	309
2,2-Dimethylpentane	11.55	309
2,3-Dimethylpentane	4.05	309
2,4-Dimethylpentane	11.7	309
2,2,3-Trimethylbutane (Triptane)	5.55	309
2,2,4-Trimethylpentane	26.5	149,311
Petroleum ether (42-62°)	2.5	149,343
Petroleum ether (80-100°)	-4.5	149,343
Lubricating oil	50	131,149
Acetamide (m.p. 81)	<30	255,270,271,392(p.121)
Ethylene glycol	67.7	256,268,271,392(p.157)

PHENYLACETIC (α-TOLUIC)
ACID (m.p. 77)   15

	CST	References
n-Dodecane, n-Tetradecane	<70	151
n-Hexadecane	<70	151
n-Octadecane	80	151
Benzene	<35	392(p.582),410
Acenaphthene (m.p. 95)	<62.8	255,264,392(p.584)
Biphenyl (m.p. 70)	<61	Ibid.
Diphenylmethane	<40.6	Ibid.
1-Bromonaphthalene	<55.3	255,264,271,392(p.584)
Chloroform	<25	177,392(p.584)
1-Chloronaphthalene(m.p. 55)	<36	255,264,271,392(p.584)
Ethyl alcohol	<0	392(p.581),452
Isoamyl benzoate	<30	255,264,271,392(p.584)
Isoamyl oxalate	<46	Ibid.
Isoeugenol methyl ether	<48.5	Ibid.
Methanol	<-17	392(p.581),452
Pentachloroethane	<30	177,392(p.584)
Phenyl ether	<30.6	255,264,271,392(p.584)
n-Propyl alcohol	<12	392(p.581),452
Tetrachloroethane	<25	177,392(p.584)
Trichloroethylene	<30	Ibid.
Water	108	153,209(p.391), 392(p.582),410

PHENYLACETONITRILE (α-TOLUNITRILE,
or BENZYL CYANIDE)

	CST	References
n-Heptane	71.3	149
2-Methylhexane	75	311
2,2-Dimethylpentane	78.5	311
2,3-Dimethylpentane	65.5	311
2,4-Dimethylpentane	79.2	311
2,2,3-Trimethylbutane (Triptane)	67.4	311
2,2,4-Trimethylpentane	73	149,311
Petroleum ether (42-62°)	>b.p.	149,343
Petroleum ether (80-100°)	47	149,343
Di-sec-butylbenzene	<25	145
Lubricating oil	83	151
Water (Isopycnic at 60°)	High	140A,151

TABLE I   **149**

	CST	References

<u>meso</u>-PHENYLACRIDINE   15

PHENYLAMMONIUM PHENOLATE
(ANILINE PHENOLATE)
   Water   140   1,153,209,389,
                                                    392(pp.415,708)

PHENYLAZO-1-NAPHTHYLAMINE   15

4-PHENYL-3-BUTENE-2-ONE
   (see BENZALACETONE, p.39)

PHENYL CELLOSOLVE
(2-PHENOXYETHANOL)   54
   <u>n</u>-Heptane   60E   130,149
   Methylcyclohexane   47   130,149
   Water   >20   284

PHENYLDIETHANOLAMINE
   Water   >20   284

<u>o</u>-PHENYLENEDIAMINE (m.p. 101)   15
   <u>n</u>-Heptane   206E   149
   Benzene   18e   411
   Diisopropylbenzene   111   140,149
   Triphenylmethane (m.p. 91)   91   149,210,244
   Glycerol   <m.p.   153,328
   Phenyl ether   <87   271
   Water   <67   392(p.425),411

<u>m</u>-PHENYLENEDIAMINE (m.p. 63)
   <u>n</u>-Heptane   289E   149
   Benzene   69   140,149,209,210(p.132),
                                                   411,445(p.570)
   Triphenylmethane (m.p. 91)   98   149,210(p.143),244,245,
                                                   353
   Glycerol   <m.p.   153,328
   Water   <28   392(p.425),411

<u>p</u>-PHENYLENEDIAMINE (m.p. 141)
   <u>n</u>-Heptane   292E   149
   Benzene   91e   411
   <u>m</u>-Xylene   <130   140
   Methylethylbenzene   150   140
   Cumene   153   140
   <u>sec</u>-Butylbenzene   169   140
   Diethylbenzene   169   140
   <u>p</u>-Cymene   170   140
   Methyldiethylbenzene   183   140
   Ethylisopropylbenzene   185   140
   Diisopropylbenzene   193   140
   Isopropylnaphthalene   <140   140
   Diisopropylnaphthalene   181   140

   Glycerol   <m.p.   153,328
   Water   <75   392(p.425),411

	CST	References
2-PHENYLETHANOL		
n-Hexane	33	139
n-Heptane	20.7,34	139,149,309
2-Methylhexane	39.1	309
2,2-Dimethylpentane	46.6	309
2,3-Dimethylpentane	28.2	309
2,4-Dimethylpentane	47.05	309
2,2,3-Trimethylbutane		
(Triptane)	34.45	309
2,2,4-Trimethylpentane	50	309
1-Heptene	-14	139
Diisobutene	-14	139
Methylcyclohexane	-10	139
Naphthalene (m.p. 80)	<59.8	271
Petroleum ether (42-62°)	30.5	149,343
Petroleum ether (80-100°)	6	149,343
Paraffin wax (m.p. 53)	99	139
Paraffinic oil	98	139
Naphthenic oil	47	139
Acetamide (m.p. 81)	<38.5	271
p-Chlorophenol (m.p. 43)	<20	270,271
p-Dibromobenzene (m.p. 87)	<67	255,270,271,392(p.341)
2,2'-Dichloroethyl ether		
(Chlorex)	<-35	455
Glycerol	4.5,59?	153,328
Menthol (m.p. 35)	<35	271
Propionamide	<34	271
PHENYLETHANOLAMINE		
(2-HYDROXYETHYLANILINE)		284
n-Heptane	133E	149
Methylcyclohexane	>102	151
Decalin	112	151
sec-Butylbenzene	<-10	140,446(p.129)
Methyldiethylbenzene	5	140,446(p.129)
Ethylisopropylbenzene	27	140,446(p.130)
sec-Amylbenzene	23	140,446(p.120)
Triethylbenzene	34	140,446(p.133)
Diisopropylbenzene	55	140,446(p.130)
Methyldiisopropylbenzene	69	145,446(p.133)
Di-sec-butylbenzene	89	151
Di-sec-amylbenzene	113	140,446(p.130)
1-Methylnaphthalene	<-35	151
Diisopropylnaphthalene	21	140,446(p.343)
Di-sec-amylnaphthalene	98	140
Isopropyltetralin	10	140,446(p.45)
Water	>20	284
PHENYL ETHER (PHENYL OXIDE)		
(m.p. 28)		
All hydrocarbons	<m.p.	131,145
Acetamide (m.p. 81)	160.8	255,256,268,270,271,
		392(p.121),445(p.997)
Benzoic acid (m.p. 122)	<99	271
Catechol (m.p. 104)	<92	271
Diethylene glycol	116	271
Isoamyl benzoate	<23.5	255,270,271,392(p.700)
Phenylacetic acid (m.p. 77)	<30.6	255,264,271,392(p.584)
o-Phenylenediamine (m.p. 101)	<87	271
Resorcinol (m.p. 110)	<93	271

TABLE I 151

	CST	References
2-PHENYLETHYLAMINE (Table VIII)		211
PHENYLGLUCOSAZONE		15
PHENYLHYDRAZINE (m.p. 19.6)		15
n-Heptane	114e	149
Cyclohexane	61	140,445(p.139)
Methylcyclohexane	86	140,445(p.541)
Decalin	75	140
Triethylbenzene	13	140
Diisopropylbenzene	27	140
Methyldiisopropylbenzene	40	140
Di-sec-butylbenzene	60	151
Di-sec-amylbenzene	81	140
Diisopropylnaphthalene	7	140
sec-Amylnaphthalene	<0	140
Di-sec-amylnaphthalene	79	140
Isopropyltetralin	<0	140,445(p.593)
Lubricating oil	148	131,149
Water	55 to 75	19,153,209(pp.389,393), 253,303,392(p.424),443
PHENYL ISOCYANATE		
n-Heptane	<-40	149
Lubricating oil	0	131,149
PHENYL ISOTHIOCYANATE		
n-Heptane	<-60	149
Lubricating oil	13	131,149
Sulfur	125.7	486
PHENYL MERCURIC BROMIDE		15
PHENYL-1-NAPHTHYLAMINE (m.p. 62)		
n-Hexane	69	139
n-Heptane	63	139,149
2,2,4-Trimethylpentane	84	139
Diisobutene	17e	139
Methylcyclohexane	0e	139
Paraffin wax (m.p. 53)	90	139
Paraffinic oil	70	139
Naphthenic oil	24	139
PHENYL OXIDE (see PHENYL ETHER, p.150)		
PHENYLPHENOLS (see HYDROXYBIPHENYLS, P·107)		
PHENYL PHOSPHITE		
n-Heptane	22E	149
2,2,4-Trimethylpentane	42E	140
Diisobutene	8	149
Methylcyclohexane	27	139
Decalin	25	140,149
Di-sec-amylbenzene	<31	140,149
Paraffin wax (m.p. 53)	67	149

	CST	References
PHENYL PHTHALATE (m.p. 70)		
n-Heptane	135	139,149
2,2,4-Trimethylpentane	145	139
1-Heptene	79	139
Cyclohexane	41	139,140,445(p.417)
Methylcyclohexane	63	139,140,445(p.419)
Decalin	57	140,445(p.423)
Diisopropylbenzene	<40	140
Methyldiisopropylbenzene	<34	140
Di-sec-amylbenzene	49	140
Paraffin wax (m.p. 53)	190	139
Paraffinic oil	174	151
Naphthenic oil	13.5	151
Aromatic oil	64	151
3-PHENYLPROPANOL		
n-Heptane	40E	149
Petroleum ether (42-62°)	31.5	149,343
Petroleum ether (80-100°)	4.5	149,343
Glycerol	>100	153,328
2-PHENYLPROPIONIC ACID		
(HYDROCINNAMIC)(m.p. 48.6)		
Benzene	<0	410
Ethyl alcohol	<-16	392(p.634),452
Isobutyl alcohol	<10	Ibid.
Methanol	<-20	Ibid.
Propyl alcohol	<0	Ibid.
Six polychlorohydrocarbons	<25	177,392(p.634)
Water	150	392(p.634),410
(this observation was assigned incorrectly in ICT to 1-phenylpropionic acid)		153,209(p.392)
2-PHENYLQUINOLINE		15
PHENYL SALICYLATE		
n-Heptane	-11E	149
n-Dodecane	<25	145
Paraffinic lubricating oil	34	139(p.766),149
PHENYLSTEARIC ACID		
Paraffinic lubricating oil	-11	139(p.766),149
PHENYLTHIOUREA (m.p. 154)		
n-Heptane	150E	149
PHENYL-p-TOLYLSULFONE		15
PHENYLUREA		15
PHLOROGLUCINOL		
(1,3,5 TRIHYDROXYBENZENE)(m.p. 219)		15
Pyridine	<20	86,392(p.404)
PHOSGENE (CARBONYL CHLORIDE)		
Toluene, Xylene, Kerosene	<17	8
Lubricating oil	<15.6	8,149
Chlorobenzene	<17	8
Chloronaphthalene	<17	8
Nitrobenzene	<17	8
Tetrachloroethane	<17	8

TABLE I   **153**

	CST	References
PHOSPHORUS (m.p. 44)(Table IV)		17
n-Hexane	210	17,149
n-Decane	>300	17,149,182,184,188,209, 253
Benzene	190	17,149,210(p.36)
Naphthalene	202.7	149,182,184,188,209,253
Phenanthrene	200	Ibid.
Anthracene	198	149,182,184,188,253
Aniline	260	17
Bromoform	<0	182,184
Carbon disulfide	-6.5	73,153,182,184,188,189, 209,210(p.36),253
Chlorobenzene	264	153,182,184,188,209 (p.394)
p-Dibromobenzene	163	Ibid.
Ethylene bromide	165	Ibid.
PHOSPHORUS OXYCHLORIDE		
2,2,4-Trimethylpentane	<0	149
PHOSPHORUS TRIBROMIDE		
Lubricating oil	<0	131,149
PHOSPHORUS TRICHLORIDE		
All hydrocarbons	<m.p.	145
PHTHALALDEHYDIC ACID (m.p. 100)		
Water	45.7m	153,209(p.391),255, 392(p.571),408
PHTHALIC ACID		15
Water	<150	473
PHTHALIC ANHYDRIDE (m.p. 131)		15
n-Hexane	197	139
n-Heptane	186	139,149
2,2,4-Trimethylpentane	193	139
1-Heptene	129	139
Diisobutene	126	139
Cyclohexane	128	139
Methylcyclohexane	132	139
Paraffin wax (m.p. 53)	215	139
Paraffinic oil	209	139
Naphthenic oil	160	139
PHTHALIMIDE		15
PHTHALYL CHLORIDE		
n-Heptane	43	151
n-Dodecane	50	151
n-Hexadecane (Cetane)	61	151
Methylcyclohexane	19	151
Crystal oil (Nujol)	73	151

α-PICOLIN (see 2-METHYLPYRIDINE, p.124 and GLYCEROL, p.100)

	CST	References

β-PICOLIN (see 3-METHYLPYRIDINE
p. 124 and WATER, p.185)

PICRIC ACID (TRINITROPHENOL)
(m.p. 122)

	CST	References
n-Heptane	400E	149
Triphenylmethane	144.5	116,149,209(pp.119-20), 210(p.121),245,353
Eleven other aromatic hydrocarbons	<m.p.	209(pp.119-20),210
Acetone	<16	92,392(pp.334-5)
Water	>165	115,393(p.647)

PICRYL CHLORIDE (see TRINITRO-
CHLOROBENZENE, p.176)

PICROTOXINE ($C_{15}H_{16}O_6$)(m.p. 201)

	CST	References
Pyridine	<25	86

PINACOL (TETRAMETHYLETHYLENE
GLYCOL)(m.p. 38)

	CST	References
n-Heptane	<12	151
n-Dodecane	<35	151
n-Tetradecane	39	151
n-Hexadecane	52	151
Naphthenic lubricating oil	53	151
Methyl oxalate (m.p. 54)	<48.5	271

PIPERIDINE (HEXAHYDROPYRIDINE)

	CST	References
Glycerol	<20	153,328
Water	Miscible	133,134
Water with 3.75% KCl	240	133

PIPERONAL (m.p. 37)

	CST	References
Methylcyclohexane	95	151
Di-sec-butylbenzene	44.5	151
Glycerol	159	153,328

POLYETHYLENE

	CST	References
n-Hexane LCST, 127		155
Cyclohexane LCST, 163		155

POLYETHYLENE GLYCOL
(miscibilities with 39 substances)   296

POLYISOBUTENE

	LCST	UCEP*	References
Ethane	<0	36	155
Propane	85	103	155
n-Butane	Miscible		155
Isobutane	114	142	155
n-Pentane	75	199	155
Isopentane	54	189	155
n-Hexane	128	-	155
2,2-Dimethylbutane	103	-	155
2,3-Dimethylbutane	131		155
n-Heptane	168		155
n-Octane	180		155
Cyclopentane	71		155
Cyclohexane	139		155
Benzene	150-170		155

* Upper critical end point, or crit.temp.upper layer.

TABLE I   **155**

	CST	References
POLYISOBUTENE		
(m.w. 22,700 to 6,000,000)		
Diisobutyl ketone	18-56	404A
POLYPROPYLENE		
n-Pentane LCST, 105-152	202	155
POLYSTYRENE		
(m.w. 43,600 to 1,270,000)		
Cyclohexane	18-32	84A,404A
POTASSIUM		
Potassium chloride (m.p. 776)	800	32
Potassium fluoride (m.p. 880)	910	32,152

POTASSIUM IODIDE (Table III)
(m.p. 723)

Methanol (max.solubility at 192)		210(pp.205,213),253
Sulfur dioxide LCST, 77.3		209,210(p.42),253,330,470

PROCAINE SALTS (see
Novocaine, under WATER, p. 186)

PROPANE (crit.temp., 95.6)
(Table III)

	CST	References
Naphthalene (m.p. 80)	<m.p.	151,192
Phenanthrene (m.p. 101)	<m.p.	151,192
9-Butylanthracene LCST,<20		153
1,1-Di(1-decalyl) hendecane		
LCST, 92		153
1,5-Dicyclohexyl-3-(2-cyclo-		
hexylethyl)pentane LCST, 100		153
Methanol LCST, 21.15?	<-32	149,247A,371A,446(p.3)
(see Table III for Propane		
phase points)		

1,2-and 1,3-PROPANDIOLS (Table VIII)	211	

PROPANOL (see n-PROPYL ALCOHOL,
p. 156)

PROPIONALDEHYDE

	CST	References
2,2,4-Trimethylpentane	<0	149,311
n-Octadecane (m.p. 28)	<21	151
Lubricating oil	<0	131

PROPIONAMIDE (m.p. 79)

	CST	References
n-Heptane	295E	149
Toluene	<57	255,263,271,392(p.198)
Naphthalene (m.p. 80)	75	149,260,271
Camphene (m.p. 51)	145	149,268,271(p.170)
Acetamide (m.p. 81)	<54	271,445(p.1145)
Acetophenone	<33	271,445(p.1021)
Benzyl acetate	<50	255,270,271,392(p.198)
Carvone	<63	271,445(p.1017)
Cineole	<60	271,445(p.995)
p-Dibromobenzene (m.p. 87)	<70	271,445(p.798)
p-Dichlorobenzene	<65	271,445(p.797)
Ethyl benzoate	<65	255,270,271,392(p.198), 445(p.1079)
Eugenol methyl ether	<55	255,264,270,271, 392(p.198)

	CST	References
PROPIONAMIDE (continued)		
Geraniol	<55	255,264,271,392(p.198)
Isoamyl isovalerate	<70	255,263,271,392(p.198),
		445(p.1043)
Menthol (Hexahydrothymol)	<36	271
p-Methylacetophenone	<50	255,263,271,392(p.198),
		445(p.1021)
Methyl benzoate	<43	263,271,445(p.1048)
Methyl salicylate	<60.2	271
Nitrobenzene	<51	271,445(p.1147)
p-Nitrochlorobenzene	<66.5	255,264,271,392(p.198),
(m.p. 83.5)		445(p.1147)
o-Nitrophenol (m.p. 45)	<45	271
2-Phenylethanol	<34	271
n-Propyl benzoate	<67	271,445(p.1049)
Pulegone	<62	271,445(p.1017)
α-Terpineol	<36.2	271
PROPIONANILIDE (m.p. 104)		
Acetic acid	<30	30,392(p.636)
PROPIONIC ACID (Table IV)		17
n-Heptane	<-70	139,147,149
2,2,4-Trimethylpentane	<0	149,311
Benzene, Toluene, Xylene	<25	165
Naphthalene (m.p. 80)	<50	452
Kerosene	<25	165
Paraffin wax (m.p. 53)	8e	139,149
Paraffinic oil	10	139,149
Naphthenic oil	-31	139,149
Another lubricating oil	55?	131,149
Aniline	>0	4A,393(p.1099)
Bromoform, Carbon disulfide	<25	165
Carbon tetrachloride	<25	165
Cottonseed oil	<25	165
Methylene iodide	52	17
Water	<-29.4	129,139,149
PROPIONITRILE (Table IV)		
n-Decane	40	17,149
2,7-Dimethyloctane	55.1	149,443
Cyclohexane	12.2	149,175,392(p.433)
Methylcyclohexane	15	445(p.540)
Carbon disulfide	-13.5	445(p.944)
Glycerol	140	17,446(p.191)
Water	112	68,153,209(pp.387,389),
		253,330,362,365,
		392(p.169),443,486
n-PROPYL ALCOHOL		
Ethane (Table III) LCST, 38.67		46,149,248,250,446(p.2)
(crit.temp.,upper layer, 41.7)		
n-Heptane	<-78	139,149
Paraffin waxes	65	139,149,340
Paraffinic oil	82,75	131,139,149,340
Naphthenic oil	48,35	131,139,340
"Paraffin oil"	13.5	79,149
"Paraffin oil" (d 0.8723)	35.2	149,487
Two other lubricating oils	37	131,139,149,340
Anisic acid (m.p. 184.2)	<30	392(p.591),452
Carbon dioxide	<-28	45(p.677),392(p.205)

TABLE I 157

	CST	References
n-PROPYL ALCOHOL (continued)		
Carbon disulfide	-52	247B,446(p.392)
2,2'-Dichloroethyl ether	-32.9	455,455A,456
1,1'-Dichloromethyl ether	-46.2	455A
3,3'-Dichloro-n-propyl ether	-90.5	455B
Diphenylamine (m.p. 53)	<50	392(p.703),452
1-Iodododecane	<-3	194
Mandelic acid (m.p. 118)	<30	452
Methylene iodide	75.7	153,209(p.397),443, 446(p.260)
Phenylacetic acid (m.p. 76.7°)	<12	392(p.581),452
2-Phenylpropionic acid (m.p. 48.6°)	<0	392(p.634),452
Resorcinol (m.p. 110)	<10	392(p.393),442,452
Trimethylamine	<25	170
Urethane (m.p. 50)	<15	392(p.202),425
Water	-23e	118,152,444
ISOPROPYL ALCOHOL (see p.111)		
p-ISOPROPYLBENZALDEHYDE		
2,2,4-Trimethylpentane	<0	149,311
n-PROPYL BENZOATE		
Acetamide	115	255,263,271,392(p.121), 445(p.1049)
Ethylene glycol	164	255,256,268,270,271, 392(p.157)
Propionamide (m.p. 79)	<67	271,445(p.1049)
PROPYLENE CARBONATE		
1-Octene	156	340
PROPYLENE CHLOROHYDRIN (1-CHLORO-2-PROPANOL)		
Water	<20	284
PROPYLENEDIAMINE		
n-Heptane	34	149
2,4-Dimethylpentane	35.5	149
2,2,3-Trimethylbutane (Triptane)	30	149
Miscibilities with 33 substances		296(p.400),483A
PROPYLENE GLYCOL (Table VI)		372
n-Heptane	300E	149
Benzene	80	140,149,327,446(p.95)
Naphthalene	100	140,149,446(p.139)
1-and 2-Methylnaphthalenes	119	140,149
Di-sec-butylbenzene	192	151
Acetonitrile	<0	151
n-Decyl alcohol	<0	151
n-Dodecyl alcohol (Lauryl alcohol, m.p. 24)	<15	151
2-Ethylhexanol	<0	151
Nitromethane	15.5	151
Miscibilities with 115 substances		296(p.530)
Water	<20	284
PROPYLENE GLYCOL MONOMETHYL ETHER		
2,2,4-Trimethylpentane	<0	149,311

	CST	References

1,2-PROPYLENE GLYCOL PROPYL
ETHERS (Table III)(see WATER,
p. 187)

PROPYLENE OXIDE (b.p. 35)
  Water   >20   296(p.673)

PROPYL FUROATE
n-Hexane	-28	139
n-Heptane	-24	73,139,149,256
2,2,4-Trimethylpentane	-20	73,139,256
Diisobutene	-70e	139
Cyclohexane	-48e	139
Methylcyclohexane	-44	139
Paraffin wax (m.p. 53)	53	139
Paraffinic oil	49	139
Naphthenic oil	12	139

Four PROPYLPHENOLS
(see WATER, p.187)

PROPYL PHOSPHATE
| n-Heptane | 4E | 149 |
| Paraffin wax (m.p. 53) | 49 | 149 |

PROPYL PHTHALATE (Table III)
  Propane (lower phase point,106)   149,192

PROPYLPIPERIDINE (Table III)
  Water (LCST)   -20e   134,153,209(p.392),253

n-PROPYL STEARATE (m.p. 28.87)
  Five organic solvents   <m.p.   390A

PROTOCATACHUALDEHYDE (m.p. 154)
  Glycerol   <153   153,328

PULEGONE (4(8)-p-MENTHEN-3-ONE)
  Acetamide (m.p. 81)   <66   256,260,268,271,392(p.121)
                                       445(p.1017)
  Propionamide (m.p.79)   <62   271,445(p.1017)

PYRAMIDONE (DIMETHYLAMINO-
ANTIPYRINE)(Table III)
  Water LCST, 69.5   190   57,153,229,253,392(p.728)
                                      393(p.753)

PYRIDINE
(Tables III,IV,V,VII,VIII)   15,17,106,121,211
n-Hexane	-25	139
n-Heptane	-22	73,139,149,392(p.290)
2,2,4-Trimethylpentane	-15	Ibid.
Diisobutene	-54e	139
Cyclohexane	-36e	139
Methylcyclohexane	-40	139
Paraffin waxes	23e	139,341
Paraffinic oils	25.7	131,139,149,341
Naphthenic oils	-10,<10	Ibid.

Diazoaminobenzene (m.p. 97)	<25	86
Diethyldiphenylurea (m.p. 71)	<50	93
2,4-Dinitroanisole (m.p. 95)	<25	88,392(p.534)

TABLE I   159

	CST	References

PYRIDINE (continued)

	CST	References
m-Dinitrobenzene (m.p.89.6)	<25	86,90
2,4-Dinitrophenetole (m.p.86)	<20	88,392(p.578)
Diphenylamine (m.p. 53)	<0	86,94,392(p.703)
Ethanolamine	<25	393(p.1085),418A
Glycerol	<20	106,153,328
Iodoform (m.p. 119)	<20	86
Maltose (m.p. 102.5)	<25	86
Methyl iodide (reacts vigorously)	<0	152(p.449)
Methyl iodide pyridine complex LCST, 78.4		7,209,253,330
Nitrobenzenes (listing in ref. 86 should be the nitrophenols)		
p-Nitrochlorobenzene (m.p. 86)	<18	86,89,392(p.345)
o-Nitrophenol (m.p. 45)	<15	86,92,392(p.364)
m-Nitrophenol (m.p. 97)	>25	86
p-Nitrophenol (m.p. 114)	<20	86,92,392(p.364)
p-Nitrotoluene (m.p. 51.3)	<18	86,90,392(p.537)
Phenolphthalein (m.p. 261)	<20	86
Phloroglucinol (m.p. 219)	<20	86,392(p.404)
Picrotoxin ($C_{15}H_{16}O_6$)(m.p.201)	<25	86
Quinine (m.p. 175)	<25	86
Rosaniline (m.p. 186d)	<20	86
Rosolic acid (Aurin, m.p.308)	<20	86
Salol (Phenyl salicylate, m.p. 43)	<20	86
Sulfur (m.p. 113)	161	2,153,172,254,255(p.474), 391(p.1451),392(p.290)
p-Toluidine (m.p. 45)	<20	86
2,4,6-Trinitroanisole (m.p.68)	<40	88
1,3,5-Trinitrobenzene (m.p.61)	<17	90
2,4,6-Trinitrochlorobenzene (Picryl chloride)(m.p. 83)	<17	89
2,4,6-Trinitromethylaniline	<24	91
2,4,6-Trinitrophenetole (m.p. 78.5)	<15	88,392(p.578)
Trinitrophenylethylnitroamine (m.p. 95.7)	<35	91
2,4,6-Trinitrotoluene (m.p.81)	<20	432
Vanillin and Veratrine	<20	86
Water (miscible)		133
Water with 8.7% KCl	112	133

PYRIDINE ZINCICHLORIDE

	CST	References
Benzyl alcohol	<-78	133
Cetyl alcohol	241	133
Ethyl alcohol	32.9	133
Isoamyl alcohol	62.9	133
Isobutyl alcohol	54.6	133
Methanol	1.9	133
Methylhexylcarbinol	97	133
Water	163	133

PYROCATECHOL (see CATECHOL, p.55)

	CST	References
PYROGALLOL (m.p. 134)		15
Diphenylmethane	122.9	210(p.141),243
Triphenylmethane (m.p. 91)	178.5	210(p.141),245
Ethyl alcohol and Ethyl ether	<25	234A,392(p.404)
Water	<35	Ibid.
PYROGALLOL TRIMETHYL ETHER		
Glycerol	230.5	153,328
PYRROLE		15
PYRUVIC ACID (ACETOFORMIC ACID) (m.p. 13.6)		
n-Heptane	245E	149
Benzene	>80	151
Toluene	<13	267,271
m-Xylene	83.5?38.5	149,267,271
(both listed by Lecat)		
Naphthalene	>150	151
Chlorobenzene	25	260,267,271
QUINALDINE, QUINALDINE PICRATE		15
QUININE (m.p. 175)		
Pyridine	<25	86
QUININE IODOBISMUTHATE		
Acetone LCST,<9		337

QUINOL (see HYDROQUINONE,p. 106)

Four QUINOL ETHERS
(see GLYCEROL, p. 100)

QUINOLINE		15
Lubricating oil	14	131,149
Catechol (m.p. 104)	<58	271,446(p.796)
Glycerol	<20	153,328
p-Nitrotoluene (m.p. 52)	<50	271
Sulfur (m.p. 113)	96.5	153,172,255(p.474), 391(p.1451)
Thymol (m.p. 51.5)	<3	271,446(p.796)
QUINOLINE METHIODIDE		15
QUINOLINE YELLOW		15
QUINONE (m.p. 116)		
n-Heptane	108	139,149
2,2,4-Trimethylpentane	116	139
Paraffin wax (m.p. 53)	162	139
Paraffinic oil	152	139
Naphthenic oil	117	139
Five polycyclic aromatics	<m.p.	149,210(p.127),247
RAPESEED OIL		
Sulfur dioxide	45.5	475

TABLE I   161

	CST	References
RESORCINOL (m.p.110)(Table IV)		17
n-Hexane		
(crit.temp.,upper layer,250)		17,149,446(p.147)
n-Decane	260	17,149
Diisobutene	>235	149
Benzene	109	17,140,149,209,253,362, 392(p.394),443,446(p.155) 471,486
Toluene	131	17,140,149,446(p.169)
Ethylbenzene	151.5	140,149,209,443,446(p.171)
m-Xylene	148.7	51,140,149,209
Biphenyl	109	140,446(p.174)
Bibenzyl	125	140,446(p.181)
Diphenylmethane	115.4	149,210(p.139),243,271
Triphenylmethane (m.p. 91)	142	149,153,209,210(p.139), 245
Naphthalene	98	140,446(p.186)
1-Methylnaphthalene	<98,108	140,271
Isopropylnaphthalene	153	140,446(p.195)
Tetralin	94	140,446(p.149)
Acenaphthene	<105	271
Fluorene	105	140,446(p.201)
Phenanthrene	111	16,140,149,245,446(p.198)
Acetic acid	<55	318,392(p.394)
Acetone	<10	392(p.394),471
1-Bromonaphthalene	135.2	153,255,256,265,268
Carbon tetrachloride	>103.7	17,392(p.394),446,471
Chlorobenzene	227	17,446(p.348)
Chloroform	>94.8	17,392(p.394),445(p.345), 471
Diphenylamine	<92	207,392(pp.393-4)
Ethyl alcohol	<0	392(pp.393-4),425,442,452, 471
Methanol	<9	392(p.393),452,469
Methylene iodide	180	17,446(p.342)
1-Naphthylamine	<m.p.	207
Nitrobenzene	<78	318,392(p.394)
Olive oil	245	17
Phenyl ether	<93	271
n-Propyl alcohol	10	392(p.393),442,452
Sulfur (m.p. 113)	>120	207
Triolein	245	17,446(p.616)
Urea (m.p. 132)	<132	207
Urethane	<40	86,318,392(p.394)
Water	<12	86,318,392(pp.392-4),425, 471
RESORCINOL DIMETHYL ETHER		
2,2,4-Trimethyl pentane	<0	149,311
Glycerol	<240	153,328
Other **RESORCINOL ETHERS** (see under GLYCEROL, p.100)		
RHAMNOSE (m.p. 126)		
Methanol	<36	392(p.448),458
Ethyl alcohol	<59	Ibid.
RICINOLEIC ACID		
Benzene	35	342
ROSANILINE (m.p. 186d)		15
Pyridine	<20	86

	CST	References
ROSIN		15
ROSOLIC ACID (AURIN)(m.p. 309d)		15
Pyridine	<20	86
RUBIDIUM (m.p. 38.5)		
Sulfur	>185,>212	210(p.26)
(two composition ranges)		
RUBBER		15
n-Pentane	130	154
SACCHARIN (BENZOIC SULFINIDE)		
Ethyl alcohol	<25	15
Ethyl ether	<25	15
Isoamylamine	<25	15
SAFROLE		
Acetamide	136.5	255,256,268,270,271, 392(p.121),445(p.999)
Benzoic acid (m.p. 122)	<47	271
Catechol (m.p. 104)	<71	271
Diethylene glycol	84.5	271
Ethylene glycol	187.5	255,256,268,270,271, 392(p.157)
SALICYL ALCOHOL (SALIGENIN) (m.p. 86)		
n-Heptane	208E	149
Methyldiethylbenzene	86	140,446(p.173)
sec-Amylbenzene	104	140,446(p.120)
Ethylisopropylbenzene	107	140,446(p.174)
Triethylbenzene	109	140,446(p.174)
Diisopropylbenzene	126	140,446(p.173)
Methyldiisopropylbenzene	142	140,446(p.174)
Hexaethylbenzene	154	140,446(p.173)
sec-Amylnaphthalene	80	140,446(p.174)
Diisopropylnaphthalene	96	140,446(p.174)
Isopropyltetralin	83	140,446(p.149)
Glycerol	<86	153,328
SALICYLALDEHYDE (m.p. 1.6) (Table VIII)		211
n-Butane	59	149
n-Pentane	41	149
n-Hexane	31	139
n-Heptane	34	139,149
2,2,4-Trimethylpentane	42	139
1-Heptene	-3	139
Disobutene	-7	139
Cyclohexane	5	139
Methylcyclohexane	10	139
Paraffin wax (m.p. 53)	80	139
Paraffinic oil	78	139,149
Naphthenic oils	35,39	131,139,149
Glycerol	176.6	153,209(p.395),287,328, 392(p.210)
Water	>200	153,209(p.391),392(p.498), 406

SALICYLIC ACID (see
o-HYDROXYBENZOIC ACID, p.106)

TABLE I   **163**

	CST	References
SALOL (PHENYL SALICYLATE) (m.p. 43)		
Pyridine	<20	86
SEBACIC ACID (m.p. 133)		
n-Heptane	100E	149
Decalin	122	140
Diisopropylbenzene	<120	140,446(p.250)
SELENIUM (m.p. 218)		15
Bismuth (m.p. 271)	>608	210(p.26)
Lead (m.p. 327)	>673	210(p.27)
Mercuric bromide	>277.4	210(p.31)
Silver	>620	210(p.27)
Thallium	>361	210(p.27)
SESAME OIL		
Ethyl alcohol	62	152,350
SHELLAC		15
A SILICONE (Table III)		
Ethane LCST, -1		155
Isobutane	miscible	155
n-Pentane	miscible	155
SILICON TETRACHLORIDE		
Ethyl malonate	-32	152,462,466
Stannic iodide	139.9	153,182,187,188, 391(p.1493)
Sulfur dioxide	-4.8	24,25,153,188,255(p.473)
SILICON TETRAETHYL		
Methanol	77.6	18,153,256,392(p.53)
SILICON TETRAMETHYL		
Perfluoro-n-pentane	-21.2	108C
SILVER		
Selenium	>620	210(p.27)
SILVER BROMIDE		
Aluminum bromide	186	18,153,209,230
SILVER NITRATE (Table IV)		17
Decane	>280	17
Chlorobenzene	>280	17
SKATOLE		15
SODIUM(Table IV)(m.p. 97.5)		17
Ammonia	-41.6	2,153,167,209,241,367, 391(p.1146)
Sodium bromide (m.p. 755)	1090	33
Sodium chloride (m.p. 801)	1060	33
Sodium fluoride	1110	32,152
Sodium iodide (m.p. 651)	1110	33
Tellurium (m.p. 452)	>435	210(p.29)
SODIUM BROMIDE		
Aluminum bromide	232	153,209(p.393),230

	CST	References
Five Organic SODIUM SALTS		15
SOY BEAN OIL		
Ethyl alcohol	65	152,350
Miscibilities with 45 solvents		296(p.137)
STANNIC BROMIDE (m.p. 31)		
Paraffin oil	<0	149
Sulfur dioxide	48.6	23,153,188,210(p.42), 255(p.473),391(p.1489)
STANNIC CHLORIDE (Table IV)		
Paraffin oil	<0	149
Antimony chloride	65.9m	153,209(p.393),210(p.46), 230,330
Perfluoro-n-heptane	97	50,152,390
Sulfur	>121	70A(p.895)
Sulfur dioxide	-44.9	23,153,188,210(p.42), 255(p.473),391(p.1491)
Valeric acid	-10	17
STANNIC IODIDE (m.p. 143.5)		
n-Pentane (probably no CST)	>199.8	20,149
Isopentane (probably no CST)	>215	20,95,149,182,188
n-Hexane	148.5	20,95,149,182,188, 391(p.1493)
2-Methylpentane	185.4	20,95,149,182,188
3-Methylpentane	147.8	Ibid.
2,2-Dimethylbutane	ca 200	Ibid.
2,3-Dimethylbutane	166.80	Ibid.
n-Heptane	136.4	20,95,149,182,188,391 (p.1493)
2-Methylhexane	160.3	20,95,149,182,188
3-Methylhexane	144.1	Ibid.
2,2,3-Trimethylbutane (Triptane)	163	149
n-Octane	132	20,95,149,182,188, 391(p.1493)
3-Methylheptane	138.3	20,149
2,2,4-Trimethylpentane	195.1	20,95,149,182,188, 391(p.1493)
Dotriacontane	194	95,149,181A,182,188,189
Diisobutene	129.0	20,149
Cyclohexane	115.4	20,149
Methylcyclohexane	119.7	20,149
Benzene	115.8	20,149
Silicon tetrachloride	139.9	153,182,187,188, 391(p.1493)
Sulfur	<104	99A,153,255(p.474)
STANNOUS BROMIDE		
Aluminum bromide	204.5	153,209(p.393),230
STANNOUS CHLORIDE		
Antimony chloride	>241	210(p.46),230,330
STARCH		15
STEARAMIDE (m.p. 109)(Table III)		
Propane	None	22,101,149
(crit.pt.upper layer 99)		

TABLE I 165

	CST	References
STEARIC ACID (m.p. 69)		15
(Table III)		22,101,149,192
Propane LCST, 91.4		198
Furfural	<62	35A,198,446(p.1006)
Nitromethane	114	197,345
Fifteen organic solvents	<m.p.	
STEARONITRILE		
Sixteen organic solvents	<m.p.	194
STRYCHNINE		15
STYPHNIC ACID		
(see TRINITRORESORCINOL, p.177)		
STYRENE (Table VII)		121
SUCCINAMIDE		15
SUCCINIC ACID AND SUCCINIMIDE		15
SUCCINONITRILE (ETHYLENE		
CYANIDE) (m.p. 54.5)		
Benzene	52	149
Di-sec-butylbenzene	>288	151
1-Methylnaphthalene	126	151
Lubricating oil	>100	131,149
Ethyl alcohol	28	153,209(pp.395,397),253,330, 387A,443,446(p.694)
Isobutyl alcohol	67	153,209(p.397),256,443,446 (p.695)
Water	54	153,209(pp.387,393),253,330, 387,387A,392(p.214),443,444, 486
SUCROSE		15
Water	<20	86
SULFANILIC ACID		15
SULFONAL		
Urea	>120	208,393(p.1075)
SULFUR (m.p. 113)		15,17
(Tables III and IV)(reacts with most organic compounds beginning at 130)		
n-Decane	>220	17,149
Decalin	170	151
Benzene LCST, 226(see Fig. 3)	163	1,17,38A,149,182,188,189, 209,210(p.35),231,247,253, 423,486
Toluene LCST, 222 (see Fig. 3)	179	1,17,149,182,188,209,247, 253,392(p.543),423,486
Ethylbenzene	189	149,182,188,247
m-Xylene	None	149,182,188,247,391(p.1451)
p-Xylene (Sλ) LCST, 206	190	149,172,391(p.1452)
p-Xylene (S, equilibrium)	None	149,172
Biphenyl	<98	149,151,182,188,423
Diphenylmethane	>170	423
Tetralin	90	151
Naphthalene	<82	149,182,188

	CST	References
SULFUR (continued)		
1-Methylnaphthalene	<100	151
2-Methylnaphthalene	<94	151
Phenanthrene	<80	149,151,182,188
Fluorene	<100	149
Triphenylmethane LCST, 199	147	149,182,188,247,423
Paraffin wax (no complete mixing)	None	149,189,247
Allyl isothiocyanate	124	1,153,209(p.394),253, 392(p.221),393(p.1066),489
Aniline	138	1,153,182,188,209(p.394), 212,253,330,392(p.417),486
Antimony	>615	210(p.25)
Benzoic acid	>257.5	22A,173
Benzyl chloride	134.2	22A,70A(p.898),153,182,188
Butyl phthalate	>197.8	35,153
Carbon tetrachloride	>220	17
Cesium	>172.8	210(p.26)
Chlorobenzene	116	1,38A,153,182,188,209(p394) 253,330,392(p.353),443,486
Chloroform	164	182
Copper (m.p. 1083)	>1485	210(p.25)
p-Dibromobenzene	<100	151,182,188
p-Dichlorobenzene (m.p.53)	103.5	38A,210(p.35),391(p.1449)
2,2'-Dichloroethyl sulfide (Mustard gas)	143	153,182,188,210(p.35),482
N,N-Dimethylaniline	ca 88	393(p.1067),489
Furfural	>130	151
Iron (m.p. 1535)	1970	322A
Isoamyl alcohol	220	17
Methylaniline	ca 110	393(p.1067),489
Methylene iodide	<100	70A(p.898),151,182,188
2-Naphthol	164	182,391(p.1452),423
1-Naphthylamine (m.p. 50)	<113	207,393(p.1067)
Olive oil	>130	70A(p.899)
Perfluorodimethylcyclo- hexane	High	151
Phenol	>175	423
Phenylisothiocyanate	125.7	486
Pyridine	161	2,153,172,254,255(p.474), 391(p.1451),392(p.290)
Quinoline	96.5	153,172,255(p.474), 391(p.1451)
Resorcinol (m.p. 110)	>120	207
Rubidium (two composition ranges)	>185,>212	210(p.26),392(p.290)
Stannic chloride	>121	70A(p.895)
Stannic iodide	<104	99A,153,255(p.474)
Sulfur dioxide	>96	151
o-Toluidine	130	393(p.1066),489
Thallium (two composition ranges)	>127,>448	210(p.25)
SULFUR BROMIDE (S_2Br_2)		
n-Heptane	<-56	149
SULFUR CHLORIDE (S_2Cl_2)		
Benzene	<20	70A(p.899)
n-Heptane	<-70	149
2,2,4-Trimethylpentane	-40	149
Lubricating oil	<0	131,149
Carbon disulfide	<20	70A(p.899)

TABLE I   167

	CST	References
SULFUR DIOXIDE (Tables III, IV)		17
Propane	-24	149(p.298),393(p.1067)
n-Butane	-4	149,255,256,276,403
Isobutane	-1	149
n-Pentane	2	149,255,256,276,317
Isopentane	-3.6	151,317
n-Hexane	11	1,17,139,149,209(p.394),
		254,256,276,399,403,443
2-Methylpentane	10	149,276
n-Heptane	19.2	130,139,149,255,256,276
n-Heptane(SO$_2$ satd.with water)	28.7	151
n-Heptane(SO$_2$ satd,with glycerol)	23	151
2-Methylhexane	18	149,276
n-Octane	26	149,255,256,276,317,398,
		403
2-Methylheptane	24	149,276
2,2,4-Trimethylpentane	18.7	139,149
n-Nonane	32	149,276,317
n-Decane	37	17,149,255,256,276,317,
		396A,403
2,7-Dimethyloctane	34.1	149,443
n-Hendecane	42	149,276,402A
n-Dodecane	47.1	149,255,256,276,403,443
n-Tetradecane	55.5	149,255,256,403,443
n-Dotriacontane	110	149,255,256,276,403,443
Propylene	<-78	149,393(p.1067)
Pentene	ca -60	149,294,317,400
Pentene and Hexene	>25?	85
1-Hexene	<25	317,393(p.1068)
1-Heptene	-21	139,149
Octene	>25?-16.5	85,149,317,400
Diisobutene	-35	139,149,317
Hexadecene (Cetene)	42.7	85,149,209(p.394),
		392(p.767),401
Methylcyclopentane	8	149,276
Cyclohexane	13	139,140,149,209(p.394),
		210(p.187),239,256,276,
		317,396A,397,399,402,443
Methylcyclohexane	15.5	130,139,140,149,276
Ethylcyclohexane	25	149,276
m-Dimethylcyclohexane	>25	85,149
1,2,4-Trimethylcyclohexane ("Nonanaphthene")	27	149,276
Hexahydromesitylene	30.5	149,276
Decalin	42	85,140,149,392(p.682),
		396A,488
Cyclohexene	<-80	149,402
Pinene	>25	85,149
Carvene (d-Limonene)	<25	85,149
Aromatic hydrocarbons to C$_{12}$	<-78	85,140,149,317
Di-sec-amylbenzene	-8	140
Styrene (Vinylbenzene)	<-60	149,294
Diisopropylnaphthalene	<-78	140
Twenty other aromatics	<m.p.	85,149
Paraffinic gasoline	>25	317,393(p.1068)
Light kerosene	44	392(p.834),488
Paraffin wax (m.p. 53)	95	139,149
Paraffinic oil	113	139
Naphthenic oil	86	139

	CST	References
SULFUR DIOXIDE (continued)		
Bone oil	35.75	475
Carbon disulfide	-2.3	151
Carbon tetrachloride	-29.27	23,153,180,188,210(p.187) 255,391(p.216),392(p.4)
Castor oil	-8	475
Cetyl alcohol (m.p. 49.3)	<25	210(p.188),392(p.767),396
Chloroform	<25	17
m-Dinitrobenzene (m.p. 89.57)	<25	85
Ethyl ether and Formic acid	<25	17
Germanium tetrachloride	-4.7	24,25,153,188,256(p.676)
Glycerol (no complete mixing)	None	151
Hydrogen cyanide	<-78	148
Hydrogen sulfide (reacts vigorously)	<-78	151
Isoamyl alcohol	<25	17
Isobutyl isobutyrate	<25	17
Linseed oil	0.5	475
Methanol	<25	17
Nitrobenzene	<25	85,151
Oleic acid	24	17,475
Olive oil	28	17,475
Perfluoromethyldecalin	68	151
Perfluorononyldecalin (Iso-optic at 74)	75	143
Phenol	<25	85
Phosphorus	>44	17
Potassium iodide LCST, 77.3		209,210(p.42),253,330,470
Rapeseed oil	45.5	475
Silicon tetrachloride	-4.8	24,25,153,188,255(p.473)
Stannic bromide	48.6	23,153,188,210(p.42), 255(p.473),391(pp.1489-91)
Stannic chloride	-44.9	Ibid.
Stearin	37.5	475
Sulfur (m.p. 113)	>96	151
Sulfur hexafluoride	High	151
Sulfuric acid (100%)	<25	151
Sulfuric acid (95%)	>25	70A(p.907),151
Sulfur trioxide	<25	70A(pp.900,907),388
Tallow	43.75	475
Titanium tetrabromide	103.8	24,25,153,188,256(p.677)
Titanium tetrachloride	12	25,153,188,255(p.473)
Valeric acid	<17	17
Eleven other nonhydrocarbons	<25	85
38 other nonhydrocarbons	>25	85
Water (Iso-optic at 0)	133	143,151,153,256(p.672), 434
SULFUR HEXAFLUORIDE (m.p. -56) (crit.temp. 45.5)		
n-Pentane	<-78	151
n-Hexane	-22.8	151
2,2,4-Trimethylpentane	<-78	151
n-Decane	High	151
Methylcyclohexane	High	151
Toluene	High	151
Carbon disulfide (incomplete mixing)	None	151
Sulfur dioxide (incomplete mixing)	None	151

TABLE I 169

	CST	References
SULFURIC ACID (Table IV)		17
Carbon disulfide	>180	17
Ethyl ether (>94.6% H_2SO_4)	<25	393(p.1065),439A
Isopropyl acetate	<25	149,393(p.1065)
Sulfur dioxide (in 100% H_2SO_4)	<25	151
(in 95% H_2SO_4)	>25	70A(p.900),151
SULFUR TRIOXIDE		
Carbon disulfide	between 15 and 30	70A(p.907),388
Sulfur dioxide	<25	70A(pp.900,907),388
SULFURYL CHLORIDE		
All hydrocarbons	<m.p.	145
TALLOW		15
Sulfur dioxide	43.75	475
TANNIC ACID, TARTARIC ACID		15
TELURIUM (m.p. 452)		
Sodium (m.p. 97)	>435	210(p.29)
Thallium (m.p. 302)	>393	210(p.28)
α-TERPINEOL		
Acetamide (m.p. 81)	<46	260,271
o-Nitrophenol (m.p. 45)	<30	271
Propionamide (m.p. 79)	<36.2	271
TETRABROMOETHANE		15
n-Dodecane	30	151
n-Hexadecane	43	151
Nonaromatic oil	43.3	151
Aromatic oil	15.5	151
1,1,2,2-TETRACHLOROETHANE		
(Table VII)		121
Paraffin wax (m.p. 50)	<50	340
Two lubricating oils	<10	340
Ethylene glycol	88.5	255,256,268,271,392(p.157)
Phenylacetic acid (m.p. 77)	<25	177,392(p.584)
Phosgene	<17	8
TETRACHLOROETHYLENE (Table VI)		372
Paraffin wax (m.p. 50)	<29	341
Lubricating oils	<10	131,341
Acetamide (m.p. 81)	>120	271
Acetonitrile	13	73,153,256,392(p.66)
2-Chloroethanol	30	Ibid.
Ethylenediamine	15.8	Ibid.
Methanol	-10	73,153,256,392(p.53)
2-Methoxyethanol	-25	73,153
Nitromethane	41	73,153,256(p.678), 392(pp.36,66)
n-TETRADECYL ALCOHOL (m.p. 38.3)		211
(Table VIII)		
Acetonitrile	48	196A
Nitroethane	35	196A
TETRAETHYLAMMONIUM IODIDE		15
TETRAETHYLLEAD		15

	CST	References
TETRAETHYLENE GLYCOL		
Water	<20	284
TETRAETHYLENEPENTAMINE		
Water	<20	284
TETRAHYDROFURFURYL ALCOHOL		
n-Hexane	82	139
n-Heptane	82	139,149
2,2,4-Trimethylpentane	90	139,149,311
1-Heptene	15	139
Diisobutene	45	139
Cyclohexane	40	139,140,446(p.40)
Methylcyclohexane	50	139,140
Decalin	27	140
Triethylbenzene	<-78	140,446(p.133)
Di-sec-amylbenzene	12	140,446(p.130)
Di-sec-amylnaphthalene	9	140
Pinene	11	151
Paraffin wax (m.p. 53)	150	139
Paraffinic oil	150	139
Naphthenic oil	115	139
Water	<25	296(p.44)
TETRAMETHYLDIAMINOBENZOPHENONE		15
2,3,5,6-TETRAMETHYLPHENOL		
Water	294	152,433
TETRAMETHYLTHIURAM DISULFIDE		
n-Heptane	>100	149
Octyltoluene	112	151
Naphthalene (m.p. 80)	<65	149
TETRYL (see TRINITROPHENYL-		
p. 177)		
THALLIUM (m.p. 302)		
Selenium (m.p. 218)	>361	210(p.27)
Sulfur (two composition		
ranges)	>127,>448	210(p.25)
Teleurium (m.p. 452)	>393	210(p.28)
THIOCARBANILIDE (m.p. 154)		
Paraffin wax (m.p. 53)	179	139,149
Paraffinic oil	177	139
Naphthenic oil	153	139
THIODIPROPIONITRILE		
Benzene	0	152,421
Toluene	61	152,421
Ethylbenzene	114	152,421
o-Xylene	107	152,421
m-Xylene	119	152,421
p-Xylene	123	152,421
THIOPHENE		
All hydrocarbons	<m.p.	145
THIOUREA		
All hydrocarbons	High	139

TABLE I   **171**

	CST	References
THIOXANE (OXATHIANE)		
All hydrocarbons	<m.p.	145
THYMOL (3-HYDROXY-p-CYMENE)		
(m.p. 51.5)		15
Paraffin oil	<40	139,149
Acetamide (m.p. 81)	<69	271
Camphor (m.p. 176)	<34	271
Carvone	<-10	271
Diethylene glycol	<33	271
Ethyl fumarate	<35.5	271
Glycerol	218.5	153,209,220,287,328
p-Methylacetophenone	<7.7	271
Quinoline	<3	271,446(p.796)
Water	271	149(p.270),153,255(p.412) 481

TIN (see STANNIC, STANNOUS p.164)

TITANIUM TETRABROMIDE		
Sulfur dioxide	103.8	24,25,153,188,256 (pp.677,680)

TITANIUM TETRACHLORIDE		
n-Heptane	<0	149
2,2,4-Trimethylpentane	<0	149
Sulfur dioxide	12	24,25,153,188,256(p.680)

o-TOLIDINE		15

p-TOLIDINE (m.p. 103)		
n-Heptane	>100	139,149

p-TOLUENESULFONAMIDE		15

α-TOLUIC ACID (see PHENYLACETIC ACID, p.148)

o-,m-, and p-TOLUIC ACIDS (see WATER, p.187)

TOLUENE (Tables III,IV,VI,VII)		17,121,340,372

o- and m-TOLUIDINES (Tables III,IV) 17

	Ortho	Meta	References
Melting point	-24	-31.5	
n-Hexane	23	21.3	87,139,149,175,392 (pp.457,559),435,442,442A 445(pp.522-3),448
2-Methylpentane	25.5		149,392(p.559),435, 445(p.522)
n-Heptane	22	18.85	139,149,309
2-Methylhexane	23.6	23.25	309
2,2-Dimethylpentane	28.2	27.61	309
2,3-Dimethylpentane	17.7	16.25	309
2,4-Dimethylpentane	28.4	28.0	309
2,2,3-Trimethylbutane	21.55	20.7	309
2,2,4-Trimethylpentane	33	30	139,149,311
n-Decane		32	17,149
2,7-Dimethyloctane		38.5	149,209(p.397),443,445 (p.529)

	CST		References

o- and m-TOLUIDINES (continued)

	Ortho	Meta	
1-Heptene	-25		139
Diisobutene	-10		139
Methylcyclopentane	-10.9		149,435,445(p.533)
Ethylcyclopentane	-8.3		Ibid.
Cyclohexane (m.p. 6)	-7	-18E	87,139,149,253
Methylcyclohexane	-5	-8.3	87,139,149,175,253,
			392(p.559),435,445(p.541)
Paraffin wax (m.p. 53)	72		139
Paraffinic oils	69		131,139,149
Naphthenic oils	34-35		Ibid.
Acetamide (m.p. 81)	<24.3	<-3	255,270,271,392(p.121),
			445(p.1108)
Ethylene glycol	<-55		151,255,256,262,268,271,
			272,392(p.157)
Glycerol LCST		(6.7)	153,209(p.395),328,330,
(Figure 2)			392(p.210)
Glycerol	154.4	120.5	153,209(pp.395-6),272,
			328,330,392(p.210)
Sulfur	130		393(p.1066),489
Water	216	High	3,140A,153,253,256,
			392(p.555),414,447
Water(Isopycnics)	(24.5)	(7)	140A,315

p-TOLUIDINE (m.p. 45)(Table III)

			15
Ethane LCST, 32.6			380
2-Methylpentane		36	149,392(p.559),435,
			445(pp.523-4)
3-Methylpentane		32.4	Ibid.
2,2,4-Trimethylpentane		<35	139,149
n-Dotriacontane		78.4	341B,445(p.529)
Paraffin wax (m.p. 53)		63	139,149
Paraffinic oil		54	139
Acetamide (m.p. 81)		<65	318,392(p.121)
Ethyl alcohol		<8	392(p.560),425
Glycerol		<42.8	153,286,328
Pyridine		<20	86

α-TOLUNITRILE
  (see PHENYLACETONITRILE, p.148)

m-TOLUNITRILE

Crystal oil (Nujol)		33	151

TWO TOLUYLENEDIAMINES

n-Heptane		>150	139,149
Glycerol		<m.p.	153,328

TRIACETIN (GLYCEROL TRIACETATE)

n-Heptane		96	151
n-Octadecane		155	151
Cyclohexane		63	151
Methylcyclohexane		70	151
Decalin		89	151
Tetralin		<0	151
Di-sec-butylbenzene		36	151
Naphthenic lubricating oil		142	151

TRIAMYLAMINE

Propane (miscible)	None <100		192

TABLE I   **173**

	CST	References

TRIAMYLAMINE STEARATE
Paraffinic oil ..... <0 149

TRI-n-BUTYLAMINE (Table V)
Aniline 43 151
Benzaldehyde ..... <25 151
Miscibilities with 160
  substances ..... 15,296(pp.404-10)

TRI-n-BUTYL PHOSPHATE (Table VIII) 211

TRICAPRYLIN (GLYCEROL TRICAPRYLATE)
(Table III)
Propane LCST, 100.5 22,149,191

TRICHLOROACETIC ACID (m.p.57.5)
2,2,4-Trimethylpentane ..... <46 149
Paraffin wax (m.p. 53) ..... <52 149

TRICHLOROACRYLIC ACID (m.p.72.9)
Water ..... 60.85 21,344,392(p.163)

1,3,5-TRICHLOROBENZENE (m.p. 63)
(Table III)
Ethane (crit.temp.,upper
  layer 46.8) LCST, 40.3 ..... 365,381,445(p.180)
Ethylene glycol ..... >181 256,271

TRICHLOROETHYLENE
(Tables VI and VII)
All hydrocarbons ..... <m.p. 151,341
Phenylacetic acid (m.p. 77) ..... <30 ..... 177,392(p.584)

1,2.3-TRICHLOROPROPANE
Ethylene glycol ..... >152.5 271

TRICHLOROGALLEIN 15

TRICHLOROMETHANE
(see CHLOROFORM, p.59)

1,1,1-TRICHLOROTOLUENE
(BENZOTRICHLORIDE)
All hydrocarbons ..... <m.p. 145

12-TRICOSANONE (LAURONE)(m.p.69.3)
Acetonitrile ..... >82 ..... 153,158,393(p.799)
Eleven other solvents ..... <m.p. ..... 158,393(p.799)

2-TRIDECANONE (m.p. 27.46)
Thirteen solvents ..... <m.p. 197A

TRIDECYLIC ACID
Five organic solvents ..... <m.p. 345

TRI-n-DODECYLAMINE (m.p. 15.7)
Acetone ..... >56 347
2-Butanone 15 347
Ethyl acetate ..... <9.8 347
Isopropyl alcohol 41.1 347
Nine other solvents ..... <m.p. 347

	CST	References
TRIETHANOLAMINE (Tables V and VII)		106,121,289
Benzene	>155	140,446(p.104)
Styrene	180	140,446(p.120)
Biphenyl	185	140,446(p.133)
Bibenzyl	215	140,446(p.134)
Naphthalene	151	140,446(p.140)
1-Methylnaphthalene	177	140,446(p.141)
2-Methylnaphthalene	178	140,446(p.142)
Isopropylnaphthalene	226	140,446(p.143)
sec-Amylnaphthalene	251	Ibid.
Diisopropylnaphthalene	265	Ibid.
Tetralin	187	140,446(p.45)
Isopropyltetralin	264	Ibid.
Anthracene (m.p. 216)	<197	140,446(p.144)
Phenanthrene (m.p. 101)	174	Ibid.
Fluorene	180	Ibid.
Water	<20	284
TRIETHYLAMINE (Tables III and IV)		17
n-Hexane	<25	170
Acetic acid	130	393(p.594),446(p.815), 460
Deuterium oxide	14.45	341A,451
Formic acid	>25	226,392(p.32)
Water LCST, 12.4 to 28		1,1A,14,72,135,152,153, 157,169,209(pp.390,393), 253,341A,344,357,362, 392(p.466),442A,443,444, 446A,451,485,486
Miscibilities with 129 substances		15,296(pp.404-10)
TRIETHYLENE GLYCOL (Table VIII)		211,284
Benzene	22	140,446(p.95)
Toluene	90	140,446(p.113)
Ethylbenzene	115	140,446(p.116)
m-Xylene	120	140,446(p.123)
Methylethylbenzene	138	140,446(p.128)
Cumene (Isopropylbenzene)	137	140,446(p.117)
Pseudocumene	152	140
tert-Butylbenzene	153	140,446(p.119)
sec-Butylbenzene	156	Ibid.
Diethylbenzene	160	140,446(p.128)
Cymene (p-Isopropyltoluene)	161	140,446(p.129)
Methyldiethylbenzene	172	Ibid.
Ethylisopropylbenzene	177	140,446(p.130)
Disopropylbenzene	191	Ibid.
sec-Amylbenzene	178	140,446(p.120)
Triethylbenzene	188	140,446(p.133)
Methyldiisopropylbenzene	203	Ibid.
Di-sec-butylbenzene	222	151
Di-sec-amylbenzene	234	140,446(p.130)
Hexaethylbenzene	235	140
Styrene	37	140,446(p.120)
Biphenyl	65	140,446(p.133)
Bibenzyl	115	140,446(p.134)
1-Methylnaphthalene	62	140,446(p.141)
2-Methylnaphthalene	61	140,446(p.142)
Isopropylnaphthalene	133	140,446(p.143)
sec-Amylnaphthalene	160	Ibid.
Diisopropylnaphthalene	177	Ibid.

TABLE I

175

	CST	References
TRIETHYLENE GLYCOL (continued)		
Di-tert-butyl naphthalene	190	140
Di-sec-amyl naphthalene	246	140
Tetralin	92	140,446(p.45)
Isopropyltetralin	179	Ibid.
Indene	53	151
Limonene	170	151
Water	<20	284
TRIETHYLENETETRAMINE (Table VIII)		211
Tetraisopropylbenzene (m.p.118.4)	174	140,149
Water	<20	284
Miscibilities with 33 substances		296(p.400),483A
TRIETHYL PHOSPHATE (Table VIII)		211
TRIGLYCOLDICHLORIDE		
Water	>20	284
TRIISOBUTYLAMINE		
Acetone	-11	445(p.964)
Methanol (Miscible)	None	446(p.655)
TRIISOPROPANOLAMINE		
Water	<20	284
TRILAURIN (GLYCEROL TRILAURATE) (m.p. 46)		
Propane (Table III) LCST, 87.4		22,153
TRIMETHYLAMINE		
Amyl alcohol	<25	170,392(p.211)
Benzyl alcohol	<25	Ibid.
Chloroform	<25	Ibid.
Ethyl alcohol	<25	Ibid.
Methanol	<25	Ibid.
n-Propyl alcohol	<25	Ibid.
TRIMETHYLENE CHLOROHYDRIN (Table VIII)		211
TRIMETHYLENE GLYCOL (Tables V and VII)		106,121
2,2,4-Trimethylpentane	>90	149,311
Benzene	>80	218
Naphthalene	155	149
Acetonitrile	-6	151
n-Decyl alcohol	-13	151
n-Dodecyl alcohol (Lauryl alcohol)	<15	151
2-Ethylhexanol	<0	151
Nitroethane	56.5	151
Nitromethane	41	151
2,6,8-TRIMETHYL-4-NONANONE (Table VIII)		211
Four TRIMETHYPHENOLS (see WATER, p.187)		

	CST	References

2,4,6-TRIMETHYLPYRIDINE
(COLLIDINE)(Table III)
  Water LCST, 3.5   >180   135,153,209(p.393),253,
                                                         362,392(p.616),443

TRIMYRISTIN (GLYCEROL TRIMYRISTATE)
(m.p. 56)
  Propane (Table III) LCST, 79.4   22,153

2,4,6-TRINITROANILINE (PICRAMIDE)
(m.p. 188)
  Six Polycyclic aromatic   <m.p.   116,149,210(p.127)
    hydrocarbons

2,4,6-TRINITROANISOLE (m.p. 68.4)
  Benzene   <15   88,392(p.495)
  Toluene   <18   Ibid.
  Acetone   <0   Ibid.
  Chloroform   <35   Ibid.
  Ethyl acetate   <15   Ibid.
  Pyridine   <40   Ibid.

1,3,5-TRINITROBENZENE (m.p. 61)
  Six Polycyclic aromatic   <m.p.   149,210(pp.118-9)
    hydrocarbons
  Acetone   <35   90,392(p.323)
  Pyridine   <17   Ibid.
  Urea (m.p. 132)   >130   459

2,4,6-TRINITROCHLOROBENZENE
(PICRYL CHLORIDE, m.p. 83)
  Benzene   <25   89,392(p.320)
  Toluene   <20   Ibid.
  Seven Polycyclic hydrocarbons   <m.p.   116,149,210(p.117)

  Acetone   <10   89,392(p.320)
  Chloroform   <40   Ibid.
  Ethyl acetate   <18   Ibid.
  Pyridine   <17   Ibid.

TRINITROCHLOROMETHANE (CHLOROPICRIN)
  n-Heptane   <-60   149

2,4,6-TRINITROMETHYLANILINE
(m.p. 81.5)
  Benzene and Pyridine   <24   91

1,4,5-TRINITRONAPHTHALENE (m.p.126)
  1,2,5-Trinitronaphthalene
    (m.p. 114)   >130   210(p.154),329
  1,3,5-Trinitronaphthalene
    (m.p. 147)   >131   210(p.155),329

2,4,6-TRINITROPHENETOLE (m.p.78.5)
  Benzene   <30   88,392(p.578),432
  Toluene   <40   Ibid.
  Acetone   <15   Ibid.
  Chloroform   <40   Ibid.
  Ethyl acetate   <35   Ibid.
  Pyridine   <15   Ibid.

TABLE I   **177**

	CST	References

2,4,6-TRINITROPHENOL (see PICRIC
ACID, p. 154)

2,4,6-TRINITROPHENYLETHYLNITRO-
AMINE (m.p. 95.7) .

	CST	References
Acetone	<25	91
Ethyl acetate	<50	91
Pyridine	<35	91

2,4,6-TRINITROPHENYLMETHYLENE-
TETRAMINE (TETRYL, m.p. 130)

	CST	References
95% Ethyl alcohol	105	80,81,153,209(p.395), 392(p.496)

2,4,6-TRINITRORESORCINOL (STYPHNIC
ACID, m.p. 180)

	CST	References
Diphenylmethane	>144.6	116,149,210(p.122)
Triphenylmethane	>167.4	Ibid.
Ten other Polycyclic aromatics	<m.p.	Ibid.
Water	>123	115,392(p.647)

2,4,6-TRINITROTOLUENE (m.p. 81)

	CST	References
Benzene	<30	88,432
Toluene	<35	Ibid.
Six Polycyclic aromatics	<m.p.	149,210(p.146)
Acetone	<20	88,392(p.493),432
Aniline	<80	Ibid.
Chloroform	<45	Ibid.
Ethyl alcohol (95%)	96.5	80,153,210(p.147)
Pyridine	<20	432

TRI-n-OCTADECYLAMINE (m.p. 54)

	CST	References
Acetone	<50	347,392(p.809)
2-Butanone (Methyl ethyl ketone)	<47	Ibid.
n-Butyl alcohol	<52	Ibid.
Ethyl acetate	<46	Ibid.
Isopropyl alcohol	144e	Ibid.
Five other solvents	<m.p.	Ibid.

TRI-n-OCTYLAMINE

	CST	References
Acetone	48	347,392(p.800)
2-Butanone (Methyl ethyl ketone)	-17.5	Ibid.
Carbon tetrachloride	<-23	Ibid.
Ethyl acetate	-22.5	Ibid.
Isopropyl alcohol	<-36	Ibid.
Eight other solvents	<m.p.	Ibid.

TRIOLEIN (GLYCEROL TRIOLEATE)

	CST	References
Propane (Table III) LCST, 64.5		149,191
Ethyl alcohol	145	17,446(p.595)
Resorcinol	245	17,446(p.616)

TRIPALMITIN (GLYCEROL TRIPALMITATE)
(m.p. 65)

	CST	References
Propane (Table III) LCST, 73.5		22,149,191

TRIPHENYLGUANIDINE (m.p. 145)

	CST	References
Paraffinic lubricating oil	151	139(p.766),149

TRIPHENYL PHOSPHITE
(see PHENYL PHOSPHITE, p. 151)

	CST	References
TRIPHENYLSELENONIUM IODIDE		15
TRI-n-PROPYLAMINE		
Acetone	-40	444,445(p.964)
TRISTEARIN (GLYCEROL TRISTEARATE, m.p. 71)		
Propane (Table III) LCST, 69.2		22,149,191
2-UNDECYLBENZOTHIAZOLE (m.p. 44)		
Acetonitrile	79	108A,445(p.1087)
Methanol	56	108A
Hexane, Benzene, Carbon tetrachloride, Chloroform, and Ethyl acetate	<0	108A
Acetone, 95% Ethyl alcohol, and Isopropyl alcohol	<10	108A
UNDECYLIC ACID (HENDECYLIC ACID)		
Fifteen organic solvents	<m.p.	197,345,392(pp.735-6)
URANIUM HEXAFLUORIDE		
Hydrogen fluoride	100.5	152,369
UREA (m.p. 132)		
All hydrocarbons	>130.6	145,459
o-Dinitrobenzene (m.p. 114.8)	<130	210(p.100),246,459
m-Dinitrobenzene (m.p. 89)	<129	Ibid.
p-Dinitrobenzene (m.p. 169.5)	<164	Ibid.
2,4-Dinitrotoluene	>130.5	353
Diphenylamine	High	207,393(p.1075)
Nitrobenzene •	>130.6	459
Phenacetin	ca 163	206
Resorcinol	<132	207
Sulfonal (m.p. 128)	>120	208,393(p.1075)
1,3,5-Trinitrobenzene (m.p. 122)	>130	459
URETHANE (ETHYL CARBAMATE, m.p. 50)		
n-Heptane	>122	151
1-Octene	92	151
Cyclohexane	95	151
Methylcyclohexane	104	151
Benzene	<0	210
Toluene	<0	210,425
1,2,4-Trimethylbenzene	<36	271
1,3,5-Trimethylbenzene (Mesitylene)	<34	271
p-Cymene (p-Isopropyltoluene)	<38	271
sec-Butylbenzene	40	151
Di-sec-butylbenzene	86	151
Naphthalene (m.p. 80)	<56	271
Indene	<32.5	271,445(p.655)
Acetamide (m.p. 81)	<44	318,392(p.121)
Acetanilide (m.p. 114)	<75	318,392(p.603)
Acetophenone	<41.5	271,445(p.1021)
n-Amyl ether	<48	271
Bromobenzene	<22	271
m-Bromotoluene	<35	271,445(p.799)
n-Butyl butyrate	<21	271

TABLE I   **179**

	CST	References
URETHANE (continued)		
Carbon dioxide (crit.temp., upper layer, 37) LCST, 30.5		45(p.678),392(p.203), 445(p.940)
Chloroform	<23	392(p.202),425
o-Chlorotoluene	<35	271,445(p.799)
o-Cresol	<8	271,446(p.926)
p-Cresol methyl ether	<23.5	271,446(p.927)
p-Dibromobenzene (m.p. 87)	<70	271,445(p.798)
o-, and p-Dichlorobenzenes	<48	271,445(p.797)
Diphenylamine	>132	206
Ethyl alcohol	<0	392(p.202),425
Ethyl caproate	<22	271,445(p.1043)
Ethyl oxalate	<19	271,445(p.1045)
n-Heptyl alcohol	<20.5	271,446(p.876)
n-Hexyl bromide	<32	271
Isoamyl butyrate	<29.5	271,445(p.1041)
Isoamyl ether	<44	271
Isoamyl isovalerate	<36	271,445(p.1043)
Isobutyl isovalerate	<24	271,445(p.1042)
Methanol	<0	392(p.202),425
Methyl benzoate	<36	271,445(p.1048)
Methyl caprylate	<37	271,445(p.1043)
Methylene iodide (Diiodomethane)	82	271
Nitrobenzene	<42.5	271,445(p.1162)
2-Octanol	<30	271,445(p.876)
n-Octyl alcohol	<39	271,445(p.876)
Phenol	<6.5	271,446(p.926)
n-Propyl alcohol	<15	392(p.202),425
Resorcinol (m.p. 110)	<40	86,318,392(p.394)
Water	<15	86,392(p.202),425
URIC ACID		15
VALERALDEHYDE		
All hydrocarbons	<m.p	145
VALERAMIDE (m.p. 115)		
Propane (crit.pt.,upper layer,98)		22
VALERIC ACID (Table IV)		17
n-Decane	-20	17,149,446(p.211)
Naphthalene (m.p. 80)	<65	452
p-Dichlorobenzene (m.p. 53)	<47	271
Methylene iodide	73	17
Stannic chloride	-10	17
ISOVALERIC ACID		
Water	95	153,209(p.393),443
γ-VALEROLACTONE		
n-Heptane	>39	130
Methylcyclohexane	>39	130
VALERONITRILE		15
n-Octadecane (m.p. 28)	<25	151
VANILLIN (4-HYDROXY-3-METHOXY-BENZALDEHYDE)(m.p. 81)		
Glycerol	<80	153,286,328
Pyridine	<20	86

	CST	References
VERATRINE (an alkaloid)		
Pyridine	<20	86
VERATROLE (see CATECHOL DIMETHYL ETHER)		
VINYL BROMIDE		
Ethylene glycol (Iso-optic at 15.7)	>15.7	143
VINYL CHLORIDE		
Water (Iso-optic at 72.3)	>72.3	143
WATER (Tables III and IV)		17
Benzene	306.4	149,209,212,351 392(p.368)
Toluene, Xylene, Tetralin	>300	149,212,324
Acetaldehyde	<20	193A
Acetamide (m.p. 81)	<25	318
Acetanilide (m.p. 114)	144	153,209(p.392),385, 392(p.600)
Acetic acid (m.p. 16.6)	<-27	129
Acetic anhydride (reacts)	>40	151
Acetone	<-11	210(p.262)
Acetonitrile	-0.9	119,126,153,392,451
Acetonylacetone(2,5-Hexanedione)	<20	193A,296(p.43)
Acetophenone (Isopycnic at 96)	220	17,140A
Acetylacetone (2,4-Pentanedione)	87.7	153,209(p.388),253,271, 330,362,365,443,486
Acetyl chloride (reacts)	>25	151
Acetyldimethylamine	<25	151
Acetylsalicylic acid (Aspirin) (m.p. 135)	89m	136,153,209(p.392),253, 362,392(p.630)
Acetyl-p-toluidide	<117.6	339
Acrolein	88	28,153,209(p.387),255 (p.469),392(p.165)
Acrylonitrile	>95	84,393(p.603)
Adiponitrile	101	493
Albumin (egg)	<25	86
o-Aldehydobenzoic acid (Phthalaldehydic acid)(m.p. 100)	45.7m	153,209(p.391),255, 392(p.571),408
m-Aldehydobenzoic acid(m.p.175)	<115	392(p.571),408
p-Aldehydobenzoic acid (m.p. 250)	<182	Ibid.
Alkylmalonic acids (Me to Am)	<25	462
Aluminum hydroxide	>25	277B(p.210)
o-Aminoacetanilide (m.p. 144.8)	<m.p.	392(p.608),411
p-Aminoacetanilide (m.p. 161)	<m.p.	Ibid.
o-Aminobenzoic acid (m.p. 147) (Anthranilic acid)	78m	136,153,209(p.391), 253,392(p.539)
m-Aminobenzoic acid (m.p. 174)	66m	136,153,392(p.539)
p-Aminobenzoic acid (m.p. 186)	47m	Ibid.
o-Aminophenol (m.p. 174)	<129	392(p.421),407
m-Aminophenol (m.p. 123)	1.9	Ibid.
p-Aminophenol (m.p. 186)	<106	Ibid.
1-Amino-2-propanol (Isopropanolamine)	<20	284
2-Aminopropanol	<20	284
Ammonia	<-80	368A,391(p.1032)
n-Amyl alcohol	182	1,118,152,176,444
Two secondary amyl alcohols	>92	271,341

TABLE I   **181**

	CST	References
WATER (continued)		
tert-Amyl alcohol	>30	392(p.316)
Aniline (Isopycnic at 77)	167	(see ANILINE, p.37)
Aniline phenolate	140	1,153,209,389, 392(pp.415,708)
Anisic acid (m.p. 122) (p-Methoxybenzoic acid)	138.2	136,153,209(p.392), 253,392(p.591)
Antipyrine	<25	86
Benzamide (m.p. 130)	<75	338,392(p.536)
Benzoic acid (m.p. 122)	117	1,27,153,209(pp.391,393) 251,253,392(pp.500-1), 410,443,473,486
Benzonitrile (Isopycnic at 34)	High	140A,151,315
Benzyl Cellosolve	>25	271,284
Benzyl cyanide (Isopycnic at 60)	High	140A
Bromal hydrate	107	116,153,209(p.387), 392(p.87),443
p-Bromobenzoic acid (m.p. 252)	170m	136,153,392(p.473)
1,3-Butanediol (Butylene glycol)	<20	284
2-Butanone (Methyl ethyl ketone) LCST, -22 to -6	139 to 151.8	153,209(pp.387,393),253 296(p.594),330,362,365, 392(p.243),418,443,486
n-Butyl alcohol	127	(see n-BUTYL ALCOHOL, p.48)
sec-Butyl alcohol	110	(see sec-BUTYL ALCOHOL, p.48)
tert-Butyl alcohol	<0	151,325,365
Butyl Carbitol	<20	284
Butyl Carbitol acetate	>20	284
Butyl Cellosolve (see Ethylene glycol n-butyl ether, p.183)		
n-Butyl lactate	>20	296(p.43)
p-n-Butylphenol	246.6	119,152
n-Butyric acid	-3	(see n-BUTYRIC ACID, p. 50)
Carbitol	<20	45,46,284
Carbitol acetate	<20	284
Carbon dioxide (crit.temp., upper layer, 31.5)		45
Carbon tetrachloride	>220	17
Catechol (m.p. 104)	<35	392(p.391),471
Cellosolve (Ethoxyethanol)	<20	284
Cellosolve acetate	181	296(pp.656,722)
Chloral hydrate (m.p. 52)	<0	86,392(p.92),425,485
Chlorex (Dichloroethyl ether)	>20	284
o-,m-,p-Chloroacetanilides	>180	153,392(p.580),413,425
o-,m-,p-Chloroanilines	>150	392(p.371),413
Chlorobenzene	>220	17
o-Chlorobenzoic acid (m.p.142)	126.2	136,153,209(p.390),253, 392(p.473)
m-Chlorobenzoic acid (m.p.158)	142.8	Ibid.
p-Chlorobenzoic acid (m.p.243)	167m	136,153,392(p.473)
2-Chloroethanol (Ethylene chlorohydrin)	<20	284
o-Chlorophenol	173	153,209(p.389)392(p.355) 417
m-Chlorophenol	130.8	Ibid.
p-Chlorophenol	129	Ibid.
Cinnamic acid (m.p. 133)	140.5	153,251,392(p.626)
Collidine (Trimethylpyridine) LCST, 3.5	>180	153,209(p.393),253,341A 362,392(p.616),443

	CST	References
WATER (continued)		
o-Cresol (Isopycnic at 145)	166	119,152,153,209(p.391), 255,305,306,392(p.547), 414,431,433
m-Cresol (Isopycnic at 148)	148	Ibid.
p-Cresol (Isopycnic at 138)	143	Ibid.
Crotyl alcohol (2-Butene-1-ol)	>100	271
Cyclohexanol	184.7	152,153,256,392(p.435), 415,493
n-Decyl alcohol	296e	118,152,176
2,2'-Dichloroethyl ether (Chlorex)	>20	284
2,2'-Dichloroisopropyl ether	>20	284
1,2-Dichloropropane (Propylene chloride)	>20	284
Diethanolamine (2,2'-Dihydroxy- diethylamine)	<20	284,296(p.43)
Diethylamine LCST, 143.5		1,135,153,169A,209 253,258,392(p.278)
Diethylaminoethanol	<20	284
Diethylcarbinol (3-Pentanol)	>91.8	271,341
Diethyl Carbitol	<20	284
Diethyl Cellosolve	>20	284
Diethyl Cellosolve acetate	<20	296(p.43)
Diethylene glycol	<20	284
Diethylene glycol monoamyl ether LCST, 30		449B
Diethylene glycol monobutyl ether	<20	296(p.43)
Diethylene triamine	<20	284
Diethyl ketone (3-Pentanone)	>160	153,209,253,362,392
3,5-Diethylphenol	248	119,152,433
Diglycolchlorohydrin	<20	284
o,o'-Dihydroxybiphenyl	186.3	152,433
Dimethoxymethane (Methylal)	160.3	26,153,209(p.393), 392(p.208),443
Dimethoxytetraglycol	<20	284
Dimethyl Cellosolve	<20	296(p.43)
2,3-Dimethylphenol (Xylenol)	209.5	119,152,433
2,4-Dimethylphenol (Xylenol)	213.2	119,152,328,433
2,5-Dimethylphenol (Xylenol)	218.9	Ibid.
2,6-Dimethylphenol (Xylenol)	238.8	119,152,433
3,4-Dimethylphenol (Xylenol)	189.5	Ibid.
3,5-Dimethylphenol (Xylenol)	198.9	Ibid.

Dimethylpyridines	LCST		
2,3-	16.5	192.6	77,152
2,4-	23.4	188.7	2,76,77,152,153,224
2,5-	13.1	206.9	2,76,77,152,153
2,6- (Lutidine)	34.06	230.7	2,76,77,78,133,134,135, 152,153,209,253,444
3,4-	-3.6	162.5	76,77,152
3,5-	-12.5	192.0	Ibid.
3,5-Dinitrobenzoic acid (m.p. 205)		123.8	136,153,209(pp.390,393) 253,392(p.471),443
2,3-Dinitrophenol (m.p. 145)		122.5	153,209(p.388), 392(pp.350-1),405,416
2,4-Dinitrophenol		>200	115,153,209(pp.388-9), 392(pp.350-1) 393(p.848),405,416

TABLE I   **183**

	CST	References
WATER (continued)		
2,5-Dinitrophenol	>200	153,209,392(pp.350-1), 405,416
2,6-Dinitrophenol	>200	Ibid.
3,4-Dinitrophenol (m.p. 134)	105.2	Ibid.
3,5-Dinitrophenol (m.p. 126)	125	Ibid.
2,4-Dinitroresorcinol (m.p. 148)	167	115,393(p.649)
p-Dioxane	<-15	162A,200A,234B,392
Diphenylamine	304	52,153,209(p.392),253, 392(p.702)
Di-n-propylamine LCST -4.9		193,296(pp.415-6)
Dipropylene glycol	<20	284
Epichlorohydrin	>80	274,392(p.169)
Ethanolamine	<20	153,284,328
2-Ethoxyethanol (Cellosolve)	<20	284
Ethylene chloride	High	284
Ethylene diacetate	>20	284
Ethylene diamine	<20	284
Ethylene glycol	<20	284
Ethylene glycol benzyl ether	>20	296(p.43)
Ethylene glycol n-butyl ether (Butyl Cellosolve, Table III) LCST, 49.1	128,140	74,153,209(p.390), 254(p.300),255,296 (p.651),392(p.461)366A
Ethylene glycol isobutyl ether (Table III) LCST, 24.5	150.4	74,78,153,209,254 (p.300),255,392(p.461)
Ethylene oxide	<2	151,283,392(p.101)
Ethyl ether (crit.temp.,upper layer, 202.2) LCST, -70e		168A,250,366A,377
Ethyl lactate	<25	296(p.737)
o-Ethylphenol	213.8	152,433
m-Ethylphenol	190.6	152,433
p-Ethylphenol	185	119,152,433
Ethylphenylethanolamine	>20	284
1-Ethylpiperidine LCST 7.45		134,135,153,209(p.391), 253
2-Ethylpyridine LCST -5	231.4	77,152
3-Ethylpyridine LCST -35e	195.6	77,152
4-Ethylpyridine LCST -19	181.8	77,152
Ethyl vinyl ether	>25	393(p.910),418A
Fluorobenzene (Isopycnic at 48)	High	140A
Formic acid	<-48	129
Freon 21 ($CHCl_2F$)(Iso-optic at 71)	>71	143
Furfural	122	(see FURFURAL, p.97)
Furfuryl alcohol	<25	296(p.43),362
Glutaric dinitrile	68.3	153,256(p.669) 392(p.290),395
Glycerol	<-23	256A,392(p.209)
n-Heptyl alcohol	248.5	118,152
Hexamethyleneimine LCST, 66.9	228	152,494
Hexamethylenetetramine	<20	392(p.434),458A
2-Hexanone	>90	271
n-Hexyl alcohol	222.2	118,152
Hydrocinnamic acid (2-Phenylpropionic acid)	150	153.209(p.392), 392(p.634),410
Hydrogen bromide (incomplete mixing)	None	56B,70A(p.114),147,359
Hydrogen chloride (incomplete mixing)	None	147,368
Hydrogen cyanide	<-24m	68,148,332

	CST	References

WATER (continued)

Hydrogen sulfide (Iso-optic at 47.6)(crit.t.,upper layer,100.2)	>47.6	143,393A
Hydroquinone (Quinol, m.p. 170)	<90	392(p.396),471
o-Hydroxybenzaldehyde (Salicylaldehyde)	>200	153,209(p.391), 392(p.498),406
m-Hydroxybenzaldehyde (m.p. 106)	66.2	Ibid.
p-Hydroxybenzaldehyde (m.p. 116)	64.4	Ibid.
o-Hydroxybenzoic acid (m.p. 159) (Salicylic acid)	90	1,11,27,136,153,209,253, 392(pp.518-9),410,486
m-Hydroxybenzoic acid (m.p. 201)	122E	153,406,410
p-Hydroxybenzoic acid (m.p.215)	<110	153,406
o-Hydroxybiphenyl (m.p. 56)	258	152,433
2-Hydroxyethyl acetate	<25	296(p.720)
Hydroxyethylethylenediamine	<20	284
5-Hydroxyhydrindine	200.8	152,453
2,5-Hydroxytolualdehyde	>200	153,209(p.392) 392(p.584),406
4,2-Hydroxytolualdehyde	125	Ibid.
4,3-Hydroxytolualdehyde	136.8	Ibid.
2,3-Hydroxytoluic acid (m.p.164)	153.5	153,209(p.392) 392(p.598),410
2,4-Hydroxytoluic acid (m.p.178)	145.2	Ibid.
2,5-Hydroxytoluic acid (m.p.152)	142.8	Ibid.
3,4-Hydroxytoluic acid (m.p.207)	9E	209,392(p.598),410
4,3-Hydroxytoluic acid (m.p.172)	17E	Ibid.
Iodine (m.p. 114)	ca 300	153,240,256(p.670), 391(p.655)
Iodobenzoic acid (m.p. 270)	175m	136,153,392(p.477)
Isoamyl alcohol	187.5	38,137,153,209,253, 330,392(p.313)
Isobutyl alcohol	129	(see ISOBUTYL ALCOHOL, p. 110)
Isobutyric acid	22	(see ISOBUTYRIC ACID, p. 111)
Isopropanolamine (1-Amino-2-propanol)	<20	284
Isopropyl alcohol	<-23	296(p.470)
Isopropyl Cellosolve	<25	296(p.44)
Isopropyl lactate	<25	296(p.44)
o-Isopropylphenol	239.8	152,433
p-Isopropylphenol	196	152,433
Isovaleric acid	95	153,209(p.393),433
Lutidine (2,6-Dimethylpyridine) LCST, 34.06	230.7	2,76,77,78,118,113,135 152,153,209,253,444
Malonic acid (m.p. 132)	<0	392(p.166)
Malonic acid, alkyl derivatives up to C$_5$	<15	392(p.167),462
Maltose	<25	86
p-Methoxybenzoic acid (Anisic acid, m.p. 184)	138.2m	136,153,209(p.392),253, 392(p.591)
2-Methoxyethanol (Methyl Cellosolve)	<20	284
2-Methoxyethyl acetate	<20	284
Methyl acetate	108	153,209(p.387)
Methyl acetoacetate	>25	296(p.44)
Methylal (Dimethoxymethane)	160.3	26,153,209(p.393), 392(p.208),443
Methylaniline (Isopycnic at 2)	High	140A
3-Methyl-2-butanone	>79	271
Methyl Carbitol	<20	284
Methyl Cellosolve acetate	<20	284

TABLE I 185

	CST	References

WATER (continued)

	CST	References
Methyl chloride (Iso-optic at 26)	>26	143
Methyldiethylamine LCST, 49.42		71,78,152,344
Methyl ethyl ketone (2-Butanone)		153,209(pp.387,393),
LCST, -22 to -6	139 to 151.8	253,330,362,365,
		392(p.243),418,443
2-Methyl-4-ethylphenol	235.4	152,433
2-Methyl-6-ethylphenol	265.3	152,433
3-Methyl-4-ethylphenol	221.5	152,433
3-Methyl-5-ethylphenol	235	119,152,433
3-Methyl-6-ethylphenol	256.2	152,433
4-Methyl-2-ethylphenol	242.5	152,433
Methyl formate	70E	137A,209(p.387)
Methyl isopropyl carbinol	>91	271(p.55)
Methyl oxalate (m.p. 54)	>96	153,231,392(pp.223-4),
		421A
	LCST	
1-Methylpiperidine	48.3	290e	134,135,153,209(p.390)
		253,392(p.452)
2-Methylpiperidine	79.3	227	135,153,209(p.390),253
3-Methylpiperidine	56.9	235	153,209(p.390),253
4-Methylpiperidine	84.9	189.5	133,153,209(p.390),253
3-Methylpyridine	49.4	152.5	2,19,71,76,78,133,153,
		209(p.389),253
3-Methylpyridine		
(β-Picoline)	None Mixes	2,133
4-Methylpyridine	None Mixes	2,133
(γPicoline)		
Methyl vinyl ether		
(Iso-optic at 66.3)	>66.3	143
Morpholine vinyl ether LCST, 70		483A
1-Naphthol	209.0	152,433
2-Naphthol	192.6	152,433
Nicotine LCST, 61	210	4A,140A,153,171,182,
Nicotine (Isopycnic at 96)		208A,209(pp.392-3)
		253,256,315,392
		(p.672),394,443,451,
		454
o-Nitroacetanilide	198	15,153,209(p.391),392
		(p.597),413
m-Nitroacetanilide	180	Ibid.
p-Nitroacetanilide (m.p. 215)	177.4	Ibid.
o-Nitroaniline	211	153,209(p.389),392
		(p.401),413
m-Nitroaniline	187.5	Ibid.
p-Nitroaniline	172.5	Ibid.
o-Nitrobenzaldehyde	>166	15,153,209(p.390),
		392(p.479),409
m-Nitrobenzaldehyde	212	Ibid.
p-Nitrobenzaldehyde	216	Ibid.
Nitrobenzene	240	28,52,79,153,209
		(p.389),253,330,
		392(p.356)
o-Nitrobenzoic acid (m.p. 147)	52e	136,153,209(p.391),
		253,392(p.481)
m-Nitrobenzoic acid (m.p. 141)	108	1,136,153,209
		(pp.391,393),253,
		392(p.481),410,443,
		486
p-Nitrobenzoic acid (m.p. 242)	118e	136,153,392(p.481),410
3-Nitrocatechol (m.p. 85)	105.3	115,153,393(p.654)
Nitroethane (Isopycnic at 60)		140A

	CST	References
WATER (continued)		
Nitrogen dioxide $(N_2O_4$ or NO_2) (Isopycnic about 60)	67	280
Nitrohydroquinone (m.p. 131.2)	120.2	115,153,393(p.654)
Nitromethane	103.3	153,209(pp.387,393), 443,444
o-Nitrophenol	>200	153,209(p.389), 392(p.361),405,414
m-Nitrophenol (m.p. 97)	98.7	Ibid.
p-Nitrophenol (m.p. 114)	93	153,209,253,392(p.361), 405,414,443,444
2-Nitroresorcinol (m.p. 84.8)	>132.7	115,153,393(p.653)
4-Nitroresorcinol (m.p. 112.2)	74.4	Ibid.
Nitrosopiperidine	150.3	133,153,209(p.388)
o-Nitrotoluene	263.5	52,153,209(p.391), 253,330,392(p.537)
Nitrous anhydride (N_2O_3)	55	280
n-Nonyl alcohol	282e	118,152
Novocaine (Procaine) bichromate	98	47,153,199,225,392 (p.730),393(p.754)
Novocaine iodide	<33	199,393(p.755)
Novocaine perchlorate	78	153,199,393(p.755)
Novocaine thiocyanate	54	Ibid.
n-Octyl alcohol	265e	118,152
2- and 3-Pentanol	>92	271
2-Pentanone	>83	209,271,362,392(p.298)
3-Pentanone (Diethyl ketone)	160	153,209,253,362, 392(p.298)
Phenol	66	(see PHENOL, p.147)
Phenylacetic acid	108	153,209(p.391), 392(p.582),410
Phenylacetonitrile (Benzyl cyanide, Isopycnic at 60)	High	140A,151
Phenylammonium phenolate	140	1,153,209,389, 392(pp.415-708)
Phenyl Cellosolve	>20	284
Phenyldiethanolamine	>20	284
o-Phenylenediamine (m.p. 101)	<67	392(p.425),411
m-Phenylenediamine (m.p. 63)	<28	Ibid.
p-Phenylenediamine (m.p. 141)	<75	Ibid.
Phenylethanolamine	>20	284
Phenylhydrazine	55.2 to 75.5	19,153,209(pp.389,393), 253,303,392(p.424),443
2-Phenylpropionic acid (Hydrocinnamic acid)	150	392(p.634),410
Phthalic acid	<150	473
Picolines (see Methylpyridines, pp. 124, 185)		
Picric acid (Trinitrophenol)	>165	115,393(p.647)
Piperidine (Hexahydropyridine)	Mixes	133,134
Piperonal	<78	193A
Procaine (see Novocaine, this page)		
Propionic acid	-29.4	129,139,149
Propionitrile	112	68,153,209(pp.387,389), 253,330,362,365, 392(p.169),443,486
n-Propyl alcohol	-23e	118,152,444
Propylene chlorohydrin (1-Chloro-2-propanol)	<20	284
Propylene glycol	<20	284

TABLE I 187

	CST	References
WATER (continued)		
1,2-Propylene glycol-1-propyl ether LCST, 34.5	171.8	153,209(p.390), 392(p.462)
1,2-Propylene glycol-2-propyl ether LCST, 42.6	162	153,209(p.390), 392(p.462)
Propylene oxide	>20	296(p.673)
o-n-Propylphenol	240.2	152,433
p-n-Propylphenol 200 to	221	119,152,433
o-Isopropylphenol	239.8	152,433
p-Isopropylphenol	196	152,433
1-Propylpiperidine LCST, -20		134,153,209(p.392),253
Pyramidone LCST, 69.5	190	57,153,229,253,
(Dimethylaminoantipyrine)		392(p.728),393(p.753)
Pyridine zincichloride	163	133
Pyrogallol (m.p. 133)	35	234A,392(p.404)
Resorcinol (m.p. 110)	<12	86,318,392(pp.392-4), 425,471
Salicylaldehyde	>200	153,209(p.391), 392(p.498),406
Salicylic acid (m.p. 109)	<90	1,11,27,136,153,209 (p.391),253,392 (pp.518-9),410,486
Succinonitrile (m.p. 54.5)	54	153,209(pp.387,393), 253,330,387,387A,392 (p.214),443,444,486
Sucrose (m.p. 186)	<20	86
Sulfur dioxide (Iso-optic at 0)	133	143,151,153,256(p.672), 434
Tetraethylene glycol	<20	284
Tetraethylene pentamine	<20	284
Tetrahydrofurfuryl alcohol	<25	193A,296(p.44)
2,3,5,6-Tetramethylphenol	294	152,433
Thymol	271	149(p.270),153,255 (p.472),481
α-Toluic acid (Phenylacetic acid)	108	153,209(p.391),392 (p.582),410
o-Toluic acid	160	136,153,209(pp.391-2), 253,392(p.586),414
m-Toluic acid	161	Ibid.
p-Toluic acid (m.p. 179.6	159	Ibid.
o-Toluidine (Isopycnic at 24.5)	216	3,140A,153,253,256, 315,392(p.555),414,447
m-Toluidine (Isopycnic at 7)	High	140A
Trichloroacrylic acid (m.p. 73)	60.85	21,344,392(p.163)
Triethanolamine	<20	284
Triethylamine LCST, 12.4 to 28		(see TRIETHYLAMINE, p.
Triethylene glycol	<20	284
Triethylene tetramine	>20	284
Triglycol dichloride	<20	284
Triisopropanolamine	<20	284
2,3,5-Trimethylphenol	248	119,152,433
2,4,5-Trimethylphenol	244.2	119,152
2,4,6-Trimethylphenol	264.5	152,433
3,4,5-Trimethylphenol	219	152,433
2,4,6-Trimethylpyridine (Collidine) LCST 3.5		135,153,209(p.393),253, 362,392(p.616),443
2,4,6-Trinitrophenol (m.p. 122) (Picric acid)	>165	115,393(p.647)
2,4,6-Trinitroresorcinol (Styphnic acid, m.p. 180)	>123	Ibid.
Urethane (Ethyl carbamate,	<15	86,392(p.202),425

	CST	References
WATER (continued)		
Vinyl chloride (Iso-optic at 72.3)	>72.3	143
Xylenols (see Dimethylphenols, p.182 XYLENOLS, below)		
92 Esters, 51 Ethers, 12 Hydrocarbons, 13 Halogenated hydrocarbons (and practically all others of these classes) CST above azeotropic boiling point.		271(pp.214-219)
WAX, CANAUBA and JAPAN		15
XENON		
Fluoroform	-87	365,439
p-XYLENE (Tables VI and VII)		131,340
XYLENOLS (see WATER-Dimethylphenols, p.182)		
2,4-XYLENOL-1 (m.p. 26)		
n-Hexane	-70	139
n-Heptane	-60	139,149
2,2,4-Trimethylpentane	-45	139
Paraffin wax (m.p. 53)	21e	139
Paraffinic oil	27	139
Naphthenic oil	-30e	139,285
Glycerol	<20	153,328
Water	213.2	119,152,328,433
2,5-XYLENOL-1 (m.p. 74.5)		
Paraffinic oil	<60	139,149
Glycerol	<m.p.	153,286,328
Water	218.9	119,152,328,433
3,5-XYLENOL-1 (m.p. 68)		15
All hydrocarbons	<m.p.	145
Water	198.9	119,152,433
m-XYLIDINE (2,4-XYLIDINE-1)		
Glycerol	196.5	153,328
3,4-XYLIDINE (Table III)(m.p. 48.5°)		
Ethane (crit.temp., 32 LCST, 28.0m)		378,380
n-Dodecane	<25	145
Carbon dioxide (LCST, 31)		378
MIXED XYLIDINES		
n-Hexane	-22	139
n-Heptane	-23	139,149
2,2,4-Trimethylpentane	-11	139
n-Octadecane	23	151
Diisobutene	-67	139
Cyclohexane	-49e	139
Methylcyclohexane	-46e	139
Paraffin wax (m.p. 53)	34e	139
Paraffin oil	29	139,149
Naphthenic oils	-14	131,139,149
XYLOSE and ZINC STEARATE		15

TABLE II

ANILINE AND FURFURAL POINTS, HIGH MOLECULAR WEIGHT HYDROCARBONS

PSU NO.	HYDROCARBON	STRUCTURE	Empirical Formula	Aniline Point	Furfural Point
			n-Paraffins and Olefins		
565	1-Undecene	C_9–C=C	$C_{11}H_{22}$	50.1	80.4
528	n-Dodecane	n-C_{12}	$C_{12}H_{26}$	83.8	112.5
566	1-Dodecene	C_{10}–C=C	$C_{12}H_{24}$	56.0	86.6
529	n-Tridecane	n-C_{13}	$C_{13}H_{28}$	88.0	115.9
530	1-Tridecene	C_{11}–C=C	$C_{13}H_{26}$	61.8	91.8
531	n-Tetradecane	n-C_{14}	$C_{14}H_{30}$	91.1	119.6
589	1-Tetradecene	C_{12}–C=C	$C_{14}H_{28}$	64.4	96.8
532	n-Pentadecane	n-C_{15}	$C_{15}H_{32}$	94.5	122.7
533	1-Pentadecene	C_{13}–C=C	$C_{15}H_{30}$	70.5	100.3
534	n-Hexadecane	n-C_{16}	$C_{16}H_{34}$	95.7	125.9
590	1-Hexadecene	C_{14}–C=C	$C_{16}H_{32}$	72.4	104.9
535	n-Heptadecane	n-C_{17}	$C_{17}H_{36}$	98.5	129.3
536	1-Heptadecene	C_{15}–C=C	$C_{17}H_{34}$	75.7	108.6
537	n-Octadecane	n-C_{18}	$C_{18}H_{38}$	99.8	131.9
540	n-Eicosane	n-C_{20}	$C_{20}H_{42}$	106.1	138.1
541	n-Tetracosane	n-C_{24}	$C_{24}H_{50}$	114.6	147.2
106	n-Hexacosane	n-C_{26}	$C_{26}H_{54}$	116.0	150.3
176	n-Octacosane	n-C_{28}	$C_{28}H_{58}$	120.8	154.7
197	n-Dotriacontane	n-C_{32}	$C_{32}H_{66}$	126.9	ca 162
190	n-Hexatria-contane	n-C_{36}	$C_{36}H_{74}$	132.0	>160.0
205	n-Tetratetra-contane	n-C_{44}	$C_{44}H_{90}$	142.1	--

PSU NO.	HYDROCARBON	STRUCTURE	Empirical Formula	Aniline Point	Furfural Point
		Branched Paraffins and Olefins			
549	4-$\underline{n}$-Propylheptane	$C_3-\overset{\underset{\displaystyle C_3}{\mid}}{C}-C_3$	$C_{10}H_{22}$	76.5	101.9
550	4-$\underline{n}$-Propyl-3-heptene	$C_2-C=\overset{\underset{\displaystyle C_3}{\mid}}{C}-C_3$	$C_{10}H_{20}$	49.5	75.7
581	2-Methyldecane	$C-\overset{\underset{\displaystyle C}{\mid}}{C}-C_8$	$C_{11}H_{24}$	82.8	109.3
546	5-$\underline{n}$-Butylnonane	$C_4-\overset{\underset{\displaystyle C_4}{\mid}}{C}-C_4$	$C_{13}H_{28}$	85.0	113.7
547	5-$\underline{n}$-Butyl-4-nonene	$C_3-C=\overset{\underset{\displaystyle C_4}{\mid}}{C}-C_4$	$C_{13}H_{26}$	67.1	95.1
512	7-Methyltridecane	$C_6-\overset{\underset{\displaystyle C}{\mid}}{C}-C_6$	$C_{14}H_{30}$	89.4	118.5
555	2,2,3,5,5,6,6-Heptamethyl-3-heptene	$C-\overset{\underset{\displaystyle C}{\mid}}{\overset{\displaystyle C}{\mid}}{C}-C=C-\overset{\underset{\displaystyle C}{\mid}}{\overset{\displaystyle C}{\mid}}{C}-\overset{\underset{\displaystyle C}{\mid}}{\overset{\displaystyle C}{\mid}}{C}-C$	$C_{14}H_{28}$	53.6	80.3
556	2,2,3,3,5,6,6-Heptamethyl-heptane	$C-\overset{\underset{\displaystyle C}{\mid}}{\overset{\displaystyle C}{\mid}}{C}-\overset{\underset{\displaystyle C}{\mid}}{\overset{\displaystyle C}{\mid}}{C}-C-\overset{\underset{\displaystyle C}{\mid}}{C}-\overset{\underset{\displaystyle C}{\mid}}{C}-C$	$C_{14}H_{30}$	84.3	106.2
582	2-Methylpentadecane	$C-\overset{\underset{\displaystyle C}{\mid}}{C}-C_{13}$	$C_{16}H_{34}$	97.0	126.2
545	7-$\underline{n}$-Propyltridecane	$C_6-\overset{\underset{\displaystyle C_3}{\mid}}{C}-C_6$	$C_{16}H_{34}$	93.9	123.1
583	2-Methylheptadecane	$C-\overset{\underset{\displaystyle C}{\mid}}{C}-C_{15}$	$C_{18}H_{38}$	102.4	131.7
557	4,9-Di-$\underline{n}$-propyl-dodecane	$C_3-\overset{\underset{\displaystyle C_3}{\mid}}{C}-C_4-\overset{\underset{\displaystyle C_3}{\mid}}{C}-C_3$	$C_{18}H_{38}$	97.9	126.8
500	7-$\underline{n}$-Hexyltridecane	$C_6\overset{\underset{\displaystyle C_6}{\mid}}{C}-C_6$	$C_{19}H_{40}$	100.5	132.2
510	4-$\underline{n}$-Propylheptadecane	$C_3-\overset{\underset{\displaystyle C_3}{\mid}}{C}-C_{13}$	$C_{20}H_{42}$	97.8	130.9
511	5-$\underline{h}$-Butylhexadecane	$C_4-\overset{\underset{\displaystyle C_4}{\mid}}{C}-C_{11}$	$C_{20}H_{42}$	102.8	134.6
588	3-Methyleicosane	$C_2-\overset{\underset{\displaystyle C}{\mid}}{C}-C_{17}$	$C_{21}H_{44}$	107.5	139.2
591	10-Methyleicosane	$C_9-\overset{\underset{\displaystyle C}{\mid}}{C}-C_{10}$	$C_{21}H_{44}$	107.2	139.6

TABLE II 191

PSU NO.	HYDROCARBON	STRUCTURE	Empirical Formula	Aniline Point	Furfural Point
		Branched Paraffins and Olefins			
554	8-n-Hexyl- pentadecane	$C_7-\underset{\underset{C_6}{\vert}}{C}-C_7$	$C_{21}H_{44}$	104.7	134.5
163	9-n-Hexyl- heptadecane	$C_8-\underset{\underset{C_6}{\vert}}{C}-C_8$	$C_{23}H_{48}$	109.1	141.7
584	2-Methyltricosane	$C-\underset{\underset{C}{\vert}}{C}-C_{21}$	$C_{24}H_{50}$	114.8	146.9
25	9-n-Octyl- heptadecane	$C_8-\underset{\underset{C_8}{\vert}}{C}-C_8$	$C_{25}H_{52}$	111.6	146.4
26	9-n-Octyl-8- heptadecene	$C_7-C=\underset{\underset{C_8}{\vert}}{C}-C_8$	$C_{25}H_{50}$	100.0	124.5
1	11-n-Butyldocosane	$C_{10}-\underset{\underset{C_4}{\vert}}{C}-C_{11}$	$C_{26}H_{54}$	113.8	147.9
2	9-n-Butyldocosane	$C_8-\underset{\underset{C_4}{\vert}}{C}-C_{13}$	$C_{26}H_{54}$	114.4	148.1
3	7-n-Butyldocosane	$C_6-\underset{\underset{C_4}{\vert}}{C}-C_{15}$	$C_{26}H_{54}$	114.2	148.0
4	5-n-Butyldocosane	$C_4-\underset{\underset{C_4}{\vert}}{C}-C_{17}$	$C_{26}H_{54}$	114.0	148.0
22	6,11-Di-n-amyl- hexadecane	$C_5-\underset{\underset{C_5}{\vert}}{C}-C_4-\underset{\underset{C_5}{\vert}}{C}-C_5$	$C_{26}H_{54}$	112.0	145.6
23	3-Ethyl-5- (2-ethyl- butyl)- octadecane	$\left[C_2-\underset{\underset{C_2}{\vert}}{C}-C-\right]_2 -C-C_{13}$	$C_{26}H_{54}$	112.1	144.5
27	11-n-Amyl- heneicosane	$C_{10}-\underset{\underset{C_5}{\vert}}{C}-C_{10}$	$C_{26}H_{54}$	114.1	147.5
51	7-n-Hexyleicosane	$C_6-\underset{\underset{C_6}{\vert}}{C}-C_{13}$	$C_{26}H_{54}$	114.4	147.7
53	11(3-Pentyl) heneicosane	$C_{10}-\underset{\underset{C_2-C-C_2}{\vert}}{C}-C_{10}$	$C_{26}H_{54}$	113.4	146.2
55	5,14-Di-n-butyl- octadecane	$C_4-\underset{\underset{C_4}{\vert}}{C}-C_8-\underset{\underset{C_4}{\vert}}{C}-C_4$	$C_{26}H_{54}$	111.3	145.7

PSU NO.	HYDROCARBON	STRUCTURE	Empirical Formula	Aniline Point	Furfural Point
		Branched Paraffins and Olefins			
67	11-Neopentyl-heneicosane	$C_{10}-\overset{\overset{\displaystyle C}{\mid}}{C}-C_{10}$ $C-\overset{\overset{\displaystyle C}{\mid}}{\underset{\underset{\displaystyle C}{\mid}}{C}}-C$	$C_{26}H_{54}$	114.9	146.3
109	3-Ethyl-tetracosane	$C_2-\overset{\mid}{\underset{\underset{\displaystyle C_2}{\mid}}{C}}-C_{21}$	$C_{26}H_{54}$	116.0	149.2
210	9-Ethyl-9-n-heptyl-octadecane	$C_8-\overset{\overset{\displaystyle C_2}{\mid}}{\underset{\underset{\displaystyle C_7}{\mid}}{C}}-C_9$	$C_{27}H_{56}$	113.6	145.7
5	7-n-Hexyl-docosane	$C_6-\overset{\mid}{\underset{\underset{\displaystyle C_6}{\mid}}{C}}-C_{15}$	$C_{28}H_{58}$	117.7	151.3
63	9-n-Octyl-eicosane	$C_8-\overset{\mid}{\underset{\underset{\displaystyle C_8}{\mid}}{C}}-C_{11}$	$C_{28}H_{58}$	117.2	151.7
184	2,2,4,10,12,12-Hexamethyl-7(3,5,5-tri-methylhexyl)tridecane	$\left[\,C-\overset{\overset{\displaystyle C}{\mid}}{\underset{\underset{\displaystyle C}{\mid}}{C}}-C-\overset{\overset{\displaystyle C}{\mid}}{C}-C-C-\right]_3 C$	$C_{28}H_{58}$	119.6	146.6
183	2,2,4,10,12,12-Hexamethyl 7(3,5,5-tri-methylhexyl)-6-tridecene	$\left[\,C\overset{\overset{\displaystyle C}{\mid}}{\underset{\underset{\displaystyle C}{\mid}}{C}}CC\overset{\overset{\displaystyle C}{\mid}}{C}C-\right]_2 C=C\overset{\overset{\displaystyle C}{\mid}}{\underset{\underset{\displaystyle C}{\mid}}{C}}CCCCCC$ $C_{28}H_{56}$		110.7	137.9
6	9-n-Octyl-docosane	$C_8-\overset{\mid}{\underset{\underset{\displaystyle C_8}{\mid}}{C}}-C_{13}$	$C_{30}H_{62}$	116.9	150.9
8	11-n-Decyl-heneicosane	$C_{10}-\overset{\mid}{\underset{\underset{\displaystyle C_{10}}{\mid}}{C}}-C_{10}$	$C_{31}H_{64}$	121.4	154.0
7	11-n-Decyl-docosane	$C_{10}-\overset{\mid}{\underset{\underset{\displaystyle C_{10}}{\mid}}{C}}-C_{11}$	$C_{32}H_{66}$	123.1	157.7
191	9-n-Octyl-tetracosane	$C_8-\overset{\mid}{\underset{\underset{\displaystyle C_8}{\mid}}{C}}-C_{15}$	$C_{32}H_{66}$	123.6	158.2
107	11-n-Decyl-tetracosane	$C_{10}-\overset{\mid}{\underset{\underset{\displaystyle C_{10}}{\mid}}{C}}-C_{13}$	$C_{34}H_{70}$	125.8	161
164	9-n-Octyl-hexacosane	$C_8-\overset{\mid}{\underset{\underset{\displaystyle C_8}{\mid}}{C}}-C_{17}$	$C_{34}H_{70}$	126.6	161.4

PSU NO.	HYDROCARBON	STRUCTURE	Empirical Formula	Aniline Point	Furfural Point
		Branched Paraffins and Olefins			
211	10-n-Heptyl-10-n-octyleicosane	$C_9-\overset{\overset{C_8}{\mid}}{\underset{\underset{C_7}{\mid}}{C}}-C_{10}$	$C_{35}H_{72}$	124.0	158.0
133	13-n-Undecyl-pentacosane	$C_{12}-\overset{\mid}{\underset{\underset{C_{11}}{\mid}}{C}}-C_{12}$	$C_{36}H_{74}$	129.0	>160
134	13-n-Dodecyl-hexacosane	$C_{12}-\overset{\mid}{\underset{\underset{C_{12}}{\mid}}{C}}-C_{13}$	$C_{38}H_{78}$	131.7	>160
182	2,2,4,15,17,17-Hexamethyl-7,12-di(3,5,5-trimethyl hexyl)-octadecane	$\left[\left(\overset{\overset{C\ \ C}{\mid\ \ \mid}}{\underset{\underset{C}{\mid}}{CCCCCC}}-\right)_2 CCC-\right]_2$	$C_{42}H_{86}$	135.0	>160
58	17-Hexadecyl-tetratri-acontane	$C_{16}-\overset{\mid}{\underset{\underset{C_{16}}{\mid}}{C}}-C_{17}$	$C_{50}H_{102}$	138.1	>160
59	11,20-Di-n-decyl-triacontane	$C_{10}-\overset{\mid}{\underset{\underset{C_{10}}{\mid}}{C}}-C_8-\overset{\mid}{\underset{\underset{C_{10}}{\mid}}{C}}-C_{10}$	$C_{50}H_{102}$	140.5	>160
		Non-Fused Aromatics			
524	Diphenylmethane	$\left[\bigcirc\right]_2 C$	$C_{13}H_{12}$	2.34	<-36
538	1-Phenyloctane	$\bigcirc-C_8$	$C_{14}H_{22}$	<-6	10.8
513	2-Phenyloctane	$\overset{C-\overset{\mid}{C}-C_6}{\underset{\bigcirc}{}}$	$C_{14}H_{22}$	<-6	7.0
521	1-Phenyl-2-cyclohexyl-ethane	$\bigcirc-C-C-⬡$	$C_{14}H_{20}$	<-6	-6.1
522	1-Phenyl-3-cyclopentyl propane	$\bigcirc-C-C-C-⬠$	$C_{14}H_{20}$	<-6	-4.6
517	1-Phenyl-1-cyclohexyl-ethane	$\bigcirc-\overset{\mid}{\underset{\underset{C}{\mid}}{C}}-⬡$	$C_{14}H_{20}$	<-6	-4.5
519	1,2-Diphenyl-ethane	$\bigcirc-C-C-\bigcirc$	$C_{14}H_{14}$	<-6	<-35

PSU NO.	HYDROCARBON	STRUCTURE	Empirical Formula	Aniline Point	Furfural Point

Non-Fused Aromatics

PSU NO.	HYDROCARBON	STRUCTURE	Empirical Formula	Aniline Point	Furfural Point
516	1,1-Diphenyl-ethane		$C_{14}H_{14}$	<-6	<-36
560	1,1-Diphenyl-ethylene		$C_{14}H_{12}$	<-6	<-36
631	1,3-Diphenyl-benzene		$C_{18}H_{14}$	<-6	<-36
571	1-Phenyldecane		$C_{16}H_{26}$	-1.2	32.1
633	1,2-Diphenyl-benzene		$C_{18}H_{14}$	<-6	<-36
502	7-Phenyl-tridecane		$C_{19}H_{32}$	27.9	59.8
506	7-Phenyl-6-tridecene		$C_{19}H_{30}$	3.4	37.1
503	1,1-Diphenyl-heptane		$C_{19}H_{24}$	<-6	<-35
87	9(2-Phenyl-ethyl)heptadecane		$C_{25}H_{44}$	53.1	85.2
10	9-p-Tolyl-octadecane		$C_{25}H_{44}$	63.3	96.0
128	1,7-Dicyclo-pentyl-4(2-phenylethyl)heptane		$C_{25}H_{40}$	31.4	78.5

TABLE II   195

PSU NO.	HYDROCARBON	STRUCTURE	Empirical Formula	Aniline Point	Furfural Point
		Non-Fused Aromatics			
130	1-Phenyl-3(2-cyclohexylethyl)-6-cyclopentylhexane		$C_{25}H_{40}$	36.7	84.3
18	1-Phenyl-3(2-phenylethyl)-undecane		$C_{25}H_{36}$	<-6	10.5
126	1-Phenyl-3(2-phenylethyl)6-cyclopentylhexane		$C_{25}H_{34}$	<-6	1.5
89	1,5-Diphenyl-3(2-phenylethyl)pentane		$C_{25}H_{28}$	<-6	<-35
119	1,5-Diphenyl-3(2-phenylethyl)-2-pentene		$C_{25}H_{26}$	<-6	<-35
99	1-Phenyleicosane		$C_{26}H_{46}$	58.9	95.8
101	2-Phenyleicosane		$C_{26}H_{46}$	57.6	94.8
79	3-Phenyleicosane		$C_{26}H_{46}$	61.3	97.5
103	4-Phenyleicosane		$C_{26}H_{46}$	61.0	96.5
80	5-Phenyleicosane		$C_{26}H_{46}$	61.4	96.4
81	7-Phenyleicosane		$C_{26}H_{46}$	62.2	96.4
82	9-Phenyleicosane		$C_{26}H_{46}$	63.4	97.8
158	2,5-Dimethyl-n-octadecylbenzene		$C_{26}H_{46}$	63.1	93.4

PSU NO.	HYDROCARBON	STRUCTURE	Empirical Formula	Aniline Point	Furfural Point
		Non-Fused Aromatics			
208	1,3-Di-n-decyl-benzene	C_{10} C_{10}	$C_{26}H_{46}$	65.8	97.7
152	1,4-Di-n-decyl-benzene	C_{10} C_{10}	$C_{26}H_{46}$	70.2	100.2
161	8-p-Tolyl-nonadecane	C_7-C-C_{11} C	$C_{26}H_{46}$	69.2	100.6
12	1,1-Diphenyl-tetradecane	$\left[\bigcirc\right]_2$ C-C_{13}	$C_{26}H_{38}$	<-6	4.8
13	1,1-Diphenyl-1-tetra-decene	$\left[\bigcirc\right]_2$ C=C-C_{12}	$C_{26}H_{36}$	<-6	
116	1,1-Di-p-tolyl-dodecane	$\left[C\bigcirc\right]_2$ C-C_{11}	$C_{26}H_{38}$	<-6	19.2
206	1,4-Di(4-phenylbutyl)benzene	C_4 C_4	$C_{26}H_{30}$	<-6	<-36
9	11-Phenyl-heneicosane	C_{10}-C-C_{10}	$C_{27}H_{48}$	66.6	101.3
52	11-Phenyl-10-heneicosene	C_9-C=C-C_{10}	$C_{27}H_{46}$	48.2	84.0
156	2,4,6-Trimethyl-n-octadecyl-benzene	C_{18} C C C	$C_{27}H_{48}$	67.9	94.1
54	11-Benzyl-heneicosane	C_{10}-C-C_{10} C	$C_{28}H_{50}$	61.8	97.7
171	1,7-Diphenyl-4(3-phenyl-propyl)heptane	$\left[\bigcirc C_3-\right]_3$ C	$C_{28}H_{34}$	<-6	<-36
170	1,7-Di-phenyl-4(3-phenyl propyl)3-heptene	$\left[\bigcirc C_3-\right]_2$ C=C-C_2 $\bigcirc$	$C_{28}H_{32}$	<-6	<-36

TABLE II 197

PSU NO.	HYDROCARBON	STRUCTURE	Empirical Formula	Aniline Point	Furfural Point
	Non-Fused Aromatics				
168	11(2,5-Dimethyl-phenyl) heneicosane	$C_{10}-C-C_{10}$ C C	$C_{29}H_{52}$	74.9	106.3
167	11(2,5-Dimethyl-phenyl)10-heneicosene	$C_9-C=C-C_{10}$ C	$C_{29}H_{50}$	67.8	101.5
68	13-Phenyl-pentacosane	$C_{12}-C-C_{12}$	$C_{31}H_{56}$	79.4	112.6
135	15-Phenyl-nonacosane	$C_{14}C-C_{14}$	$C_{35}H_{64}$	90.8	127.2
137	17-Phenyl-tritriacontane	$C_{16}-C-C_{16}$	$C_{39}H_{72}$	100.3	134.7
	Fused Ring Aromatics				
567	1-Methyl-naphthalene m.p. -31	CH_3	$C_{11}H_{10}$	<-6	<-31
568	2-Methylnaph-thalene m.p. 34.3	CH_3	$C_{11}H_{10}$	<34	<34
592	2(ar)Butyl-tetralin	C_4	$C_{14}H_{20}$	<-6	0.0
606	2-n-Butyl-naphthalene	C_4	$C_{14}H_{16}$	<-6	<-36
576	1,2,3,4-Tetra-hydrofluor-anthene m.p. 74		$C_{16}H_{14}$	<74	<74
526	9-n-Butyl-anthracene m.p. 48.9	C_4	$C_{18}H_{18}$	<-6	<49
574	1,2,3,4,5,6,7,8,13,14,15,16-Dodecahydro-chrysene		$C_{18}H_{24}$	<-6	26.0

PSU NO.	HYDROCARBON	STRUCTURE	Empirical Formula	Aniline Point	Furfural Point

Fused Ring Aromatics

PSU NO.	HYDROCARBON	STRUCTURE	Empirical Formula	Aniline Point	Furfural Point
595	2-Decylindan	C_{10}	$C_{19}H_{30}$	15.2	53.9
597	5-Decylindan	C_{10}	$C_{19}H_{30}$	19.8	53.3
599	2-Butyl-1-hexylindene	$C_6 C_4$	$C_{19}H_{28}$	<-6	13.8
600	2-Butyl-1-hexylindan	C_6 C_4	$C_{19}H_{30}$	12.1	49.3
602	2-Butyl-5-hexylindan	C_6 C_4	$C_{19}H_{30}$	28.1	57.1
604	5-Butyl-6-hexylindan	C_4 C_6	$C_{19}H_{30}$	17.3	46.7
593	2(ar)Decyl-tetralin	C_{10}	$C_{20}H_{32}$	25.0	58.4
614	2(ar)-n-Butyl-3(ar)-n-hexyl-tetralin	C_4 C_6	$C_{20}H_{32}$	19.4	49.9
611	7(ar)-n-Butyl-1-n-hexyltetralin	C_6 C_4	$C_{20}H_{32}$	23.4	54.5
613	2-n-Butyl-3-n-hexyl naphthalene	C_4 C_6	$C_{20}H_{28}$	<-6	-1.8
610	7-n-Butyl-1-n-hexyl naphthalene	C_6 C_4	$C_{20}H_{28}$	-6.2	2.7
559	1-α-Naphthyl-undecane m.p. 22.9	C_{11}	$C_{21}H_{30}$	<23	17.0
16	1-n-Hexadecylindan	C_{16}	$C_{25}H_{42}$	47.0	85.8
120	2-n-Hexadecylindan	C_{16}	$C_{25}H_{42}$	47.4	87.7
188	1(1-ar-Tetralyl) pentadecane	C_{15}	$C_{25}H_{42}$	57.0	95.3

TABLE II 199

PSU NO.	HYDROCARBON	STRUCTURE	Empirical Formula	Aniline Point	Furfural Point
		Fused Ring Aromatics			
174	1-α-Naphthyl-pentadecane m.p. 41.6		$C_{25}H_{38}$	<42	<42
165	1,2,3,4,5,6,7,8,9,10,17,18-Dodecahydro-9(n-octyl)naphthacene		$C_{26}H_{40}$	29.7	72.1
142	2-n-Dodecyl-9,10-dihydro-phenanthrene		$C_{26}H_{36}$	<-6	35.8
124	9-n-Dodecyl-anthracene m.p. 49.3		$C_{26}H_{34}$	<-6	<49
140	9-n-Dodecyl-phenanthrene m.p. 75.8		$C_{26}H_{34}$	<76	<76
179	9-n-Octyl-(1,2,3,4-tetrahydro)naphthacene		$C_{26}H_{32}$	<-6	8.8
144	1,10-Di(5-indanyl)-decane		$C_{28}H_{38}$	<-6	35.5
131	1,10-Di-(α-naphthyl)-decane		$C_{30}H_{34}$	<-6	22.4
173	11-α-ar-Tetralyl-heneicosane		$C_{31}H_{54}$	65.6	105.1
61	11-α-Naphthyl-10-heneicosene		$C_{31}H_{48}$	43.3	75.0
121	1,1-Di(α-naphthyl)1-undecene		$C_{31}H_{34}$	<-6	-13.4
		Non-Fused Naphthenes			
551	Bicyclopentyl		$C_{10}H_{18}$	36.0	78.4
608	Bicyclohexyl		$C_{12}H_{22}$	48.1	90.4

PSU NO.	HYDROCARBON	STRUCTURE	Empirical Formula	Aniline Point	Furfural Point
		Non-Fused Naphthenes			
580	1,1-Dicyclo-pentylethane		$C_{12}H_{22}$	46.1	87.2
525	Dicyclohexyl-methane		$C_{13}H_{24}$	57.9	99.4
539	1-Cyclohexyl-octane		$C_{14}H_{28}$	77.4	110.7
514	2-Cyclohexyl-octane		$C_{14}H_{28}$	72.5	108.5
520	1,2-Dicyclo-hexylethane		$C_{14}H_{26}$	61.7	104.8
518	1,1-Dicyclo-hexylethane		$C_{14}H_{26}$	57.9	100.7
523	1-Cyclo-hexyl-3-cyclopentyl-propane		$C_{14}H_{26}$	59.6	103.5
573	1-Cyclopentyl-decane		$C_{15}H_{30}$	79.2	114.3
548	1,3-Dicyclo-pentylcyclo-pentane		$C_{15}H_{26}$	66.1	101.3
572	1-Cyclohexyl-decane		$C_{16}H_{32}$	83.1	118.2
585	1,3-Dicyclo butyl-2(cyclobutyl-methyl) propene		$C_{16}H_{26}$	3.8	39.9
564	Tricyclopentyl-methane		$C_{16}H_{28}$	50.8	99.3
634	1,2-Dicyclohexyl-cyclohexane		$C_{18}H_{32}$	64.4	112.3
632	1,3-Dicyclohexyl-cyclohexane		$C_{18}H_{32}$	59.5	108.3

TABLE II   **201**

PSU NO.	HYDROCARBON	STRUCTURE	Empirical Formula	Aniline Point	Furfural Point
		Non-Fused Naphthenes			
630	1,4-Dicyclo-hexyl-cyclohexane		$C_{18}H_{32}$	<-6	116.0
542	7-Cyclopentyl-methyl-tridecane	C_6-C-C_6	$C_{19}H_{38}$	89.2	125.4
504	7-Cyclohexyl-tridecane	C_6-C-C_6	$C_{19}H_{38}$	89.4	125.4
505	1,1-Dicyclo-hexylheptane	$\left[\bigcirc \right]_2 C-C_6$	$C_{19}H_{36}$	79.6	122.2
507	Tricyclohexyl-methane	$\left[\bigcirc \right]_3 C$	$C_{19}H_{34}$	71.4	ca 121.7
553	1,5-Dicyclo-pentyl-3 (2-cyclo-pentylethyl) pentane	$\left[\bigcirc - C_{\overline{2}} \right]_3 C$	$C_{22}H_{40}$	80.4	126.6
552	1,5-Dicyclo-pentyl-3 (2-cyclo-pentyl-ethyl)2-pentene	$\left[\bigcirc - C_{\overline{2}} \right]_2 C=C-C-\bigcirc$	$C_{22}H_{38}$	68.0	114.4
509	9-Cyclohexyl-heptadecane	C_8-C-C_8	$C_{23}H_{46}$	99.8	136.5
110	9(3-Cyclopentyl-propyl)-heptadecane	C_8-C-C_8 C_3	$C_{25}H_{50}$	104.0	141.5
88	9(2-Cyclohexyl-ethyl) heptadecane	C_8-C-C_8 C_2	$C_{25}H_{50}$	104.8	141.9
111	1-Cyclo-pentyl-4 (3-cyclo-pentyl-propyl) dodecane	$\left[\bigcirc C_3 - \right]_2 C-C_8$	$C_{25}H_{48}$	96.0	137.5

PSU NO.	HYDROCARBON	STRUCTURE	Empirical Formula	Aniline Point	Furfural Point
	Non-Fused Naphthenes				
19	1-Cyclohexyl-3(2-cyclohexylethyl) undecane	$\left[\text{⬡-S} \cdot C_2\right]_2 C\text{-}C_8$	$C_{25}H_{48}$	98.4	139.6
113	1,7-Dicyclopentyl-4 (3-cyclopentyl-propyl)heptane	$\left[\text{⬠-}C_3\right]_2 C_3$	$C_{25}H_{46}$	88.6	135.5
112	1,7-Dicyclo-pentyl-4(3-cyclo-pentyl-propyl)3-heptene	$\left[\text{⬠-}C_3\right]_2 C\text{=}C\text{-}C_2\text{-⬠}$	$C_{25}H_{44}$	75.1	
129	1,7-Dicyclo-pentyl-4(2-cyclohexyl-ethyl)heptane	$\left[\text{⬠-}C_3\text{-}\right]_2 C\text{-}C_2\text{-⬡-S}$	$C_{25}H_{46}$	90.0	136.6
127	1-Cyclohexyl-3-(2-Cyclo-hexylethyl) 6-cyclo-pentyl hexane	$\left[\text{⬡-S}\cdot C_2\right]_2 C\text{-}C_3\text{-⬠}$	$C_{25}H_{46}$	91.2	137.7
90	1,5-Dicyclo-hexyl-3(2-cyclohexyl-ethyl)pentane	$\left[\text{⬡-S}\cdot C_2\text{-}\right]_3 C$	$C_{25}H_{46}$	92.1	139.1
115	1,5-Dicyclo-hexyl-3(2-cyclohexyl-ethyl) 2-pentene	$\left[\text{⬡-S}\cdot C_2\text{-}\right]_2 C\text{=}C\text{-}C\text{-⬡}$	$C_{25}H_{44}$	80.3	121.0
207	1,4-Di(4-cyclo-hexylbutyl)-çyclohexane	⬡-S·C_4-⬡-S·C_4-⬡-S	$C_{26}H_{48}$	100.6	143.5
117	1-Cyclopentyl-heneicosane	⬠-C_{21}	$C_{26}H_{52}$	109.8	147.7
64	11-Cyclopentyl-heneicosane	$C_{10}\text{-}C\text{-}C_{10}$ ⬠	$C_{26}H_{52}$	106.5	143.5

TABLE II 203

PSU NO.	HYDROCARBON	STRUCTURE	Empirical Formula	Aniline Point	Furfural Point
		Non-Fused Naphthenes			
100	1-Cyclohexyl-eicosane	(S)-C_{20}	$C_{26}H_{52}$	110.8	148.2
102	2-Cyclohexyl-eicosane	C-C-C_{18} (S)	$C_{26}H_{52}$	109.0	146.5
75	3-Cyclohexyl-eicosane	C_2-C-C_{17} (S)	$C_{26}H_{52}$	107.7	145.1
104	4-Cyclohexyl-eicosane	C_3-C-C_{16} (S)	$C_{26}H_{52}$	107.3	145.0
76	5-Cyclohexyl-eicosane	C_4-C-C_{15} (S)	$C_{26}H_{52}$	107.0	144.5
77	7-Cyclohexyl-eicosane	C_6-C-C_{13} (S)	$C_{26}H_{52}$	106.7	144.1
78	9-Cyclohexyl-eicosane	C_8-C-C_{11} (S)	$C_{26}H_{52}$	106.4	144.1
159	2,5-Dimethyl-n-octadecyl-cyclohexane	C_{18} C (S) C C	$C_{26}H_{52}$	111.3	146.7
209	1,3-Di-n-decyl-cyclohexane	C_{10} (S) C_{10}	$C_{26}H_{52}$	110.8	146.6
153	1,4-Di-n-decyl-cyclohexane	C_{10}-(S)-C_{10}	$C_{26}H_{52}$	111.6	147.1
162	8(4-Methyl-cyclohexyl) nonadecane	C_7-C-C_{11} (S) C	$C_{26}H_{52}$	117.9	143.5
15	1-Cyclo-pentyl-2-hexadecyl-cyclopentane	⬡⬡ C_{16}	$C_{26}H_{50}$	102.3	143.1
202	1,1-Dicyclo-pentyl-hexadecane	⬡-C-C_{15} ⬡	$C_{26}H_{50}$	99.4	140.5

PSU NO.	HYDROCARBON	STRUCTURE	Empirical Formula	Aniline Point	Furfural Point
		Non-Fused Naphthenes			
11	1,1-Dicyclo-hexyltetra-decane	$[\text{(S)}-\overset{}{\underset{2}{\text{C}}}-\text{C}_{13}]$	$C_{26}H_{50}$	100.0	141.8
139	1,1-Di(4-methyl cyclohexyl) dodecane	$[\text{C}-\text{(S)}]_2-\text{C}-\text{C}_{11}$	$C_{26}H_{50}$	111.5	139.5
74	11-Cyclopentyl-methyl-heneicosane	$\text{C}_{10}\overline{}\overset{}{\underset{C}{\text{C}}}-\text{C}_{10}$	$C_{27}H_{54}$	108.3	146.0
60	11-Cyclohexyl-heneicosane	$\text{C}_{10}-\overset{}{\underset{(S)}{\text{C}}}-\text{C}_{10}$	$C_{27}H_{54}$	108.5	146.8
157	2,4,6-Trimethyl-n-octadecyl-cyclohexane	$\text{C}\overset{\text{C}_{18}}{\underset{\underset{\text{C}}{(S)}}{}}\text{C}$	$C_{27}H_{54}$	113.2	147.6
199	1,3-Dicyclo-pentyl-2-dodecyl-cyclopentane	C_{12}	$C_{27}H_{50}$	95.9	140.1
91	11-Cyclohexyl-methyl-heneicosane	$\text{C}_{10}\overline{}\overset{}{\underset{C}{\text{C}}}-\text{C}_{10}$	$C_{28}H_{56}$	108.1	145.9
65	1-Cyclohexyl 2-(cyclohexyl methyl) pentadecane	$[\text{(S)}-\text{C}]_2\text{C}-\text{C}_{13}$	$C_{28}H_{54}$	105.1	146.3
172	1,7-Dicyclo-hexyl-4(3-cyclohexyl-propyl) heptane	$[\text{(S)}-\text{C}_3]_3\text{C}$	$C_{28}H_{52}$	99.5	145.0
180	11(2,4-Dimethyl cyclopentyl-methyl) heneicosane	$\text{C}_{10}\overset{}{\underset{C}{\text{C}}}-\text{C}_{10}$ $\text{C}-\underset{}{}\text{C}$	$C_{29}H_{58}$	115.1	149.6

TABLE II   **205**

PSU NO.	HYDROCARBON	STRUCTURE	Empirical Formula	Aniline Point	Furfural Point
	Non-Fused Naphthenes				
169	11(2,5-Dimethyl-cyclohexyl)heneicosane	C_{10}–C–C_{10}	$C_{29}H_{58}$	111.8	148.0
69	13-Cyclohexyl-pentacosane	C_{12}–C–C_{12}	$C_{31}H_{62}$	115.5	153.3
136	15-Cyclohexyl-nonacosane	C_{14}–C–C_{14}	$C_{35}H_{70}$	123.2	>160
138	17-Cyclohexyl-tritriacontane	C_{16}–C–C_{16}	$C_{39}H_{78}$	128.0	>160
	Fused Ring Naphthenes				
569	cis-Decahydro-naphthalene		$C_{10}H_{18}$	33.3	77.2
570	trans-Decahydro-naphthalene		$C_{10}H_{18}$	37.7	79.2
561	Perhydro-fluorene		$C_{13}H_{22}$	41.6	89.7
607	2-n-Butyldecalin	–C_4	$C_{14}H_{26}$	61.4	102.9
626	Perhydrophenan-threne		$C_{14}H_{24}$	46.2	95.1
625	1,2,3,4,5,6,7,8-Octahydro-phenanthrene		$C_{14}H_{18}$	<−6	<−36
577	Perhydro-fluoranthene		$C_{16}H_{26}$	48.4	101.7
578	Perhydropyrene		$C_{16}H_{26}$	47.8	102.3
527	9-n-Butyl-perhydro-anthracene	C_4	$C_{18}H_{32}$	64.4	124

PSU NO.	HYDROCARBON	STRUCTURE	Empirical Formula	Aniline Point	Furfural Point

Fused Ring Naphthenes

PSU NO.	HYDROCARBON	STRUCTURE	Empirical Formula	Aniline Point	Furfural Point
575	Perhydro-chrysene		$C_{18}H_{30}$	60.6	112.7
596	2-Decylhydrindan	C_{10}	$C_{19}H_{36}$	84.2	125.6
598	5-Decylhydrindan	C_{10}	$C_{19}H_{36}$	83.9	124.6
601	2-Butyl-1-hexyl-hydrindan	C_6 C_4	$C_{19}H_{36}$	81.9	122.2
603	2-Butyl-5-hexyl-hydrindan	C_6 C_4	$C_{19}H_{36}$	87.0	125.5
605	5-Butyl-6-hexyl-hydrindan	C_4 C_6	$C_{19}H_{36}$	80.4	121.3
611	7(ar)-n-Butyl-1-n-hexyltetralin	C_6 C_4	$C_{20}H_{32}$	23.4	54.5
594	2-Decyldecalin	C_{10}	$C_{20}H_{38}$	87.6	127.9
615	2-n-Butyl-3-n-hexyldecalin	C_4 C_6	$C_{20}H_{38}$	83.3	124.1
612	7-n-Butyl-1-n-hexyldecalin	C_6 C_4	$C_{20}H_{38}$	85.3	124.7
544	1-α-Decalyl-undecane	C_{11}	$C_{21}H_{40}$	88.7	130.3
586	Di(α-decalyl)methane	C	$C_{21}H_{36}$	73.2	125.7
587	Perhydrodibenzo-(a,i)fluorene		$C_{21}H_{34}$	71.7	127.2
579	9-Cyclohexyl-perhydro-anthracene		$C_{20}H_{34}$	104.4	120.8
562	1,2-Di(α-decalyl)ethane	C-C	$C_{22}H_{38}$	77.2	126

TABLE II 207

PSU NO.	HYDROCARBON	STRUCTURE	Empirical Formula	Aniline Point	Furfural Point
	Fused Ring Naphthenes				
563	1,1-Di(α-decalyl) ethane		$C_{22}H_{38}$	72.1	123.9
108	1-n-Hexadecyl-hydrindan		$C_{25}H_{48}$	101.7	141.9
118	2-n-Hexadecyl-hydrindan		$C_{25}H_{48}$	102.1	143.0
175	1-α-Decalyl-pentadecane		$C_{25}H_{48}$	101.0	142.5
196	6-n-Octylper-hydrobenz(de) anthracene		$C_{25}H_{44}$	89.7	136.3
178	9 (cis-0,3,3-Bicyclooctyl-) methyl heptadecane		$C_{26}H_{50}$	100.1	140.1
125	9-n-Dodecyl-perhydroan-thracene		$C_{26}H_{48}$	95.7	140.1
143	2-n-Dodecyl-perhydro-phenanthrene		$C_{26}H_{48}$	100.8	143.8
141	9-n-Dodecyl-perhydro-phenanthrene		$C_{26}H_{48}$	96.5	141.9
200	1,1-Di(5-per-hydroacenaph-thyl)ethane		$C_{26}H_{42}$	79.2	139.4
193	1(5-Perhydro-acenaphthyl) pentadecane		$C_{27}H_{50}$	101.5	145.4

PSU NO.	HYDROCARBON	STRUCTURE	Empirical Formula	Aniline Point	Furfural Point
		Fused Ring Naphthenes			
155	Cholestane	C–C$_3$–C–C	$C_{27}H_{48}$	96.3	139.4
181	9(5-<u>Exo</u>-per-hydro-4,7-methano-indenylmethyl) heptadecane	-C-C-C$_8$ C$_8$	$C_{28}H_{52}$	100.4	141.6
145	1,10-Di(5-hydrindanyl) decane	C$_{10}$	$C_{28}H_{50}$	97.0	145.1
198	9,9-Perhydro-biphenanthryl m.p. 70		$C_{28}H_{46}$	<70	<70
177	9(4-<u>as</u>-Perhy-droindacenyl) heptadecane	C$_8$-C-C$_8$	$C_{29}H_{54}$	97.6	141.7
192	1-Cyclohexyl-4(α-decalyl)-tetradecane	C$_3$-C-C$_{10}$	$C_{30}H_{56}$	101.6	146.1
132	1,10-Di(α-decalyl) decane	C-C$_8$-C	$C_{30}H_{54}$	101.7	154.5
62	11-α-Decalyl-heneicosane	C$_{10}$-C-C$_{10}$	$C_{31}H_{60}$	108.9	150.3
122	1,1-Di(α-decalyl) undecane	[ ]$_2$ C-C$_{10}$	$C_{31}H_{56}$	95.4	Indistinct
203	Tri(α-decalyl)-methane	[ ]$_3$ C	$C_{31}H_{52}$	83.3	143.0
204	13(α-Decalyl)-perhydrodibenzo-(<u>a</u>,<u>i</u>)fluorene		$C_{31}H_{50}$	85.8	149.0

TABLE III   **209**

Table III

LOWER CRITICAL SOLUTION TEMPERATURES*

	LCST	CST
WATER		
2-Butanone (MEK)	-22 to -6 139 to	151.8
Diethylamine	143.5	---
2,3-Dimethylpyridine	16.5	192.6
2,4-Dimethylpyridine	23.4	188.7
2,5-Dimethylpyridine	13.1	206.9
2,6-Dimethylpyridine	34.06	230.7
3,4-Dimethylpyridine	-3.6	162.5
3,5-Dimethylpyridine	-12.5	192
Di-n-propylamine	-4.9	---
Ethylene glycol n-butyl ether	49.1	128
Ethylene glycol isobutyl ether	24.5	150.4
1-Ethylpiperidine	7.45	---
2-Ethylpyridine	-5	231.4
3-Ethylpyridine	-35e	195.6
4-Ethylpyridine	-19	181.8
Hexamethyleneimine	66.9	228
Methyldiethylamine	49.42	---
Methyl ethyl ketone	-22 to -6 139 to	151.8
1-Methylpiperidine	48.3	>280
2-Methylpiperidine	79.3	227
3-Methylpiperidine	56.9	235
4-Methylpiperidine	84.9	189.5
3-Methylpyridine	49.4	152.5
Nicotine	61	210
1,2-Propylene glycol 1-propyl ether	34.5	171.8
1,2-Propylene glycol 2-propyl ether	42.6	162
1-Propylpiperidine	-20e	---
Pyramidone	69.5	190
Triethylamine	18.5	---
2,4,6-Trimethylpyridine (Collidine)	3.5	---
DEUTERIUM OXIDE		
2,4-Dimethylpyridine	16.2	196.0
2,5-Dimethylpyridine	8.5	211.6
2,6-Dimethylpyridine	28.7	228
2-Methylpyridine	93.8	111.8
3-Methylpyridine	38.5	117
Nicotine	54	
GLYCEROL		
Ethylbenzylamine	50	281
Guaiacol	39.5	83.5
m-Toluidine (Figure 2)	6.7	120.5
SULFUR		
Benzene	226	163
Toluene	222	179
Triphenylmethane	199	147
p-Xylene	206	190

*Taken from Table I, which gives references.

	LCST	UCEP*
CARBON DIOXIDE (crit. temp. 31.04)		
1-Chloropropionic acid	12	
Diphenylamine (m.p. 53)		38.8
Ethyl phthalate	25	
Nitrobenzene	30	40
o-Nitrobromobenzene (m.p. 42)	0	
o-Nitrochlorobenzene (m.p. 32)	<3	34.5
m-Nitrochlorobenzene (m.p. 45)	8.5	37.5
p-Nitrochlorobenzene (m.p. 83)		37
Six Nitrodichlorobenzenes	<0	
o-Nitrophenol (m.p. 45)	25.9	39
p-Nitrotoluene (m.p. 51)	15	
Urethane (Ethyl carbamate, m.p. 50)	30.5	37
3,4-Xylidine (m.p. 49)	<31.0	
ETHANE (crit. temp. 32.2)		
5-n-Butyleicosane	27.7	34.5
11-n-Decyldocosane	10.6	32.6
18-Ethylpentatriacontane (m.p. 28)	<15	32.5
n-Octadecylcyclohexane (m.p. 40)	<17	33.4
11-(Cyclohexylmethyl)heneicosane	13.4	33.4
Squalane ($C_{36}H_{62}$)	22.6	33.6
Squalene ($C_{30}H_{50}$)	3.7	33.3
Di-sec-butylbenzene	<20	
Naphthalene (m.p. 80)	37.4	39.4
1-Methylnaphthalene	<20	
Polyisobutene	<0	
Four oils	<20	
Amyl alcohol	43.15	
Amyl stearate	19	
n-Butyl alcohol	38.1	39.8
p-Chlorobromobenzene (m.p. 65)	40m	47.2
p-Chloroiodobenzene (m.p. 57)	34.4m	38.5
Ethyl alcohol	31.9	40.7
Isopropyl alcohol		44
Methanol		35.37
o-Nitrochlorobenzene (m.p. 32)	22	32
m-Nitrochlorobenzene (m.p. 44)	32	44
o-Nitrophenol (m.p. 45)	34.5	
n-Propyl alcohol	38.67	41.7
A Silicone	-1	
p-Toluidine (m.p. 45)	32.6	
1,3,5-Trichlorobenzene (m.p. 63)	40.3	46.8
3,4-Xylidine (m.p. 48.5)	28.0m	
POLYISOBUTENE		
Ethane	<0	36
Propane	85	103
Isobutane	114	142
n-Pentane	75	199
Isopentane	54	189
n-Hexane	128	
2,2-Dimethylbutane	103	
2,3-Dimethylbutane	131	
n-Heptane	168	
n-Octane	180	
Cyclopentane	71	

*Upper critical end point, or critical temperature, upper layer.'

TABLE III   **211**

	LCST
POLYISOBUTENE (continued)	
Cyclohexane	139
Benzene	150-170
ACETONE	
Quinine iodobismuthate	9
ANILINE	
Hydrogen chloride	10.5
ETHYLENE (crit. temp. 9.7)	
p-Dichlorobenzene (m.p. 53)	26
d-Menthol (m.p. 35)	-9
ETHYL ETHER (crit. temp. 194)	
Chrysene (m.p. 254)	213
ISOBUTANE (crit. temp. 134)	
Cottonseed oil	126
Phenanthrene (m.p. 101)	<100
Polyisobutene	114
POLYETHYLENE	
n-Hexane	127
Cyclohexane	163
PROPANE (crit. temp. 95.6)	
9-n-Butylanthracene	<20
1,1-Di(1-decalyl)hendecane	92
1,5-Dicyclohexyl-3-(2-cyclo-hexylethyl)pentane	100
Amyl phthalate	105
n-Butyl phthalate	106
Cetyl stearate	95.2
Cottonseed oil	66.2
Di-n-octadecylamine	94.2
Ethyl phthalate	100.5
Isoamyl phthalate	105
Lauric acid	111
Linoleic acid	79.8
Methyl ricinoleate	91.3
Myristic acid	104.5
n-Octadecyl stearate	94.9
n-Octyl phthalate	105e
Oleic acid	91.1
Palmitamide	<92
Palmitic acid	96.9
Polyisobutene	85
n-Propyl phthalate	106
Stearic acid	91.4
Tricaprylin	100.5
Trilaurin	87.4
Trimyristin	79.4
Triolein	64.5
Tripalmitin	73.5
Tristearin	69.2
PYRIDINE	
Methyl iodide - pyridine complex	78.4
SULFUR DIOXIDE	
Potassium iodide	77.3

Table IV

Mutual Miscibility of Liquids - Bingham[a] (17)

No.	Liquid	Immiscible Liquids[b]
1	Acetaldehyde	---
2	Acetic acid	15,25,30
3	Acetone	19
4	Acetophenone	9,19
5	Ammonia	15,20,30
6	Aniline	15,20,30
7	Benzaldehyde	19
8	Benzene	18,19
9	Bromine	4,18,19
10	Carbon disulfide	18,19,24
11	Carbon tetrachloride	18,19
12	Castor oil	15,20,30
13	Chlorobenzene	18,19
14	Chloroform	19
15	Decane	2,5,6,12,18,19,24,25,27,33,36
16	Ethyl alcohol	25,29,30
17	Ethyl ether	19
18	Formic acid	8,9,10,11,13,15,18,20,25,28,30,35
19	Glycerol	3,4,7,8,9,10,11,13,14,15,17,20,21,22,26,27,28,30,33,35,36,37
20	n-Hexane	5,6,12,18,19,24
21	Isoamyl alcohol	19
22	Isobutyl isobutyrate	19
23	Isobutyric acid	---
24	Methanol	10,15,20,30
25	Methylene iodide	2,15,16,18,28,29,30,32,38
26	Methyl formate	19
27	Nitrobenzene	15,19
28	Oleic acid	18,19,25
29	Olive oil	16,25
30	Paraffin (at m.p.)	2,5,6,12,16,18,19,24,25,36
31	Phenol (at m.p.)	---
32	Propionic acid	25
33	Propionitrile	15,19
34	Pyridine	---
35	Toluene	18,19
36	m-Toluidine	15,19,30
37	Triethylamine	19
38	Valeric acid	25

a) Bingham listed 50 substances. The following were omitted from the above compilation: Mercury, phosphorus, silver nitrate, sodium, sulfur, sulfuric acid, and water because they are immiscible with most of the other liquids; carbon dioxide and sulfur dioxide because of limited data; stannic chloride because most of the data are wrong (substance not anhydrous); benzoic acid and resorcinol (and four of the first group above) because of their high melting points.

b) Each liquid is miscible in all proportions at 25°C with all other liquids listed in this table except those numbered under "Immiscible Liquids".

TABLE V   **213**

Table V

Mutual Miscibility of Liquids - Drury (106)

No.	Liquid	Immiscible Liquids*
1	Glycerol	6?(10,13)14-38
2	Ethylene glycol	16,20,23,24?(26)27-37(38)
3	Formamide	18,19,21,23,27-38
4	Trimethylene glycol	20,23,27-38
5	Hydroxyethylethylenediamine	22,24,30-38
6	Diethanolamine	1?15,20,22,24?26,27,29-38
7	Triethanolamine	27,29-38
8	2-Amino-2-methyl-1-propanol	28,29,34-38
9	Aniline	35-38
10	Furfuryl alcohol	(1),37,38
11	Benzyl alcohol	38
12	Ethyl alcohol	None
12	Pyridine	None
13	n-Butyl alcohol	(1)
14	Acetone	1
15	Dibutoxytetraethylene glycol	1,6
16	Adiponitrile	1,2,17?21,32-38
17	Isoamyl alcohol	1,16?
18	Benzothiazole	1,3
19	Capryl alcohol	1,3,20
20	Nitromethane	1,2,4,6,19,21,31?35?36,37(38)
21	2-Ethylhexanol	1,3,16,20
22	Diethyl Cellosolve	1,5,6
23	Ethyl thiocyanate	1-4
23	Ethyl benzoate	1-4
23	Benzonitrile	1-4
24	Benzaldehyde	1,2?5,6?
25	Diacetone alcohol	1,31?32?34?36?37?38?
26	Acetylacetone	1(2)6
27	Methyl isobutyl ketone	1-4,6,7
28	Ethyl isothiocyanate	1-4,8
29	Benzyl mercaptan	1-4,6,7,8
30	Isobutyl mercaptan	1-7
30	Methyl disulfide	1-7
30	Dimethylaniline	1-7
30	n-Butyl acetate	1-7
31	Benzene	1-7,20?25?
32	Carbon tetrachloride	1-7,16,25?
33	Ethyl ether	1-7,16
34	Di-n-propylaniline	1-8,16,25?
35	n-Butyl ether	1-9,16,20?
36	Tri-n-butylamine	1-9,16,20,25?
37	Isoamyl sulfide	1-10,16,20,25?
38	Petroleum ether (Benzine)	1(2)3-11,16(20)25?

*Each liquid is miscible in all proportions at 25°C with probably all other liquids in this table except those listed under "Immiscible Liquids". Liquids represented by numbers in parentheses are listed by Drury as miscible but found by Francis to be immiscible. Those followed by question marks are listed by Drury as immiscible, but found by Francis to be miscible. Liquids with the same number (bracketed) are miscible with the same group of other liquids in this table. It was necessary to supplement Drury's table with some estimates. The arrangement is that mentioned in reference 146, p. 21, Cf. reference 140 and Fig. 6.

Table VI

Mutual Miscibility of Liquids - Sample et al (372)

Letter	Liquids	Immiscible Liquids*
a	Glycerol	deg?(h)j?l-w
b	Ethylene glycol	de,n-w
c	Propylene glycol	op(q)rtuvw
d	Nitromethane	abimstvw
e	Nitroethane	abs
f	Methanol	tuw
g	Furfural	a?uvw
h	Furfuryl alcohol	(a)o?uvw
i	Cyclohexanol	d
j	n-Butyl alcohol	a?
k	Isopropyl alcohol	None
l	Acetone	a
l	2-Butanone (MEK)	a
l	n-Butyl lactate	a
l	Diethylcarbinol	a
m	Amyl alcohol	ad
n	n-Butyl acetate	ab
n	Chloroform	ab
n	Ethyl acetate	ab
n	Ethyl ether	ab
o	n-Butyl ether	abch?
p	Carbon tetrachloride	abc
p	p-Chlorotoluene	abc
p	o-Dichlorobenzene	abc
p	1-Nitropropane	abc
p	Trichloroethylene	abc
p	Xylene	abc
p	Benzene	abc
q	Ethylene chloride	ab(c)r?
r	Toluene	abcq?
s	Lauryl (Dodecyl) alcohol	abde
s	Oleic acid	abde
t	Tetrachloroethylene	a-d,f
u	Cyclohexane	abcfgh
v	n-Pentane	a-d,gh
w	n-Butyl stearate	a-d,fgh

*Each liquid is miscible in all proportions at 25° with all other liquids in this table except those listed under "Immiscible Liquids". Liquids represented by letters in parentheses are listed by the authors as miscible but found by Francis to be immiscible. Those followed by question marks are listed by the authors as immiscible but found by Francis to be miscible. Liquids with the same letter are miscible with the same group of other liquids in this list. The arrangement of liquids is similar to that of Table V. (Cf. Figure 6)

TABLE VII   **215**

Table VII

Mutual Miscibility of Liquids - Eslami and Dubois (121)

No.	Liquids	Immiscible Liquids*
1	Benzyl alcohol	18?25
2	Butyl alcohol	6,7?11?13?15?18?
3	Cyclohexanol	15,18,39,43
4	Ethyl alcohol	None
5	Furfuryl alcohol	24,25
6	Glycerol	2,8?9,10?12,14?16?18?19-40,42-4
7	Ethylene glycol	2?12?16?19-26(27)28-30,34-7, 39-40,43(44)
8	Methanol	6?
9	Isoamyl alcohol	6,39,43
10	Isopropyl alcohol	6?18?
11	Trimethylene glycol	2?16?19-26(27)28-30,34-37,39,40
12	Benzaldehyde	6,7?15?23?
13	Formamide	2?16?19-30,32,34,35,37,40,44
14	Aniline	6?16?24(25)
15	Diethanolamine	2?3,12?19-30,33?34-36(37),38,42?
16	Dimethylamine	6?7?11?13?14?
17	Pyridine	None
18	Triethanolamine	1?2?3,6?10?(19)20-28(29), 30,34-36,37(38)42?
19	Benzene	6,7,11,13,15(18)20?39?
20	Carbon disulfide	6,7,11,13,15,18,19?39,43
21	Carbon tetrachloride	6,7,11,13,15,18,33?43
22	Chlorobenzene	6,7,11,13,15,18,33?
23	Chloroform	6,7,11,12?13,15,18
24	Cyclohexane	5,6,7,11,13,14,15,18(39)43
25	Petroleum ether	1,5,6,7,11,13(14)15,18(39)42,43
26	Styrene	6,7,11,13,15,18
27	Tetrachloroethane	6(7,11)13,15,18
28	Toluene	6,7,11,13,15,18
29	Trichloroethylene	6,7,11,13,15(18)
30	Xylene	6,7,11,13,15,18
31	Acetone	6
32	Cyclohexanone	6,13,39,43
33	2-Butanone (MEK)	6,15?21?22?
34	Amyl acetate	6,7,11,13,15,18,39,43
35	Butyl acetate	6,7,11,13,15,18
36	Ethyl acetate	6,7,11,15,18
37	Ethyl benzoate	6,7,11,13,18(15)
38	Ethyl formate	6,15(18)
39	Nitromethane	3,6,7,9,11,19?20(24,25)32,34
40	Ethyl ether	6,7,11,13,43,44?
41	Cellosolve	None
42	Carbitol	6,15,18,25
43	Adiponitrile	3,6,7,9,20,21,24,25,32,34,40
44	Benzonitrile	6(7)13,40?

*Each liquid is miscible in all proportions at 20° with all other liquids in this table except those listed under "Immiscible Liquids". Liquids represented by numbers in parentheses are listed by Eslami as miscible but found by Francis to be immiscible. Those followed by question marks are listed by Eslami as immiscible, but found by Francis to be miscible. The arrangement of Eslami is retained to facilitate comparison.

Table VIII

Mutual Miscibility of Liquids - Jackson and Drury (211)

No.	Liquids	Immiscible Liquids[a]
1	Acetone	(b)
2	1-Amino-2-propanol (isopropanolamine)	(b)
3	n-Amyl cyanide	(b)
4	Anisaldehyde	(b)
5	Benzene	7?45
6	Benzyl ether	45
7	Bromoethyl acetate	5?30?
	1,3-Butanediol	4,5,6,9,17,18,20,23, 24,26,29,30,31,47
	2,3-Butandiol	5,6,17,20,30,47
	2-Chloroethanol	(b)
8	Chloroform	(b)
	3-Chloro-1,2-propanediol	5,17,20,30,43,47
9	Cinnamaldehyde	(b)
10	o-Cresol	(b)
11	Di-n-amylamine	15?45,46
12	Di-n-butylamine	(b)
13	Di-n-butyl carbonate	45,46
	Dibutyl hydrogen phosphite	(b)
14	Diethylacetic acid	(b)
	Diethylene glycol dibutyl ether	34
	Diethylene glycol diethyl ether	(b)
	Diethylene glycol monobutyl ether	(b)
	Diethylene glycol monoethyl ether (Carbitol)	17,30
	Diethylene glycol monomethyl ether	17,30
15	Diethylenetriamine	11?30,47
16	Diethylformamide	30
17	Di(2-ethylhexyl)amine	45
18	Diisobutyl ketone	45
19	Diisopropylamine	(b)
20	Di-n-propylaniline	45
	Dipropylene glycol	17,30
21	Ethyl alcohol	(b)
22	Ethyl benzoate	(b)
23	Ethyl chloroacetate	(b)
24	Ethyl cinnamate	(b)
	Ethylene diacetate	17,30
	Ethylene glycol	3-9,11,13,17,18,20,22- 26,30,31,37,42,43,44,47
	Ethylene glycol ethyl butyl ether	(b)
	Ethylene glycol monobutyl ether	(b)
	Ethylene glycol monoethyl ether (Cellosolve)	(b)
	Ethylene glycol monomethyl ether (Methoxyethanol)	(b)
25	Ethyl ether	45
26	Ethyl phenylacetate	(b)
	Glycerol	1,3-9,11-14,17,18, 20,22-31,34,37-39, 42-44.47
27	Heptadecyl alcohol	45
28	3-Heptanol	(b)
29	n-Heptyl acetate	45
30	n-Hexyl ether	7?15,16,45,46
31	Isoamyl acetate	45
32	Methylbenzylamine	(b)
33	1-Methylbenzydiethanolamine	(b)

TABLE VIII   **217**

No.	Liquids	Immiscible Liquids[a]
34	1-Methylbenzyldimethylamine	(b)
35	1-Methylbenzylethanolamine	(b)
36	2-Methyl-5-ethylpyridine	(b)
37	Methyl isopropyl ketone	(b)
38	4-Methyl-n-valeric acid	(b)
39	o-Phenetidine	(b)
40	2-Phenylethylamine	(b)
	1,2-Propanediol	5,6,17,18,20,24-26, 30,47
	1,3-Propanediol	3-6,9,17,18,20,23-26, 29-31,42-3,47
41	Pyridine	(b)
42	Salicylaldehyde	(b)
43	Tetradecyl alcohol	45
44	Tri-n-butyl phosphate	(b)
45	Triethylene glycol	5,6,11,13,17,18,20, 25,27,29-31,43,47
46	Triethylenetetramine	11,13,30,47
	Triethyl phosphate	17
	Trimethylene chlorohydrin	(b)
47	2,6,8-Trimethyl-4-nonanone	15,45-46

(a) Each liquid is reported to be miscible in all proportions at 25° (or reacting) with all numbered liquids except those indicated by numbers in above column. Sulfuric acid is omitted from the above list because it is immiscible with practically all liquids except when it reacts with them.

(b) Miscible with all liquids numbered in column one. They are immiscible with some of the unnumbered liquids in this table.

BIBLIOGRAPHY

(1)   Alekseev, V., *Ann. physik. Chem.*, (2) 28, 305 (1886);
      through ref. 392, pp. 221,500,708, and ref. 209, p. 394,
      Water, Sulfur.

(1A) Alfrey, G. F., Schneider, W. G., *Discussions, Faraday* Soc.,
      15, 224 (1953), Nitrobenzene, Triethylamine.

(2)   Andon, R. J. V., Cox, J. D., *J. Chem. Soc.*, 1952, 4602,
      Water-Pyridine derivatives.

(3)   Angelescu, E., *Bull. sect. sci. acad, roumaine*, 7, 79
      (1925); Chem. Abstr., 20, 1348, Water-o-Toluidine.

(4)   Angelescu, E., coworkers, *Ibid.*, 23, 515 (1941);
      Chem. Abstr., 37, 6180, Acetic anhydride, Anisidine,
      Phenetidine.

(4A) Angelescu, E., Giusca, R., *Z. physik. Chem.*, A191, 145
      (1942), Acetic acid, o-Toluidine

(5)   Atack, D., Rice, O. K., *J. Chem. Phys.* 22, 382 (1954),
      Aniline-Cyclohexane.

(6)   Atack, D., Rice, O. K., *Discussions, Faraday* Soc., 15,
      212 (1953), Aniline-Cyclohexane.

(7)   Aten, A. H. W., *Z. physik. Chem.*, 54, 124 (1906), Methyl
      iodide-Pyridine.

(8)   Atkinson, R. C., Heycock, C. T., Pope, W. J., *J. Chem.
      Soc.*, 117, 1422 (1920), Phosgene.

(9)   Aubert, M., Moutte, R., *Ann. Comb. Liq.*, 4, 683 (1929),
      Aniline-1-Olefins.

(10) Avenarius, M., Tarasenkov, D. N., *J. Gen. Chem.* (USSR)
      16, 1776 (1946), *Chem. Abstr.* 41, 5372, Formic acid-
      Benzene, Bromoform.

(11) Bailey, C. R., *J. Chem. Soc.*, 126, 1953 (1925), Phenol,
      Salicylic acid.

(11A) Baker, L. C. W., Anderson, T. F., *J. Amer. Chem.* Soc., 79,
      2071 (1957), Carbon dioxide, Ethyl alcohol.

(12) Ball, J. S., "Aniline Points of Hydrocarbons", R. I.
      3721, U. S. Dept. of Interior, Bureau of Mines, 1943.
      Most of the aniline points of this reference are listed
      also in ref. 100.

(12A) Ibid., Original observations or estimates. Aniline.

(13) Bastic, B. L., Pushin, N. A.,*Bull. Soc. Chim. Belgrade*,
      12, 109 (1947), *Chem. Abstr.* 43, 6066b. Formic acid-
      Diphenylamine.

(14) Bellemans, A., *J. Chem. Phys.*, 21, 368 (1953). Triethyl-
      amine.

(15) Bergstrom, F. W., Gilkey, W. M., Lung, P. E., Ind. Eng. Chem., 24, 57 (1932); Ref. 296, pp. 404-10. Aliphatic amines.

(16) Bernoulli, A. L., Sarasin, A., Helv. Chem. Acta, 13, 520 (1930). Dihydroxybenzenes.

(17) Bingham, E. C., Am. Chem. J., 37, 549 (1907).(Table IV).

(18) Bjerrum, N., Jozefowicz, E., Z. physik. Chem., A 159, 202 (1932). Silicon tetraethyl.

(19) Blanksma, J. J., Chem. Weekblad, 7, 418 (1910); through ref. 392(p.424). Phenylhydrazine.

(19A) Bloch, I., Höhn, F., Ber. 41, 1977 (1908). Hydrogen disulfide.

(20) Bocharov, A. A., Obolentsev, R. D., J. Applied Chem.(U.S.S.R.) 19, 492 (1946); U.O.P. Survey Foreign Petroleum Litt., Nov. 8-15 (1946). Stannic iodide.

(21) Boeseken, J., Carrière, J. F., Rec. trav. chim., 34,181(1915); Chem. Abstr. 9, 2382. Trichloroacrylic acid.

(22) Bogash, R., Hixson, A. N., Chem. Eng. Progress, 45, 597 (1949). Propane—Glycerides.

(22A) Boguski, J. J. von, Jakubowski, W., J. Russ. Phys. Chem. Soc. 37, 92 (1905); Chem. Zentr. 1905 I, 1207. Sulfur-Benzyl chloride.

(23) Bond, P. A., Beach, H. T., J. Am. Chem. Soc., 48, 348 (1926). Sulfur dioxide-Tetrahalides.

(24) Bond, P. A., Crone, E. B., Ibid., 56, 2028 (1934). Sulfur dioxide-Tetrahalides.

(25) Bond, P. A., Stephens, W. R., Ibid., 51, 2910 (1929). Sulfur dioxide—Tetrachlorides.

(26) Bourgoin, A., Bull. soc. chim. Belg., 33, 101 (1924); through ref. 392(p.208). Methylal.

(27) Boutaric, A., Corbet, G., Compt. rend. 179, 1320 (1924). Phenol, etc.

(28) Boutaric, A., Corbet, G.,Ibid., 183, 42 (1926). Acrolein.

(29) Ibid., 184, 1446 (1927). Methanol.

(30) Bradfield, A. E., Williams, A. F., J. Chem. Soc., 1929, 2544. Acetic acid-Methyl acetanilide.

(31) Brame, J. S. S., Hunter, T. G., J. Inst. Petroleum Technol., 13, 798 (1927). Nitrobenzene.

(32) Bredig, M. A.,Bronstein, H. R., Smith, W. T., Jr., J. Am Chem. Soc., 77, 1454 (1955). Alkali metals-Fluorides.

(33) Bredig, M. A., Johnson, J. W., Smith, W. T. Jr., Ibid. 307 (1955). Sodium-NaF

(34) Briggs, S. W., Comings, E. W., Ind. Eng. Chem., 35, 411
(1943). Furfural.

(35) Brooke, M., J. Am. Chem. Soc., 72, 5749 (1950). Sulfur-
Butyl phthalate.

(35A) Broughton, G., Jones, D. C., Trans. Faraday Soc.,
32, 686 (1936). Nitromethane.

(36) Brown, C., Berger, A. W., Hersh, C. K., J. Chem. Phys.
23, 1340 (1955). Oxygen-Ozone.

(37) Brown, C. W., Ind. Eng. Chem., Anal. Ed., 18, 739 (1946).
Automatic CST determination.

(38) Brun, P., Compt. rend., 180, 1745 (1925). Butyl and
Amyl alcohols.

(38A) Bruni, G., Pelizzola, C., Atti, Accad. Lincei, 30, ii,
158 (1921); Chem. Abstr. 17, 2814. Sulfur.

(39) Bruun, J. H., Hicks-Bruun, M. M., J. Research Natl. Bur.
Standards, 6, 877 (1931). Aniline-Hexane.

(40) Ibid., 7, 612 (1931). Aniline-Cyclohexane.

(41) Ibid. , 7, 807 (1931). Aniline-Methylcyclopentane.

(42) Ibid., 8, 534 (1932). Aniline-n-Heptane.

(43) Ibid., 8, 587 (1932). Aniline-n-Decane.

(44) Ibid., 10, 472 (1933). Aniline-2-Methylhexane.

(45) Büchner, E. H., Z. physik. Chem., 54, 665 (1906).
Carbon dioxide.

(46) Ibid., 56, 257 (1906). Aniline-Water.

(47) Büchner, E. H., Kleyn, D., Rec. trav. chim., 43,
153 (1924). Aniline-Cyclohexane.

(48) Butler, J. A. V., Thomson, D. W., Maclennan, W. H.,
J. Chem. Soc., 1933, 680. Butyl alcohol.

(48A) Calingaert, G., (1921), (through ref. 445(p.517).
Aniline-Isopentane.

(49) Calingaert, G. Saroos, H., J. Am. Chem. Soc.,
58, 635 (1936). Aniline-Decanes.

(49A) Cameron, F. K., J. Phys. Chem., 2, 376,(1898); Brit.
Chem. Abstr., 1899i, 206. Acetohydroxamic acid-
Benzoate.

(49B) Campbell, A. N., Campbell, A. J. R., J. Am. Chem. Soc.,
59, 2485 (1937). Phenol.

(50) Campbell, D. N., Hickman, J. B., Ibid., 75, 2879 (1953).
C_7F_{16}.

(51) Campetti, A., Atti. accad. sci. Torino, 52, 114 (1917);
Chem. Abstr., 11, 3150. Diphenylamine, Resorcinol.

(52) Campetti, A., del Grosso, Mem. R, Accad. Sci. Torino, 61, 187 (1911). Chem. Abstr., 8, 2294; through ref. 209 (pp.396-7); Nuovo cimento, 6, 379 (1913). Various.

(53) Carpenter, J. A., J. Inst. Petroleum Technol., 12, 561 (1926). Aniline-C_7 to C_{60}.

(54) Carpenter, J. A., Ibid., 14, 461 (1928). Aniline.

(55) Carrick, L. L., J. Phys. Chem., 25, 628 (1921). Nitrophenols.

(56) Carter, S. R., Megson, N. J. L., J. Chem. Soc., 1927, 2024. Isobutyric acid, Phenol.

(56A) Cernatescu, R., Papafil, E., Z. Physik. Chem., 125, 333 (1927). Phenol.

(56B) Champion, P., Pellat, H., Compt. rend., 70, 620(1870); through ref. 70A(p.114). Hydrogen bromide.

(57) Charonnet, R., Ibid., 185, 284 (1927). Pyramidone.

(58) Chavanne, G., Bull. sci. acad. roy. Belg., (5) 12, 105 (1926); Chem. Abstr., 20, 2664. Aniline-Dimethyl-cyclopentane.

(59) Chavanne, G., Bull. soc. chim. Belg., 31, 331 (1922); reported in ref. 12, 93, 161. Aniline-Paraffins.

(60) Ibid., 39, 402 (1930); Chem. Zentr. 1931, I, 597. Aniline-Dimethylcyclopentane.

(61) Chavanne, G., Becker, P., Ibid., 36, 591 (1927); through ref. 12. Aniline-Alkylcyclopentanes.

(61A) Chavanne, G., La Jeune, B., Ibid., 31, 98 (1922); through ref. 442. Aniline-Olefins.

(62) Chavanne, G., Miller, O., Ibid., 39, 287 (1930); through ref. 12. Aniline-Dimethylcyclopentanes.

(63) Chavanne, G., Simon, L. J., Compt. rend., 168, 1111 (1919); Chem. Abstr. 13, 2125. Aniline-Paraffins and Naphthenes.

(64) Ibid., 1324 (1919); Chem. Abstr., 13, 3182. Aniline-Paraffins and Naphthenes.

(64A) Chipman, J., J. Amer. Chem. Soc., 46, 2446 (1924). Benzoic acid.

(65) Chiurdoglu, G., Bull. soc. chim. Belg., 42, 347 (1933); Chem. Abstr., 28, 2336. Aniline-Cyclopentanes.

(66) Ibid., 43, 35 (1934); Chem. Abstr., 28, 3061. Aniline-Alkylcyclopentanes.

(67) Ibid., 47, 363 (1938); Chem. Zentr., 1939, II, 73. Aniline-Naphthenes.

(68) Coates, J. E., Hartshorne, N. H., J. Chem. Soc., 1931, 657. Hydrogen cyanide.

(69) Collett, A. R., Johnston, J., _J_. _Phys_. _Chem_., _30_, 70 (1926). Nitroanilines.

(70) Collett, A. R., Lazzell, C. L., _Ibid_., _34_, 1838 (1930) Nitrobenzoic acids.

(70A) Comey, A. M.,"_Dictionary of Chemical Solubilities_," Macmillan, London, 1921. Various.

(71) Copp, J. L., _Trans_. _Faraday Soc_., _51_, 1056 (1955). Methyldiethylamine.

(72) Copp, J. L., Everett, D. H., _Faraday Soc_. _Discussions_, _15_, 179 (1953). Triethylamine.

(72A) Corcoran, W. H., Reamer, H. H., Sage, B. H., _Ind_. _Eng_. _Chem_., _46_, 2541(1954). Nitric acid-Nitrogen dioxide.

(73) Cornish, R. E., Archibald, R. C., Murphy, E. A., Evans, H. M., _Ibid_., _26_, 399 (1934). Various.

(73A) Cornog, J., Olson, L. E., _J_. _Am_. _Chem_. _Soc_., _62_, 3328 (1940). CCl_4-1Cl.

(74) Cox, H. L., Cretcher, L. H., _J_. _Am_. _Chem_. _Soc_., _48_, 451 (1926). Glycol butyl ethers.

(75) Cox, H. L., Nelson, W. L., Cretcher, L. H., _Ibid_., _49_, 1080 (1927). Glycol propyl ethers.

(76) Cox, J. D., _J_. _Chem_. _Soc_., _1952_, 4606. Deuterium oxide.

(77) _Ibid_., _1954_, 3185. Alkylpyridines.

(78) Cox, J. D., Herrington, E. F. G., _Trans_. _Faraday Soc_., _52_, 928 (1956). Aniline-Cyclohexane. Dimethyl-pyridine.

(79) Crismer, L., _Bull_. _soc_. _chim_. _Belg_., _18_, 18·(1904); _Chem_. _Zentr_., _1904_, _I_, 1480. TNT.

(80) _Ibid_., _34_, 28 (1920); _Chem_. _Abstr_., _15_, 2724; through ref. 392(p.647). Nitronaphthalene.

(81) Crismer, L., Timmermans, J., _Ibid_., 34 (1920); _Chem_. _Abstr_., _15_, 2725. Tetryl.

(82) Croll, J. M., Scott, R. L., _J_. _Phys_. _Chem_., _62_, 954 (1958). Carbon tetrafluoride.

(82A) Culbertson, J. L., Palmer, E. S., _J_. _Phys_. _Chem_., _35_, 3063 (1931). Phenol

(82B) Curtis, R. G., Hatt, H. H., _Australian J_. _Sci_. _Research Sect_. _A_, _I_, 213 (1948). Furfural-Water.

(83) Darwent, B. deB., Winkler, C. A., _J_. _Phys_. _Chem_., _47_, 449 (1943). Aniline-Hexane.

(84) Davis, H. S., Wiedeman, O. F., _Ind_. _Eng_. _Chem_., _37_, 482 (1945). Acrylonitrile.

(84A) Debye, P., Coll, H., Woermann, D., _J_. _Chem_. _Phys_., _33_, 1746 (1960). Polystyrene.

(85)   DeCarli, F., Gazz. chim. ital., 57, 347 (1927); Chem. Abstr., 21, 3047. Ammonia, Sulfur dioxide.

(86)   Dehn, W. M., J. Am. Chem. Soc., 39, 1400 (1917). Pyridine, Water.

(86A) Delcourt, Y., (1927); through ref. 445(p.605). Nitrobenzene.

(87)   Dessart, A., Bull. soc. chim. Belg., 35, 9 (1926); Chem. Zentr., 1926, II, 157. Aniline, Toluidine, Nitrobenzene.

(88)   Desvergnes, L., Mon. Sci., 14, 249 (1924); through ref. 392(pp.495,534,578). TNT, Nitroanisoles, Nitrophenetoles.

(89)   Ibid., 15, 73 (1925); Chem. Abstr., 19, 2036. Nitrochlorobenzenes.

(90)   Ibid., 149 (1925); Chem. Abstr., 19, 3257. Nitroaromatics.

(91)   Ibid., 16, 201 (1926); Chem. Abstr., 21, 740. Nitroaromatics.

(92)   Desvergnes, L., Rev. chim. ind., 36, 194, 224 (1927); through ref. 392 (pp.351,364). Nitrophenols.

(93)   Desvergnes, L., Ann. chim. anal. chim. appl , 10, 226 (1928); Chem. Abstr., 22, 4034. Alkyl Ureas.

(94)   Ibid., 253; Chem. Abstr., 22, 4504. Diphenylamine.

(95)   Dice, M. E., Hildebrand, J. H., J. Am. Chem. Soc., 50, 3023 (1928). Stannic iodide.

(96)   Diepen, G. A. M., Scheffer, F. E. C., Ibid., 70, 4081 (1948). Ethylene.

(97)   Dobryanskii, A. F., Khesin, I., Neftyanoe Khoz., 1929, Nos. 8, 9, 80; Chem. Zentr., 1930 I, 2662. Nitrobenzene, Aniline.

(98)   Dolgolenko, V. I., J. Russ. Phys. Chem. Soc., 39, 841 (1907); Chem. Abstr., 2, 1374; Z. physik. Chem., 62, 499 (1908). Butyl alcohols.

(99)   Dolique, R., Compt. rend., 194, 289 (1932). Phenol.

(99A) Dorfman, M. E., Hildebrand, J. H., J. Am. Chem. Soc., 49, 729 (1927). Stannic iodide.

(100) Doss, M. P., "Physical Constants of Principal Hydrocarbons", 4th ed., The Texas Co., 1943. Aniline.

(101) Drew, D. A., Hixson, A. N., Trans. Am. Inst. Chem. Engrs., 40, 675, 690 (1944). Propane-Fatty acids and glycerides.

(102) Dros, A., Tulleners, A. J., Waterman, H. I., J. Inst. Petroleum Technol., 19, 784 (1933). Aniline-Naphthenes.

(103) Drouillon, F., J. chim. phys., 22, 149 (1925): through ref. 392 (pp.135, 266). n-Butyl alcohol.

(104)   Drucker, C., <u>Rec</u>. <u>trav</u>. <u>chim</u>., <u>42</u>, 552 (1923); data
        given in ref. 392 (p. 10). Methanol-Carbon disulfide.

(105)   Drucker, K., Moles, E., <u>Z</u>. <u>physik</u>. <u>Chem</u>., <u>75</u>, 405
        (1910). Isobutyric acid.

(106)   Drury, J. S., <u>Ind</u>. <u>Eng</u>. <u>Chem</u>., 44, 2744 (1952)
        (Table V); reproduced in ref. 193A, pp. 1500-3.

(107)   Dubrisay, R., Toquet, <u>Bull</u>. <u>soc</u>. <u>chim</u>. (4) <u>25</u>, 354
        (1919). Phenol.

(107A) Dubrisay, R., Tripier, Toquet, <u>Compt</u>. <u>rend</u>., <u>167</u>,
        1036 (1918). Phenol.

(108)   Dubroka, M., <u>J</u>. <u>chim</u>. <u>physik</u>., <u>5</u>, 463 (1907): <u>Chem</u>.
        <u>Abstr</u>., <u>2</u>, 934. Methyl sulfate.

(108A) DuBrow, P. L., Hoerr, C. W., Harwood, H. J., <u>J</u> <u>Am</u>.
        <u>Chem</u>. <u>Soc</u>., <u>74</u>, 6243 (1952). Undecylbenzothiazole.

(108B) Duckett, J., Patterson, W. H., <u>J</u>. <u>Phys</u>. <u>Chem</u>., <u>29</u>,
        295 (1925). Phenol.

(108C) Dunlap, R. D., Digman, R., Vreeland, J., Abstr.,
        124th Meeting, A.C.S., Chicago, Sept. 1953. Perfluoro-
        <u>n</u>-pentane.

(108D) Dunlap, R. D., Smyth, D., <u>Ibid</u>., Silicon tetramethyl.

(109)   Du Pont Circular, "<u>Dimethylformamide</u>", Grasselli Chem.
        Dept., May 2, 1958.

(110)   Durandet, J., Gladel, Y. L., Graziani, F., <u>Rev</u>. <u>Inst</u>.
        <u>franc</u>. <u>petrole</u>, <u>10</u>, 585 (1955). Benzyl alcohol.

(111)   Dyakova, M. K., Lozovoi, A. V., <u>J</u>. <u>Gen</u>. <u>Chem</u>.,(U.S.S.R.)
        <u>9</u>, 26 (1939); <u>Chem</u>. <u>Abstr</u>., <u>33</u>, 6254. Aniline-
        Naphthenes.

(112)   Dyakova, M. K., Lozovoi, A. V., Stepantsova, T. G.,
        <u>Ibid</u>., <u>7</u>, 722 (1937); <u>Chem</u>. <u>Abstr</u>., <u>31</u>, 5770. Aniline-
        Npahthenes.

(113)   Dyke, D. E. L., Rowlinson, J. S., Thacker, R. L.,
        <u>Trans</u>. <u>Faraday</u> <u>Soc</u>., <u>55</u>, 903 (1959). Fluorocarbons.

(113A) Eckfeldt, E. L., Lucasse, W. W., <u>J</u>. <u>Phys</u>. <u>Chem</u>., <u>47</u>,
        169 (1943). Methanol.

(114)   Edgar, G., Calingaert, G., Marker, R. E., <u>J</u>. <u>Am</u>.
        <u>Chem</u>. <u>Soc</u>., <u>51</u>, 1488, 1545 (1929). Aniline-Paraffins.

(115)   Efremov, N. N., <u>Bull</u>. <u>acad</u>. <u>sci</u>. <u>U</u>. <u>R</u>. <u>S</u>. <u>S</u>., <u>Clas</u>.
        <u>sci</u>. <u>chim</u>., <u>1940</u>, 651; <u>Chem</u>. <u>Abstr</u>., <u>35</u>, 4665; through
        ref. 392 (pp. 648-54). Nitrophenols.

(116)   Efremov, N. N., <u>J</u>. <u>Russ</u>. <u>Phys</u>. <u>Chem</u>. <u>Soc</u>., <u>50</u>, <u>I</u>, 338,
        372, 421, 441 (1918); <u>Chem</u>. <u>Abstr</u>., <u>17</u>, 3327-8.
        Picric and Styphnic acids.

(117)   Egan, C. J., U.S. Patent 2,582,197 (1952); data given
        in ref. 153 (p. 218). Fluorocarbons.

(117A) Erdman, E., Bedford, F., <u>Ber</u>., <u>37</u>, 1191 (1904).
        Nitrogen-Oxygen.

(118)   Erichsen, L. v., <u>Brennstoff-Chem</u>., <u>33</u>, 166 (1952).
        Alcohols-Water.

(119)   Erichsen, L. v., Dobbert, E., <u>Ibid</u>.,<u>36</u>, 338 (1955).
        Phenols.

(120)   Erskin, A. M., <u>Ind</u>. <u>Eng</u>. <u>Chem</u>., <u>18</u>, 694 (1926).
        Nitrobenzene.

(121)   Eslami, I., Du Bois, P., <u>Chemie et Ind</u>., <u>80</u>, 766
        (1958). (Table VII).

(122)   Evans, E. B., <u>J</u>. <u>Inst</u>. <u>Petroleum Technol</u>., <u>23</u>, 222
        (1937). Aniline.

(123)   <u>Ibid</u>., <u>24</u>, 328 (1938). Aniline-Naphthenes.

(124)   <u>Ibid</u>., 539 (1938). Aniline-Aromatics.

(125)   Evans, W. V., Aylesworth, M. B., <u>Ind</u>. <u>Eng</u>. <u>Chem</u>.,
        <u>18</u>, 24 (1926). Furfural.

(126)   Ewert, M., <u>Bull</u>. <u>soc</u>. <u>chim</u>. <u>Belg</u>., <u>46</u>, 90 (1937);
        through ref. 392 (p. 85). Acetonitrile.

(127)   Ewins, A. J., <u>J</u>. <u>Chem</u>. <u>Soc</u>., <u>105</u>, 357 (1914). Formic
        acid.

(128)   Faucon, A., <u>Ann</u>. <u>chim</u>. <u>phys</u>., (8) <u>19</u>, 70 (1910);
        through ref. 392 (p.250). Isobutyric acid.

(129)   Faucon, A., <u>Compt</u>. <u>rend</u>., <u>148</u>, 1189 (1909); <u>Chem</u>.
        <u>Abstr</u>. <u>3</u>, 1710. Water-Lower acids.

(130)   Fenske, M. R., McCormack, R. H., Lawroski, H., Geier,
        R. G., <u>Am</u>. <u>Inst</u>. <u>Chem</u>. <u>Eng</u>. <u>J</u>., <u>1</u>, 335 (1955). Various.

(130A) Ferguson, J. B., <u>Trans</u>. <u>Roy</u>. <u>Soc</u>. <u>(Canada)</u>(3), <u>21</u>,
        Part. II, Sect. III, 265 (1927); through ref. 392
        (p. 375). Phenol.

(130B) Ferguson, J. B., <u>J</u>. <u>Phys</u>. <u>Chem</u>., <u>36</u>, 1123 (1932).
        Methanol.

(131)   Ferris, S. W., Birkhimer, E. R., Henderson, L. M.,
        <u>Ind</u>. <u>Eng</u>. <u>Chem</u>., <u>23</u>, 753 (1931). Lube oils-Many
        solvents.

(132)   Fischer, J., Steunenberg, R. K., Vogel, R. C., <u>J</u>.
        <u>Am</u>. <u>Chem</u>. <u>Soc</u>., <u>76</u>, 1497 (1954). Bromine-BrF_3.

(133)   Flaschner, O., <u>J</u>. <u>Chem</u>. <u>Soc</u>., <u>95</u>, 668 (1909).
        Pyridine derivatives.

(134)   Flaschner, O., <u>Z</u>. <u>physik</u>. <u>Chem</u>., <u>62</u>, 493 (1908).
        Piperidine.

(135)   Flaschner, O., McEwen, B. C., <u>J</u>. <u>Chem</u>. <u>Soc</u>.,
        <u>93</u>, 1000 (1908). Methylpiperidine.

(136) Flaschner, O., Rankin, I. G., <u>Monatsh</u>, <u>31</u>, 36 (1910); through ref. 392 (pp. 471,473,477,481,518,539,586,630). Aromatic acids.

(137) Fontein, F., <u>Z</u>. <u>physik</u>. <u>Chem</u>., <u>73</u>, 212 (1910). Isoamyl alcohol.

(138) Francis, A. W., <u>Ind</u>. <u>Eng</u>. <u>Chem</u>., <u>33</u>, 554 (1941). Aniline-Paraffins.

(139) <u>Ibid</u>., <u>36</u>, 764 (1944); quoted in ref. 296 (pp. 144-7); ref. 393, 445, 446. Nonaromatic hydrocarbons.

(140) <u>Ibid</u>., <u>36</u>, 1096 (1944); quoted in ref. 296 (pp. 148-50); ref. 393, 445, 446. Cyclic hydrocarbons.

(140A) <u>Ibid</u>., <u>45</u>, 2789 (1953). Isopycnics, Iso-optics.

(141) Francis, A. W., <u>Ind</u>. <u>Eng</u>. <u>Chem</u>., <u>Anal</u>. Ed., <u>15</u>, 447 (1943) <u>Natl</u>. <u>Petroleum News</u>, <u>35</u>, 35R, 418 (1943); <u>Petroleum Refiner</u>, <u>23</u>, 109 (1944); U.S. Patent 2,303,265 (1942). <u>o</u>-Nitrotoluene.

(142) Francis, A. W., <u>J</u>. <u>Am</u>. <u>Pharm</u> <u>Assn</u>., <u>30</u>, 229 (1941); <u>Chem</u>. <u>Abstr</u>., <u>35</u>, 8207. Camphor-Phenols.

(143) Francis, A. W., <u>J</u>. <u>Chem</u>. <u>Eng</u>. <u>Data</u>, <u>5</u>, 534 (1960). $C_{19}F_{36}$, Ammonia.

(144) Francis, A. W., <u>J</u>. <u>Phys</u>., <u>Chem</u>., <u>56</u>, 510 (1952). Nitromethane.

(145) <u>Ibid</u>., <u>58</u>, 1099 (1954). Carbon dioxide, Various.

(146) <u>Ibid</u>., <u>60</u>, 20 (1956). Ethylene glycol, Nitroparaffins, Higher alcohols.

(147) <u>Ibid</u>., <u>62</u>, 579 (1958). Hydrogen halides.

(148) <u>Ibid</u>., <u>63</u>, 753 (1959). Hydrogen cyanide.

(149) Francis, A. W., in "<u>Physical Chemistry of the Hydrocarbons</u>", A. Farkas, ed., Vol. I, pp. 273-300, Academic Press, New York, 1950. Hydrocarbons.

(150) Francis, A. W., U. S. Patent 2,402,954 (1946). Methanol, Carbitol.

(151) **Francis, A. W., Unpublished observations in this laboratory. Various.**

(152) Francis, A. W., King, W. H., in "<u>Advances in Petroleum Chemistry and Refining</u>", K. A. Kobe and J. J. McKetta, Jr., eds. Vol. I. pp. 452-6, Interscience, New York, 1958. Various.

(153) Francis, A. W., King, W. H., in "<u>Chemistry of the Petroleum Hydrocarbons</u>", B. T. Brooks and others, eds., Vol. I, pp. 218-26, Reinhold, New York, 1954. Various.

(153A) Frankland, P. F., Farmer, R. C., <u>J</u>. <u>Chem</u>. <u>Soc</u>., <u>79</u>, 1361 (1901). Bromine-Nitrogen dioxide.

(153B)   Franklin, E. C., Kraus, C. A., Am. Chem. J., 20, 820
         (1898). Ammonia.

(154)   Freed, M., Trans. Roy. Soc. Canada, Sect. III, 27, 179
         (1933). Methanol.

(155)   Freeman, P. I., Rowlinson, J. S., Polymer (London) I,
         20 (1960). Ethane-Polymers.

(156)   Freund, M., Petroleum Z., 35, 297 (1939); through ref.
         12. Aniline-High paraffins.

(157)   Friedlander, J., Z. physik. Chem., 38, 389 (1901).
         Isobutyric acid.

(158)   Garland, F. M., Hoerr, C. W., Pool, W. O., Ralston, A.
         W., J. Org. Chem., 8, 344 (1943). High ketones.

(159)   Garner, F. H., J. Inst. Petroleum Technol., 14, 715
         (1928). Aniline.

(160)   Garner, F. H., Evans, E. B., Ibid., 18, 762 (1932).
         Aniline-Naphthenes.

(161)   Garner, F. H., Wilkinson, R., Nash, A. W., J. Soc.
         Chem. Ind., 51, 265T (1932). Aniline-Olefins.

(162)   Gillam, N. W., Australian Chem. Inst. J. and Proc.,
         11, 67 (1944); Chem. Abstr., 38, 3806. Aniline-Aromatics.

(162A)   Gillis, J., Delaunois, A., Rec. trav. chim., 53, 186
         (1934). Dioxane-Water.

(163)   Glasgow, A. R., Jr., J. Research Natl. Bur. Standards,
         24, 509 (1940). Aniline-Paraffins, Naphthenes.

(163A)   Glockler, G., Fuller, D. L., Roe, C. P., J. Chem. Phys.,
         1, 714 (1933). Krypton.

(164)   Goheen, G. E., J. Am. Chem. Soc., 63, 748 (1941).
         Aniline-Bicyclic naphthenes.

(165)   Gordon, N. S., Reid, E. E., J. Phys. Chem., 26, 773
         (1922). Lower Fatty acids.

(166)   Greenish, H. G., Smith, F.A.U., Pharm. J. (London) 71,
         881 (1903); through ref. 392 (pp.379,678). Camphor,
         Olive Oil.

(167)   Griengl, F., Steyskal, F., Steyskal, K., Monatsh. Chem.,
         63, 394 (1933); Chem. Abstr., 28, 3292. Sodium.

(167A)   Griswold, W., Klecka, M. E., West, R. V., Chem. Eng.
         Progress, 44, 839 (1948). Furfural.

(168)   Grimme, C., Seifensieder Ztg., 46, 358, 379 (1919); Chem.
         Abstr., 14, 1054; through ref. 392 (p.830). Diethylamine.

(168A)   Guempel, O., Bull. soc. chim. Belg., 38, 443 (1929);
         through ref. 277B (p.737). Ether-Water.

(168B)   Gunther, P., Peiser, M., Z. physik. Chem., 128, 189
         (1927). Camphor-Phenol.

(169)   Guthrie, F., _Phil_. Mag., (5) _18_, 22, 105 (1884); _Brit_. _Chem_. _Abstr_., _1885_, 337-339. Triethylamine.

(169A) _Ibid_., 495. Diethylamine.

(170)   Halban, H. v., _Z_. _physik_. _Chem_., _84_, 144 (1913). p-Nitrobenzyl chloride.

(171)   Hall, N. F., Wentzel, H. R., Smith, T., _J_. _Am_. _Chem_. _Soc_. _56_, 1822 (1934). Deuterium oxide.

(172)   Hammick, D. L., Holt, W. E., _J_. _Chem_. _Soc_., _1926_, 1995. Sulfur-Hydrocarbons.

(173)   _Ibid_., _1927_, 493. Sulfur-Benzoic acid.

(174)   Hammick, D. L., Howard, J., _Ibid_., _1932_, 2915. Carbon disulfide.

(175)   Hartenberg, W., Thesis, Brussels, (1926); through ref. 392 (pp. 169,180,433,457,559,563). o-Toluidine.

(176)   Hennaut-Roland, Mme., _Bull_. _soc_. _chim_. _Belg_., _42_, 80 (1933); _Chem_. _Abstr_., _27_, 3920; data given in ref. 392 (p.312) o-Nitrotoluene.

(177)   Herz, W., Rathmann, W., _Z_. _Elektrochem_., _19_, 553, 887 (1913); through ref. 392 (pp. 584, 634). Phenylacetic acid.

(178)   Herz, W., Schuftan, P., _Z_. _physik_. _Chem_., _101_, 284 (1922). Lower alcohols-Dicyclics.

(179)   Hickman, J. B., _J_. _Am_. _Chem_. _Soc_., _77_, 6154 (1955). Perfluoro-n-heptane.

(180)   Hicks-Bruun, M., Bruun, J. H., _J_. _Research_ _Natl_. _Bur_. _Standards_, _8_, 534 (1932). Aniline-Heptane.

(181)   Hildebrand, J. H., _J_. _Am_. _Chem_. _Soc_., _59_, 2083 (1937). Iodine.

(181A) Hildebrand, J. H., _Discussions_, _Faraday Soc_., _15_, 9 (1953). Stannic iodide, Perfluoroheptane.

(182)   Hildebrand, J. H., "_Solubility_ _of_ _Nonelectrolytes_", 2nd ed., (pp. 147-9), Reinhold, New York, 1939, Various.

(183)   Hildebrand, J. H., Alder, B. J., Beams, J. W., Dixon, H. H., _J_. _Phys_. _Chem_., _58_, 578 (1954). Fluorocarbons.

(184)   Hildebrand, J. H., Buehrer, T. F., _J_. _Am_. _Chem_. _Soc_., _42_, 2216 (1920). Various.

(185)   Hildebrand, J. H., Cochran, D.R.F., _Ibid_., _71_, 24 (1949). Fluorocarbons.

(186)   Hildebrand, J. H., Fisher, B. B., Benesi, H. A., _Ibid_., _72_, 4348 (1950). Fluorocarbons.

(187)   Hildebrand, J. H., Negishi, G. R., _Ibid_., _59_, 339 (1937). Stannic iodide.

(188)   Hildebrand, J. H., Scott, R. L., "Solubility of Nonelectrolytes", 3rd ed., Reinhold, New York, 1950. Various.

(189)   Hildebrand, J. H., Wachter, A., J. Am. Chem. Soc., 57, 870 (1935). Stannic iodide, Phosphorus.

(190)   Hill, A. E., Malisoff, W. M., Ibid., 48, 918 (1926). Phenol.

(191)   Hixson, A. W., Bockelmann, J. B., Trans. Am. Inst. Chem. Engrs., 38, 891 (1942). Propane, Glycerides.

(192)   Hixson, A. W., Hixson, A. N., Ibid., 37, 927 (1941). Propane-Fatty acids.

(193)   Hobson, R. W., Hartman, R. J., Kanning, E. W., J. Am. Chem. Soc., 63, 2094 (1941). Dipropylamine.

(193A) Hodgman, C. D., Editor, Handbook of Chemistry and Physics. Chemical Rubber Publishing Co., Cleveland, Ohio, 42nd Edition (1960-1). Various.

(194)   Hoerr, C. W., Binkerd, E. F., Pool, W. O., Halston, A. W., J. Org. Chem, 9, 68 (1944). Nitriles.

(194A) Hoerr, C. W., Harwood, H. J., Ibid., 16, 771 (1951). Haloalkanes.

(194B) Ibid., 779. n-Hexane.

(195)   Hoerr, C. W., Harwood, H. J., J. Phys. Chem., 56, 1068 (1952). Oleic acids.

(196)   Hoerr, C. W., Harwood, H. J., Ralston, A. W., J. Org. Chem., 9, 201 (1944). Secondary amines.

(196A) Ibid., 267 (1944). Primary alcohols.

(197)   Hoerr, C. W., Ralston, A. W., Ibid., 9, 329 (1944). Fatty acids.

(197A) Hoerr, C. W., Reck, R. A., Corcoran, G. B., Harwood, H. J., J. Phys. Chem., 59, 457 (1955). Methylalkyl Ketones.

(198)   Hoerr, C. W., Sedgwick, R. S., Ralston, A. W., J. Org. Chem., 11, 603 (1946). Fatty acids.

(199)   Holleman, L. W. J., Jong, H. G. B. de, Rec. trav. chim., 59, 1055 (1940). Novocaine salts.

(200)   Hoog, H., Smittenberg, J., Visser, G. H., Second World Petroleum Congress, Paris, Vol. 2, Sect. 2, 495 (1937); data given in ref. 100. Aniline-Paraffins.

(200A) Hovorka, F., Schaefer, R. A., Dreisbach, D., J. Am. Chem. Soc., 58, 2264 (1936). Dioxane.

(201)   Howard, E. J., Patterson, W. H., J. Chem. Soc., 1926, 2787. Ethyl alcohol-Paraffin oil.

(202) Howell, O. R., _Proc. Roy. Soc._, _A137_, 418 (1932). Phenol.

(203) Howes, D. A., _J. Inst. Petroleum Technol._, _16_, 75 (1930). Aniline-Hydrocarbons.

(204) Howes, D. A., _Ibid._, _19_, 319 (1933). Methanol, Aniline.

(206) Hrynowkowski, K., Adamanis, F., _Bull. soc. chim._, (4) _53_, 1168 (1933). Phenacetin, Urea.

(207) Hrynowkowski, K., Staszewski, H., Szmyt, M., _Z. physik. Chem._, _178_, 293 (1937). Urea, Resorcinol, Sulfur.

(208) Hrynowkowski, K., Szmyt, M., _Ibid._, _181_, 113 (1937). Urea, Sulfonal.

(208A) Hudson, C. S., _Z. physik. Chem._, _47_, 113 (1904). Nicotine.

(209) "_International Critical Tables_", Vol. III., pp. 387-398, Mc Graw-Hill, New York, 1928, Various.

(210) _Ibid._, Vol. IV, pp. 23-44, 100, 123-143, 154-5, 186-205 (1929). Various.

(211) Jackson, W. M., Drury, J. S., _Ind. Eng. Chem._, _51_, 1491 (1959). (Table VIII); reproduced in Ref. 193A, pp. 1504-7.

(212) Jaeger, A., _Brennstoff-Chem._, _4_, 260 (1923); _Chem. Abstr._ _18_, 459. Water-Aromatic hydrocarbons.

(213) Jänecke, E., _Z. Elektrochem._, _35_, 718 (1929). Ammonia.

(214) Jänecke, E., _Z. physik. Chem._, _164_, 401 (1933). Iso-butyl alcohol.

(215) _Ibid._, _184_, 59 (1939). Formamide.

(216) Jasper, J. J., Pohrt, H. E., _J. Chem. Ed._, _26_, 485, (1949). 2-Chloroethanol.

(217) Jenkins, A. C., DiPaolo, F. S., Birdsall, C. M., _J. Chem. Phys._, _23_, 2049 (1955). Oxygen-Ozone.

(218) Johnson, G. C., Unpublished observations in this laboratory. Glycols-Benzene.

(219) Johnson, G. C., Francis, A. W., _Ind. Eng. Chem._, _46_, 1662 (1954). Diethylene glycol.

(219A) Jolley, J. E., Hildebrand, J. H., _J. Phys. Chem._, _61_, 791 (1937). Fluorine Compounds.

(220) Jones, D. C., _J. Chem. Soc._, _123_, 1374 (1923). Acetic acid.

(221) _Ibid._, _1929_, 799. _n_-Butyl alcohol, Isobutyric acid.

(222) Jones, D. C., Amstell, S., _Ibid._, _1930_, 1316. Methanol.

(223) Jones, D. C., Betts, H. F., _Ibid._, _1928_, 1180. Acetic anhydride.

(224)   Jones, W. J., Speakman, J. B., J. Am. Chem. Soc.,
        43, 1869 (1921). Dimethylpyridine.

(225)   Jong, H. G. B. de, Holleman, L. W. J., Proc. Acad., Sci.
        Amsterdam, 40, 69 (1937); through ref. 392, pp. 730. Cf.
        ref. 199. Novocaine salts.

(226)   Joukovski, N. I., Bull. soc. chim. Belg., 43, 397 (1934);
        through ref. 392, pp. 10, 32. Acetonitrile, Formic acid,
        Nitromethane.

(227)   Ju, T. Y., Shen, G., Wood, C. E., J. Inst. Petroleum
        Technol., 26, 519 (1940). Aniline-Aromatics.

(228)   Ju, T. Y., Wood, C. E., Garner, F. H., Ibid., 28, 159
        (1942). Aniline-Aromatics.

(229)   Kaplan, S. I., Rabinowich, F. E., Zhur. Priklad, Khim.,
        21, 1163 (1948); through ref. 393, p. 753. Pyramidone.

(230)   Kendall, J., Crittenden, E. D., Miller, H. K., J. Am.
        Chem. Soc., 45, 963 (1923). Aluminum halides.

(231)   Kendall, J., Harrison, L. E., Trans. Faraday Soc.,
        24, 588 (1928); through ref. 392, p.223. Methyl
        oxalate.

(232)   Keyes, D. B., Hildebrand, J. H., J. Am. Chem. Soc.,
        39, 2126 (1917). Aniline-Hexane.

(233)   Klatt, W., Z. anorg. allgem. Chem., 234, 189 (1937).
        Hydrogen fluoride.

(233A) Klemenc, A., Spiess, T., Monatsh., 77, 216 (1947).
        Nitric acid-Nitrogen dioxide.

(234)   Klos, S., Neiman-Pilyat, E., Pilyat, S., J. Applied
        Chem., (U.S.S.R.) 13, 1369 (1940): through ref. 12.
        Aniline-High paraffins.

(234A) Knox, J., Richards, M. B., J. Chem. Soc., 115, 508
        (1919). Pyrogallol.

(234B) Kobe, K. A., Strong, J. P., Jr., J. Phys. Chem.,
        44, 629 (1940). Dioxane.

(235)   Koch, H., Steinbrink, H., Brennstoff-Chem., 19, 282
        (1938); through ref. 100. Aniline-Naphthenes and
        Aromatics.

(236)   Kohn, J. P., Kurata, F., Am. Inst. Chem. Engrs. J.,
        4, 211 (1958). Hydrogen sulfide-Methane.

(237)   Kohnstamm, P., Reeders, J. C., Proc. Roy. Acad. Sci.,
        Amsterdam, 14, 270 (1911-12); through ref. 365.
        Carbon dioxide-Nitrobenzene.

(238)   Kohnstamm, P., Timmermans, J., Proc. Koninkl. Acad.
        Wetenschap., 13, 865 (1911); Chem. Abstr., 5, 3532.
        Phenol, Nitrobenzene.

(239)   Konovalov, D., Ann. Phys., (4) 10, 375 (1903); through
        ref. 392, p.298. Aniline-Amylene.

(240)　Kracek, F. C., J. Phys. Chem., 35, 420 (1931). Iodine.

(241)　Kraus, C. A., Lucasse, W. W., J. Am. Chem. Soc.,
　　　　44, 1949 (1922). Sodium-Ammonia.

(242)　Kraus, C. A., Zeitfuchs, E. H., Ibid., 1249 (1922).
　　　　Ammonia-Xylene.

(242A)　Kremann, R., Monatsh., 28, 8, 895, 1125 (1907).
　　　　Nitrochlorobenzenes.

(243)　Kremann, R., Fritsch, J., Ibid., 41, 631 (1920)
　　　　through ref. 210, pp. 139, 141. Resorcinol, Pyrogallol.

(244)　Kremann, R., Mauermann, O., Müller, R., II, Rösler,
　　　　W., Ibid., 43, 321 (1922); through ref. 210, p. 143.
　　　　Phenylene diamines.

(245)　Kremann, R., Odelga, F., Zowadsky, O., Ibid., 42, 117
　　　　(1921); Chem. Abstr., 16, 89; through ref. 210, 139-43.
　　　　Dihydroxybenzenes.

(246)　Kremann, R., Petritschek, B., Ibid., 38, 385 (1917).
　　　　Urea-Dinitrobenzenes.

(246A)　Krishnan, R. S., Proc. Indian Acad. Sci., 1A, 915
　　　　(1935); Brit. Chem. Abstr. 1935¡A, 1200. Various.

(246B)　Ibid., 5A, 577-93 (1937); Chem. Abstr., 31, 8288.
　　　　Phenol.

(247)　Kruyt, H. R., Z. physik. Chem., 65, 486 (1909). Sulfur.

(247A)　Keunen, J. P., Phil. Mag., (6) 6, 642 (1903); through
　　　　ref. 371A. Propane-Methanol.

(247B)　Kuenen, J. P., (1897); through ref. 446. Ethyl alcohol-
　　　　Carbon disulfide.

(248)　Kuenen, J. P., Proc. Akad. sci. Amsterdam, 5, 473(1903);
　　　　Brit. Chem. Abstr., 84, ii, 410. Ethane.

(249)　Keunen, J. P., Ibid., 14, 644 (1912); Chem. Abstr.,
　　　　7, 2507. Butanes-Methanol, Ethyl alcohol.

(250)　Keunen, J. P., Robson, W. G., Z, physik. Chem., 28, 356,
　　　　(1899); Brit. Chem. Abstr., 76 ii, 356. Ether, Ethane.

(251)　Kume, T., Rev. Phys. Chem. Japan, 11, 22 (1937); through
　　　　ref. 392, p. 626. Benzoic acid.

(252)　Kyle, B. G., Reed, T. M. III, J. Am. Chem. Soc.,
　　　　80, 6170 (1958). Fluorine compounds.

(253)　Landolt-Börnstein-Roth-Scheel, "Tabellen", Julius
　　　　Springer, Berlin, Hauptwerke, pp. 751-761 (1923). Various.

(254)　Ibid., Erg. I, pp. 300-1 (1927). Various.

(255)　Ibid., Erg. IIa, pp. 397-402, 469-78 (1931). Various.

(256)　Ibid., Erg. IIIa, pp. 667-81 (1935). Various.

(256A) Lane, L. B., Ind. Eng. Chem., 17, 924 (1925). Water-
        Glycerol.

(257)   Larsen, R. G., Thorpe, R. E., Armfield, F. A., Ind. Eng.
        Chem., 34, 186 (1942). Aniline-Naphthenes, Aromatics.

(258)   Lattey, R. T., Phil. Mag., (6) 10, 398 (1905); through
        ref. 392, p. 278. Diethylamine.

(259)   Lazzell, C. L., Johnston, J., J. Phys. Chem., 32, 1331
        (1928). Aminobenzoic acids.

(260)   Lecat, M., Ann. soc. sci. Bruxelles, 45B, 169 (1926);
        Chem. Abstr., 22, 3561; Chem. Zentr., 1927 I 2282-3.
        Ethylene glycol.

(261)   Ibid., 289 (1926) (same abstract ref.). Acetamide.

(262)   Ibid., 47B, 108 (1927); through ref. 255, pp. 476-8.
        Ethylene glycol.

(263)   Ibid., 149 (1927); through ref. 255. Acetamide, Prop-
        ionamide.

(264)   Ibid., 49B, 17 (1929); through ref. 255. Acetamide,
        Phenylacetic acid.

(265)   Ibid., 109 (1929); through ref. 255. Acetamide, Bromo-
        naphthalene.

(266)   Ibid., 50B, 21 (1930); through ref. 256. Nitromethane.

(267)   Lecat, M., Compt. rend. 222, 734 (1946). Ethanolamine,
        Diethylene glycol.

(268)   Lecat, M., J. chim. phys., 27, 75 (1930); Chem. Abstr.,
        24, 3154; Data given in ref. 256, pp. 678-80. Aceta-
        mide, Ethylene glycol.

(268A) Lecat, M., Rec. trav. chim., 45, 623 (1926). Methanol.

(269)   Ibid., 46, 240 (1927). Ethylene glycol, Phenol.

(270)   Ibid., 47, 13 (1928). Acetamide, Ethylene glycol.

(271)   Lecat, M., "Tables Azeotropiques", Bruxelles, 1949.
        Various.

(272)   Lecat, M., Z. anorg. Chem., 186, 119 (1930); data
        given in ref. 256 and 392 (p. 157). Ethylene glycol,
        Glycerol.

(273)   Leone, P., Angelescu, E., Gazz. chim. ital., 52 II, 61
        (1922); Chem. Abstr., 17, 662. Phenol.

(274)   Leone, P., Benelli, M., Ibid., 75 (1922); Chem. Abstr.,
        17, 662. Epichlorohydrin.

(275)   Leopold, G. H., Z. physik. Chem., 71, 65 (1910). HCl-
        Aniline.

(276)   Leslie, R. T., J. Research Natl. Bur. Standards,
        13, 595 (1934). Sulfur dioxide.

(277)   Lespieau, R., Wakeman, R. L., Bull. soc. chim.,
        (4) 51, 396 (1932). Aniline, Phenol, Nitrobenzene.

(277A) Lien, A. P., Mc Caulay, D. A.,Evering, B. L., Ind. Eng.
        Chem., 41, 2698 (1949). HF-Mercaptans.

(277B) Linke, W. F., Solubilities of Inorganic and Metal Organic
        Compounds, 4th Ed., Van Nostrand, New York, 1958. Various.

(278)   Lloyd, B. A., Thompson, S. O., Ferguson, J. B., Can. J.
        Research, 15B, 98 (1937). Ethyl acetate, Furfural.

(278A) Lobry de Bruyn, C. A., Z. physik. Chem., 10, 784 (1892)
        Diphenylamine.

(278B) Long, J. R., Dissertation, Ohio State Univ., 1938;
        through ref. 12, 100. Aniline-2-Octenes.

(279)   Louise, E., Compt. rend., 150, 526 (1910); Chem. Abstr.,
        4, 1368. Aniline-Turpentine.

(280)   Lowry, T. M., Lemon, J. T., J. Chem. Soc., 1936, 5, 9.
        Nitrogen oxides.

(281)   Lozovoi, A. V., D'yakova, M. K., Stepantsevo, T. G.,
        J. Gen. Chem., (U.S.S.R.) 9, 540 (1939); through ref.
        445, p. 542. Aniline-Naphthenes.

(282)   Luderman, C. G., Ind. Eng. Chem., Anal. Ed., 12, 446
        (1940). Aniline, Butanes, Isobutene.

(283)   Maass, O., Boomer, E. H., J. Am. Chem. Soc., 44, 1721
        (1922). Ethylene oxide.

(283A) Maass, O., McIntosh, D., Ibid., 34, 1284 (1912). HBr-
        Methanol.

(284)   McClure, H. B., Ind. Eng. Chem., News Ed., 17, 152
        (1939); quoted in ref. 296, p. 526. Glycol derivatives.

(285)   McCombie, H., Scarborough, H. A., Smith, F. F. P.,
        J. Chem. Soc., 1927, 802. Nitrobenzyl chlorides.

(286)   McEwen, B. C., Ibid., 123, 2279 (1923). Glycerol-
        Ketones, Benzaldehyde.

(287)   Ibid., 2284 (1923). Glycerol-Alcohols, Aldehydes,
        Phenols.
(288)   McKelvy, E. C., Simpson, D. H., J. Am. Chem. Soc.,
        44, 115 (1922). Carbon disulfide-Methanol.

(289)   Mair, B. J., Willingham, C. B., Streiff, A. J., J.
        Research Natl. Bur. Standards, 21, 599 (1938). Aniline.

(290)   Maman, A., Compt. rend., 198, 1324 (1934). Nitrobenzene,
        Benzyl alcohol, Aniline-Hexanes.

(291)   Ibid., 205, 320 (1937). Aniline-Octanes.

(292)   Ibid., 207, 1401 (1938). Aniline-Octanes.

(293)   Maman, A., Pub. sci. tech. ministere air (France)
        No. 66, 55pp. (1935). Chem. Abstracts, 30, 7095.
        (olefin names inaccurate in abstract). Nitrobenzenes-
        n-Paraffins.

(294)   Marvel, C. S., Glavis, F. J., J. Am. Chem. Soc., 60, 2622 (1938). Sulfur dioxide-1-Pentene.

(294A) Maryott, A. A., J. Am. Chem. Soc., 63, 3079 (1941). Carbon disulfide-Ethyl alcohol.

(295)   Mazee, W. A., Report 8975 from Phillips Petroleum Co., U.S. TOM Mis. Reel 79. Aniline-$C_{34}H_{70}$.

(296)   Mellan, I., "Industrial Solvents", Reinhold, New York, 1950. Various.

(297)   Menshutkin, B. N., Mem. St. Petersburg Poly. Inst., 5, 355 (1906); through ref. 391, p. 973. MgI_2-Ether.

(298)   Ibid., 13, 1, 263, 411, 505 (1910); 14, 251 (1911); 15, 793 (1911); through ref. 210, pp. 191, 195, and ref. 391, pp. 1471-2. Antimony halides.

(299)   Menshutkin, B. N., Z. anorg. allgem. Chem., 49, 34 (1906); through ref. 209, p. 394, and ref. 210, p. 204. MgI_2-Ether.

(300)   Ibid., 49, 207 (1906); through ref. 210, p. 203, and ref. 391, p. 937. $MgBr_2$-Ether.

(301)   Ibid., 53, 26 (1907); through ref. 210, p. 204. MgI_2-Acetal, Methylal.

(302)   Ibid., 61, 100 (1909); through ref. 210, p. 204, and ref. 391, p. 974. MgI_2-Methyl acetate.

(303)   Mertzlin, R. V., Ust-Kachkintzev, V. F., J. Gen. Chem. (U.S.S.R.) 5, 904 (1935); Chem. Abstr., 30, 943. Aniline, Phenyl hydrazine.

(304)   Michels, A., Arch. neerl. Sci. Ex. et Nat., (3) A6, 127, (1922); Chem. Abstr., 16, 4118. Isobutyl alcohol.

(305)   Michels, A., ten Haaf, E.C.F., Proc. Akad. Sci. (Amsterdam) 30, 52 (1927); through ref. 392, p. 547. Cresols.

(306)   Michels, A., ten Haaf, E.C.F., Verslag Akad. Wetenschappen (Amsterdam) 35, 1050 (1926); Chem. Abstr., 21, 1583. Cresols.

(307)   Mikeska, L. A., Ind. Eng. Chem., 28, 970 (1936). Aniline--High hydrocarbons.

(308)   Miller, O., Bull. soc. chim. Belg., 44, 513 (1935); Chem. Abstr., 30, 2180. Aniline-Dimethylcyclohexanes.

(309)   Miller, V. A., Anal. Chem., 17, 6 (1945). Heptanes.

(310)   Ibid., 566 (1945). Hexanes.

(311)   Miller, V. A., Private communication (1945); data given in ref. 149. Isooctane.

(312)   Moles, E., Jimeno, E., Anales Soc. espan. fis. quim., 11, 393 (1913); through ref. 392, p. 121. Acetamide.

(313)   Mondain-Monval, P., Compt. rend., 183, 1104 (1926). Methanol-Cyclohexane.

(314) Compt. rend., 205, 1154 (1937). Aniline, Nitrobenzene.

(315) Mondain-Monval, P., Quiquerez, J., Bull. soc. chim.,
       (5) 11, 26 (1944); Chem. Abstr., 39, 8. Aniline-
       Nitrobenzene.

(316) Ibid., 12, 380 (1945); Chem. Abstr., 40, 270. Nitro-
       benzene.

(317) Moore, R. J., Morrell, J., Egloff, G., Met. Chem. Eng.,
       18, 396 (1918); data given in ref. 393, p. 1068.
       Sulfur dioxide.

(318) Mortimer, F. S., J. Am. Chem. Soc., 45, 633 (1923).
       Various.

(319) Mukhin, G. E., Mukhina, A. A., Ukrainskii Khem. Zhur.,
       5, Sci. pt. 251 (1930); Chem. Zentr., 1931, I, 3434.
       Ethylene glycol-Esters.

(320) Mulliken, S. P., Wakeman, R. L., Ind. Eng. Chem., Anal.
       Ed., 7, 276 (1935). Quoted in ref. 296 p. 242.
       Nitromethane.

(321) Mulliken. S. P., Wakeman, R. L., Rec. trav. chim.,
       54, 367 (1935). Nitromethane, Aniline, Benzyl alcohol
       Ethyl sulfate.

(321A) Negishi, G. R., Donnally, L. H., Hildebrand, J. H.,
       J. Am. Chem. Soc., 55, 4793 (1933). Iodine.

(322) Neyman-Pilyat, E., Pilyat, S., Ind. Eng. Chem.,
       33, 1382 (1941). Aniline-High aromatics.

(322A) Norro, A., Lundquist, S., Jernkontorets Ann.,
       130, 118 (1946); Chem. Abstr., 41, 3358c. Iron-Sulfur.

(322B) Olivari, F., Atti. accad. Lincei, 20, I, 474 (1911);
       through ref. 210, p. 34. Iodine.

(323) Ormandy, W. R., Craven, E. C., J. Inst. Petroleum
       Technol., 12, 89 (1926). Aniline.

(324) Orton, K. J. P., Jones, D. C., J. Chem. Soc.,
       115, 1060 (1919). Water, Acetic acid-Aromatics

(325) Ibid., 1194 (1919). Butyl alcohols.

(325A) Ottenweller, J. H., Hollaway, C., Jr., Weinrich, W.,
       Ind. Eng. Chem., 35, 207 (1943). HCl-Butane.

(326) Page, J. M., Buchler, C. C., Diggs, S. H., Ind. Eng.
       Chem., 25, 419 (1933). Chlorex, Acetone, Nitrobenzene-
       Lube oil.

(327) Palit, S. R., Mc Bain, J. W., Ibid., 38, 741 (1946).
       Propylene glycol.

(328) Parvatiker, R. R., Mc Ewen, B. C., J. Chem. Soc.,
       125, 1484 (1924). Glycerol.

(329) Pascal, P., Bull. soc. chim. (4) 27, 406 (1920).
       Trinitronaphthalenes.

(329A)   Pascal, P., Garnier, M., Ibid., (4), 25, 315 (1919).
         Nitric acid-Nitrogen dioxide.

(330)   Pasquinelli, E. A., Trans. Faraday Soc., 53, 935 (1957).
         Various.

(331)   Patterson, W. H., J. Chem. Soc., 1938, 1559. Deuterium
         oxide-Butyric acids.

(332)   Peiker, A. L., Coffin, C. C., Can. J. Research, 8, 114
         (1933). Hydrogen cyanide.

(333)   Pennington, E. N., Marwil, S. J., Ind. Eng. Chem.,
         45, 1371 (1953). Furfural.

(333A)   Petrov, A. D., Bull. acad. Sci. (U.S.S.R.), Classe sci.
         chim., 1941 533; through ref. 12 and 100. Aniline-
         Naphthalenes.

(334)   Petrov, A. D., Andreev, D. N., J. Gen. Chem. (U.S.S.R.),
         12, 95 (1942); Chem. Abstr., 37, 2006. Aniline-
         Bicyclics.

(335)   Petrov, A. D., Chel'tsova, M. A., Ibid., 87 (1942);
         Chem. Abstr. 37, 1993. Aniline-Naphthenes.

(336)   Petrov, A. D., Kaplan, E. P., Ibid., 99 (1942); Chem.
         Abstr., 37, 1984. Aniline-High paraffins.

(337)   Picon, M., Compt. rend., 198, 926 (1934); data given in
         ref. 392, p. 808. Quinone iodobismuthate.

(337A)   Piekara, A., Phys. Rev., 42, 448 (1932). Nitrobenzene.

(338)   Pleuger, G., Physik. Z., 26, 167 (1925); through ref.
         392, p. 536. Benzamide.

(338A)   Poffenberger, N., Horsley, L. H., Nutting, H. S.,
         Britton, E. C., Trans. Am. Inst. Chem. Engrs., 42, 820
         (1946). Ammonia-1-Butene.

(339)   Pollock, D. L., Collett, A. R., Lazzell, C. L.,
         J. Phys. Chem., 50, 23 (1946). Acet-p-toluide.

(339A)   Ponomarev, K. K., J. Gen. Chem. (U.S.S.R.), 8, 544
         (1938); through ref. 393, p. 1086. Glycerol-Acetic
         anhydride.

(340)   Poole, J. W., and coauthors., Ind. Eng. Chem., 21, 1099
         (1929). Lube oils.

(341)   Ibid., 23, 170 (1931). Lube oils.

(341A)   Poppe, G., Bull. soc. chim. Belg., 44, 640 (1935);
         Chem. Abstr., 30, 2826. Deuterium oxide, Glycerol.

(341B)   Poppe, G., (1934-5); through ref. 445, 446. Various.

(342)   Powney, J., Addison, C. C., Trans. Faraday Soc.,
         34, 627 (1938). Ricinoleic acid.

(342A)   Prins., A., Proc. Acad. Sci., Amsterdam, 17, 1095(1915);
         through ref. 445, p. 41. Ethane.

(343) Prins, H. J., Rec. trav. chim., 42, 25 (1928). Petroleum
       ethers.

(344) Quantie, C., Proc. Roy. Soc., A224, 90 (1954). Aniline-
       Cyclohexane.

(345) Ralston, A. W., Hoerr, C. W., J. Org. Chem., 7, 546
       (1942). Fatty acids.

(346) Ralston, A. W., Hoerr, C. W., Crews, L. T., Ibid.,
       9, 319 (1944). n-Hydrocarbons.

(347) Ralston, A. W., Hoerr, C. W., DuBrow, P. L., Ibid., 259
       (1944). Tri-n-alkylamines.

(348) Ralston, A. W., Hoerr, C. W., Pool, W. O., Ibid., 8, 473
       (1943). Amides.

(349) Ralston, A. W., Hoerr, C. W., Pool, W. O., Harwood, H. J.,
       Ibid., 9, 102 (1944). Primary amines.

(350) Rao, R. K., Krishna, M. G., Zaheer, S. H., Arnold, L. K.,
       J. Am. Oil Chem. Soc., 32, 420 (1955). Ethyl alcohol-
       Vegetable oils.

(351) Rebert, C. J., Kay, W. B., Am. Inst. Chem. Engrs. J.,
       5, 285 (1959). Water-Benzene.

(352) Reinders, W., de Minjer, C. H., Rec. trav. chim.,
       66, 564 (1947). Formic acid-m-Xylene.

(353) Rheinboldt, H., Kircheisen, M., J. prakt. Chem., (ii)
       112, 187 (1926); Brit. Chem. Abstr., 1926A, 476. Picric
       acid, Phenylene diamines, Urea.

(354) Rice, H. T., Lieber, E., Ind. Eng. Chem., Anal. Ed.,
       16, 107 (1944). Furfural.

(355) Rice, O. K., J. Chem. Phys., 23, 164 (1955). Aniline-
       Cyclohexane.

(356) Riesenfeld, E. H., Schwab, G. M., Ber., 55, 2096 (1922).
       Oxygen-Ozone.

(357) Roberts, L. D., Mayer, J. L., J. Chem. Phys., 9, 852
       (1941). Triethylamine.

(358) Roof, J. G., Crawford, N. W., Jr., J. Phys. Chem.,
       62, 1138 (1958). Isobutane-Phenanthrene.

(359) Roozeboom, H. W. B., Z. physik. Chem., 2, 457 (1888).
       Hydrogen bromide.

(360) Rose, F. W., Jr., White, J. D., J. Research Natl. Bur.
       Standards, 15, 160 (1935). Aniline-Ethylcyclohexane.

(361) Rotariu, G. J., Hanrahan, R. J., Fruin, R. E., J. Am.
       Chem. Soc., 76, 3752 (1954). Perfluorotributylamine.

(362) Rothmund, V., Z. physik. Chem., 26, 457, 475 (1898).
       Triethylamine, Phenol.

362A) Rousset, A., Ann. phys., (11) 5, 5 (1936); through
       ref. 446. Aniline-Turpentine.

(362B)   Rousset, A., Compt. rend., 198, 2152 (1934). Isobutyric acid.

(363)   Rowden, R. W., Rice, O. K., J. Chem. Phys., 19, 1423 (1951). Aniline-Cyclohexane.

(364)   Rowley, H. H., J. Am. Chem. Soc., 58, 1337 (1936).MgBr$_2$-Ether.

(365)   Rowlinson, J. S., "Liquids and Liquid Mixtures", Academic Press, New York, pp. 171-185, 232, 234, 241. Various.

(366)   Rowlinson, J. S., Freeman, P. I., Manchester, England, **Preliminary Report to A.P.I. Project 42 at Pennsylvania State Univ. (1959); data released by permission of Professor Rowlinson. Ethane.**

(366A)   Rudd, De F. P., Widom, B., J. Chem. Phys., 33, 1816 (1960). Glycol butyl ether-Water.

(367)   Ruff, O., Zedner, J., Ber. 41, 1958 (1908). Ammonia.

(368)   Rupert, F. F., J. Am. Chem. Soc., 31, 851 (1909). Hydrogen chloride.

(368A)   Ibid., 32, 748 (1910). Ammonia-Water.

(369)   Rutledge, G. P., Jarey, R. L., Davis, W., Jr., J. Phys. Chem., 57, 541 (1953). Hydrogen fluoride.

(370)   Rysselberge, M. van, Bull. soc. chim. Belg., 35, 311 (1926); through ref. 12. Aniline-Dimethylcyclopentane.

(371)   Sachanen, A. N., Tilicheev, M. D., "Chemistry and Technology of Cracking", translated into English by A. A. Boehtlingk, D. F. Brown, K. T. Steik, Chemical Catalog Co., New York, pp. 177, 180 (1932). Aniline.

(371A)   Sage, B. H., Lacey, W. N., "Volumetric and Phase Behavior of Hydrocarbons," Gulf, Houston, Texas 1949, p. 118. Propane-Methanol.

(372)   Sample, N. L., Bennett, C. O., Holcomb, D. E., Ind. Eng. Chem., Chem. Eng. Data Series, 1, 17 (1956).(Table VI).

(373)   Sapgir, S., Bull. soc. chim. Belg., 38, 392(1929); through ref. 149. Carbon disulfide, Acetone, Ethyl bromide.

(374)   Savorro, E., Atti. accad. sci., (Torino), 48, 948 (1914); Chem. Abstr., 8, 340. Methanol.

(375)   Scarpa, O., J. chim. physik., 2, 447 (1904). Phenol.

(376)   Schaarschmidt, A., Hofmeier, H., Leist, H., Z. angew. Chem., 43, 955 (1930); through ref. 392, p. 418. Aniline.

(377)   Scheffer, F.E.C., Z. physik. Chem., 84, 730 (1913). Ether.

(378)   Scheffer, F. E. C., Smittenberg, J., Rec. trav. chim., 51, 1008 (1932). Carbon dioxide, o-Xylidine.

(379) Rec. trav. chim., 52, 1 (1933). Carbon dioxide.

(380) Ibid., 607 (1933). Ethane.

(381) Ibid., 982 (1933). Ethane.

(382) Schiessler, R. W., Whitmore, F. C., and others, Ind. Eng.
       Chem., 47, 1660 (1955): Document 4597, Auxiliary Publ-
       ications Project, Library of Congress, Washington, D. C.
       Aniline, Furfural.

(383) Schiessler, R. W., Dixon, J. A., and others, "Properties
       of Hydrocarbons of High Molecular Weight", Research
       Project 42 of the A.P.I. at Pennsylvania State University,
       Sept., 1958. Published with the permission of the
       Director, Professor Dixon. Aniline, Furfural.

(384) Schlegal, H., J. chim. phys., 31, 517, 668 (1934); Chem.
       Abstr., 29, 1704, 2804. Aniline.

(385) Schoorl, N., de Weerd, F. N. B., Rec. trav. chim.,
       41, 15 (1922). Acetonitrile.

(386) Schoorl, N., Regenbogen, A., Rec. trav. chim., 41, 125
       (1922). Ethyl alcohol–CS_2.

(387) Schreinemakers, F. A. H., Z. physik. Chem., 23, 417
       (1897); 25, 543 (1898). Succinonitrile–Water.

(387A) Ibid., 27, 105 (1898). Succinonitrile-Ethyl alcohol.

(387B) Ibid., 29, 577 30, 460 (1899). Phenol, Aniline.

(387C) Ibid., 33, 78 (1900). Phenol–Water.

(388) Schultz-Sellock, C., Pogg. Ann., 139, 480 (1870);
       through ref. 70A, p. 907. SO_3– SO_2, CS_2.

(388A) Schwab, G. M., Z. physik., 110, 606 (1924). Oxygen-
       Ozone.

(389) Scott, R. L., J. Am. Chem. Soc., 70, 4090 (1948).
       Fluorine compounds.

(390) Scott, R. L., J. Phys. Chem., 62, 136 (1958). Fluorine
       compounds.

(390A) Sedgwick, R. S., Hoerr, C. W., Harwood, H. J., J. Org.
       Chem., 17, 327 (1952). Esters of Fatty acids.

(391) Seidell, A., "Solubilities of Inorganic and Metal
       Organic Compounds", Vol. I, Van Nostrand, New York, 1940.
       Various.

(392) Seidell, A., "Solubilities of Organic Compounds", Vol.
       II, Van Nostrand, New York, 1941. Various.

(393) Seidell, A., Linke, W. F., "Solubilities of Inorganic
       and Organic Compounds, Supplementary Volume"., Van
       Nostrand, New York, 1951. Various.

(393A) Selleck, F. T., Carmichael, L. T., Sage, B. H., Ind.
       Eng. Chem., 44, 2223 (1952). H_2S–Water.

(394) Semenchenko, V. K., Grachevo, S., Davuidovskaya, E. A., Kolloid Z., 68, 275 (1934); through ref. 392, pp. 53,672. Nicotine.

(395) Serwy, H., Bull. soc. chim. Belg., 42, 487 (1933); through ref. 392, p. 290. Glutaronitrile.

(396) Seyer, W. F., Ball, R. W., Trans. Roy. Soc. Canada, Sect. III, 19, 149 (1925); through ref. 392. p. 767. SO_2-Cetyl alcohol.

(396A) Seyer, W. F., Cornett, W. F., Ind. Eng. Chem., 29, 91 (1937). SO_2-Decalin.

(397) Seyer, W. F., Dunbar, V., Trans. Roy. Soc. Canada, Sect. III, 16, 307 (1922); Chem. Abstr., 17, 2072. SO_2-Cyclohexane.

(398) Seyer, W. F., Gallaugher, A. F., Ibid., 20, 343 (1926); Chem. Abstr., 21, 2592. SO_2-n-Octane.

(399) Seyer, W. F., Gill, A. F., Ibid., 18, 209 (1924); Chem. Abstr. 19, 917. SO_2-n-Hexane.

(400) Seyer, W. F., Hodnett, L., J. Am. Chem. Soc., 58, 997 (1936). SO_2-Caprylene.

(401) Seyer, W. F., Hugget, J. L., Trans. Roy. Soc. Canada, Sect. III, 18, 213 (1924); Chem. Abstr., 19, 917. SO_2-Cetane.

(402) Seyer, W. F., King, E. G., J. Am. Chem. Soc., 55, 3140 (1933). SO_2-Cyclohexene.

(403) Seyer, W. F., Todd, E., Ind. Eng. Chem., 23, 325 (1931). SO_2-Paraffins C_4 to C_{32}.

(404) Shepard, A. F., Henne, A. L., Midgley, T., J. Am. Chem. Soc., 53, 1948 (1931). Aniline-n-Paraffins.

(404A) Shultz, A. R., Flory, P. J., J. Am.Chem. Soc., 74, 4760 (1952). Polymers.

(405) Sidgwick, N. V., Aldous, W. M., J. Chem. Soc.,119, 1001 (1921). Nitrophenols.

(406) Sidgwick, N. V., Allott, E. N., Ibid., 123, 2819 (1923). Hydroxybenzaldehydes.

(407) Sidgwick, N. V., Callow, R. K., Ibid., 125, 525 (1924). Aminophenols.

(408) Sidgwick, N. V., Clayton, H., Ibid., 121, 2263 (1922). Aldehydobenzoic acids.

(409) Sidgwick, N. V., Dash. W. M., Ibid., 121, 2586 (1922). Nitrobenzaldehydes.

(410) Sidgwick, N. V., Ewbank, E. K., Ibid., 119, 979 (1921). Aromatic acids.

(411) Sidgwick, N. V., Neill, J. A., Ibid., 123, 2818 (1923). Phenylene diamines.

(412) Sidgwick, N. V., Pickford, P., Wilsdon, B. H., Ibid.,
       99, 1122 (1911). Aniline-Water.

(413) Sidgwick, N. V., Rubie, H. E., Ibid., 119,1013 (1921).
       Nitroanilines, Chloroanilines.

(414) Sidgwick, N. V., Spurrell, W. J., Davies, T. E., Ibid.,
       107, 1202 (1915). Nitrophenols, Cresols.

(415) Sidgwick, N. V., Sutton, L. E., Ibid., 1930, 1323.
       Cyclohexanol.

(416) Sidgwick, N. V., Taylor, T. W. J., Ibid., 121, 1853
       (1922). Dinitrophenols.

(417) Sidgwick, N. V., Turner, S. L., Ibid., 121, 2259 (1922).
       Chlorophenols.

(418) Siegelman, I., Paper presented before Inorganic Analy-
       tical Symposium, Univ. of Pennsylvania,.April 20, 1960.
       2-Butanone.

(418A) Siggia, S., Hanna, J. G., Anal. Chem., 21, 1086 (1949).
       Various.

(419) Simons, J. H., Dunlap, R. D., J. Chem. Phys., 18, 341
       (1950). Perfluoropentane.

(420) Simons, J. H., Mausteller, J. W., J. Chem. Phys.,
       20, 1516 (1952). Perfluorobutane.

(421) Skinner, D. A., Ind. Eng. Chem., 47, 225 (1955).Diethyl-
       ene glycol, Thiodipropionitrile.

(421A) Skrabel, A., Monatsh. Chem., 38, 25 (1917); through ref.
       392, p. 224. Methyl oxalate.

(422) Smirnov, V. I., Z. physik. Chem., 58, 674 (1907).
       Isobutyric acid.

(423) Smith, A., Holmes, W. B., Hall, E. S., J. Am. Chem. Soc.,
       27, 806 (1905); Z. physik. Chem., 52, 613 (1905).
       Sulfur-Hydrocarbons.

(423A) Smith, A. S., Braun, T. B., Ind. Eng. Chem., 37, 1047
       (1945). Furfural.

(424) Smith, R. A., Mikrochemie, 11, 227 (1931); Chem. Abstr.,
       26, 5233. Phenol.

(425) Speyers, C. L., Am. J. Sci., (4) 14, 294 (1902); data
       given in ref. 392, pp. 92, 202, 393, 560, 602, and
       ref. 210, p. 112. Chloral hydrate.

(426) Squires, through ref. 392, pp. 93, 678. Camphor, Chloral
       hydrate.

(427) Staveley, L. A. K., Tupman, W. I., Hart, K. R., Trans.
       Faraday Soc., 51, 340 (1955). Acetone-Carbon disulfide.

(428) Stevens, D. R., Nickels, J. E., Ind. Eng. Chem., Anal.
       Ed., 18, 260 (1946). Diethylene glycol-Phenols.

(429) Sunier, A. A., J. Phys. Chem., 34, 2589 (1930).
       Naphthalene.

(430)   Sweeney, W. J., Fenske, M. R., Cummings, G. H., U. S. Patent 2,396,299, (1941), Column 3b. Ammonia.

(431)   Szelenyi, G. v., Z. Elektrochem., 35, 34 (1929). o-Cresol.

(432)   Taylor, C. A., Rinkenbach, W. H., J. Am. Chem. Soc., 45, 44 (1923). Trinitrotoluene.

(432A) Taylor, W. W., Proc. Roy. Soc. Edinburgh, 49, Pt. 3, 198 (1928-9); Chem. Abstr., 23, 5082. Phenol.

(433)   Terres, E., Gebert, F., Hülsemann, H., Petereit, H., Toepsch, H., Ruppert, W., Brennstoff Chem., 36, 289 (1955). Phenols.

(434)   Terres, E., Rühl, G., Z. Angew. Chem., 47, 331 (1934); through ref. 256, p. 672. Phenols.

(435)   Thiry, R., Thesis, Brussels, 1925, through ref. 392, pp. 418, 457, 553, 559, 615. Toluidines.

(436)   Thompson, T. G., Black, J. H., Sohl, G. T., J. Am. Chem. Soc., 43, 877 (1921). Dichloroethyl sulfide.

(437)   Thompson, T. G., Odeen, H., J. Ind. Eng. Chem., 12, 1057 (1920). Dichloroethyl sulfide.

(438)   Thorp, N., Scott, R. L., J. Phys. Chem., 60, 670 (1956). Fluoroform.

(439)   Ibid., 1441 (1956). Fluoroform.

(439A) Tian, A., Bull. soc. chim., 1946, 583; Chem. Abstr., 41, 3358. Sulfuric acid-Ether.

(440)   Tilicheev, M. D., Khim. Tverdogo Topliva, 9, (2) 181 (1938): J. Inst. Petroleum Technol., 23, 642 (1937); Chem. Abstr., 34, 926. Aniline-Aromatics.

(441)   Tilicheev, M. D., Kuruindin, K. S., Neftyanoe Khoz., 19, 586 (1930); Chem. Zentr., 1931, I, 2561. Aniline-Aromatics.

(442)   Timmermans, J., "Annual Table of Physical Constants" 1941, Sect. 554. Aniline, Nitrobenzene.

(442A) Timmermans, J., Arch. Neerland. Sci., 6, 147 (1922); Chem. Abstr., 16, 4110. Isobutyric acid.

(443)   Timmermans, J., J. chim. phys., 20, 502 (1923); Chem. Zentr., 1924 I, 1734. Various.

(444)   Timmermans, J., Z. physik. Chem., 58, 129 (1907). Various.

(445)   Timmermans, J., "Physical Chemical Constants of Binary Systems", Interscience, New York (1959) Vol. I. Various.

(446)   Ibid., Vol. II (1959). Various.

(446A) Timmermans, J., Delcourt, Y., J. chim. phys., 31, 110 (1934); through ref. 442. Isobutyric acid.

(446B)   Timmermans, J., Mme. Hennaut-Roland, J. chim. phys., 27, 401 (1930); through ref. 442. Formic acid, CS_2.

(447)   Ibid., 29, 529 (1932); through ref. 442. Various.

(448)   Ibid., 32, 501, 589 (1935); through ref. 442. Nitrobenzene, Aniline, o-Toluidine.

(449)   Ibid., 34, 693 (1937); through ref. 442. Phenol.

(449A)   Timmermans, J., Kohnstamm, P., (1909-11); through ref. 445, 446. Various.

(449B)   Timmermans, J., Lewin, J., Discussions, Faraday Soc., 15, 197 (1953). Diethylene glycol, Amyl ether.

(450)   Timmermans, J., Martin, F., J. chim. phys., 23, 747 (1926); Chem. Zentr., 1927 I, 836. Aniline.

(450A)   Ibid., 25, 411 (1928); through ref. 442. Nitrobenzene.

(451)   Timmermans, J., Poppe, G., Compt. rend., 201, 524 (1935). Deuterium oxide.

(452)   Timofeev, V. F., Dissertation (Kharkov)(1894); through ref. 392, pp. 393, 488,513, 581, 634. Resorcinol, Aromatic acids.

(453)   Timofeev, V. F., Stakhorskii, K. M., Ukrainskii Khem. Zhurnal, 2, 395 (1926); through ref. 392, pp. 358-9, 458. Nitrobenzene.

(453A)   Trimble, H. M., Frazer, G. E., Ind. Eng. Chem., 21, 1063 (1929). Acetone-Ethylene glycol.

(454)   Tsakalotos, D. E., Bull. soc. chim., (4) 5, 397 (1909); Chem. Abstr., 3, 1954. Nicotine.

(454A)   Tschamler, H., Monatsh., 79, 223 (1948). Chlorex.

(455)   Ibid., 80, 431 (1949). Chlorex-Alcohols.

(455A)   Tschamler, H., Krischai, H., Ibid., 81, 612 (1950). M-Chlorex.

(455B)   Ibid., 82, 564 (1951). P-Chlorex.

(456)   Tschamler, H., Richter, E., Wettig, F., Ibid., 80, 749 (1949). Chlorex

(457)   Tschamler, H., Wettig, F., Richter, E., Ibid., 80, 572 (1949). Chlorex.

(457A)   Ibid., 856 (1949). Chlorex, Halogen hydrocarbons.

(457B)   Tyrer, D., J. Chem. Soc., 97, 621 (1910). Potassium iodide in alcohols.

(458)   Upson, F. W., Fluevog, E. A., Albert, W. D., J. Phys. Chem., 39, 1079 (1935). Sugars-Alcohols.

(458A)   Utz, F., Süddeut Apoth. Ztg., 59, 832 (1919); Chem. Abstr., 14, 3345. Hexamethylenetetramine.

(459) Van Dorp., D. A., Limburg, J., Nobel, P. C., Rec. trav. chim., 56, 983 (1937). Urea, Nitrobenzene.

(460) Van Klooster, N. S., Douglas, W. A., J. Phys. Chem., 49, 67 (1945). Acetic acid-Triethylamine.

(461) Vellinger, E., Herrenschmidt, J. D., Marchand, IIe., Congr. mondial petrol. 2, Sect. 2, Phys. Chem. raffinage 871-8 (1937). Acetone-Oils.

(462) Vercade, P. E., Coops, J., Jr., Rec. trav. chim., 49, 576 (1930). Alkyl malonic acids.

(463) Verschaffelt, J. E., Ibid., 42, 683 (1923). Isobutyl alcohol.

(463A) Vezes, M., Compt. rend. 150, 698 (1910), through ref. 445, p. 544. Aniline-Turpentine.

(464) Vieth, L., Physik. Z., 30, 126 (1929); Chem. Abstr., 23, 2869: through ref. 392, pp. 10, 152, 183, 208. (listed as "Wieth" there). Carbon disulfide.

(465) Vlugter, J. C., Waterman, H. I., van Westen, H. A., J. Inst. Petroleum Technol., 21, 669-70 (1935). Aniline-Hexadecane.

(466) Vol'nov, Y. N., J. Phys. Chem. (U.S.S.R.), 28, 1382 (1954). Ethyl malonate.

(467) Vondracek, R., Collection Czechoslov. Chem. Commun., 9, 168 (1937); Chem. Abstr., 31, 5232. Phenol.

(468) Vreeland, J., Dunlop, R., J. Phys. Chem., 61, 329 (1957). Nitroethane.

(469) Vrevskii, M. S., Held, N. A., Shchukarev, S. A., J. Russ. Phys. Chem. Soc., 59, 625 (1927); Z. physik. Chem., 133, 385 (1928). Formic acid.

(470) Walden, P. T., Centnerszwer, M., Z. physik. Chem., 42, 432 (1902). KI-SO$_2$.

(471) Walker, W. H., Collett, A. R., Lazzell, C. L., J. Phys. Chem., 35, 3259 (1931). Dihydroxybenzenes.

(472) Ward, H. L., Ibid., 30, 1316 (1926). Naphthalene.

(473) Ward, H. L., Cooper, S. S., Ibid., 34, 1484 (1930). Benzoic and Phthalic acids.

(474) Waterman, H. I., Leendertse, J. J., Van Krevelen, D. W., J. Inst. Petroleum Technol., 25, 801 (1939). Aniline.

(475) Weisz, H., Opalski, H., Z. angew. Chem., 35, 253 (1922); through ref. 392, p. 832. SO$_2$-Fatty oils.

(476) White, J. D., Glasgow, A. R., J. Research Natl. Bur. Standards, 19, 423 (1937). Aniline-Nonanes.

(477) Ibid., 22, 143 (1939). Aniline-Trimethylcyclohexane.

(478) White, J. D., Rose, F. W., Jr., Ibid., 17, 952 (1936). Aniline-Isononane.

(479)   White, J. D., Rose, F. W., Jr., Calingaert, G., Saroos, H., *Ibid.*, 22, 315 (1939). Aniline-Isononane.

(480)   Wibaut, J. P., others, *Rec. trav. chim.*, 58, 373 (1939). Aniline-Paraffins, Naphthenes.

(481)   Wilcox, K. W., Bailey, C. R., *J. Phys. Chem.*, 33, 706 (1929). Thymol.

(482)   Wilkinson, J. A., Neilson, C., Wylde, H. M., *J. Am. Chem. Soc.*, 42, 1377 (1920). Sulfur-Mustard Gas.

(483)   Wilkinson, R., *J. Chem. Soc.*, 1931, 3057. Aniline-Olefins.

(483A)   Wilson, A. L., *Ind. Eng. Chem.*, 27, 869 (1935). Ethylene diamine, Morpholin.

(484)   Wolff, H., Bernstoff, K., *Z. physik. Chem.*, N. F., 14, 208 (1958). Acetone.

(484A)   Wood, J. K., Scott, J. D., *J. Chem. Soc.*, 97, 1573 (1910). Camphor-Phenol.

(485)   Woodburn, H. M., Smith, K., Tetewsky, H., *Ind. Eng. Chem.*, 36, 588 (1944). Chlorex, Nitrobenzene.

(486)   Wratschko, F., *Pharm. Presse*, 34, 143 (1929); *Chem. Abstr.*, 23, 3539. Various.

(487)   Zepalova-Mikhailova, L. A., *Trans. Inst. Pure Chem. Reagents* (U.S.S.R.), No. 15, 3 (1937); *Chem. Zentr.*, 1939, I, 4914. Lower alcohols.

(488)   Zerner, E., Weisz, H., Opalski, H., *Z. angew. Chem.*, 35, 253 (1922); through ref. 392, pp. 682,834. SO_2.

(489)   Zhuravlev, E. F., *J. Gen. Chem.* (U.S.S.R.), 10, 1926 (1940); through ref. 393, pp. 1066-7. Sulfur-Methyl-anilines.

(489A)   Zhuravlev, E. F., *J. Phys. Chem.*, 12, 639 (1938), 13, 679 (1939); *Chem. Abstr.*, 34, 1544; through ref. 393, p. 1076. Acetic acid.

(490)   Zieborak, K., Maczynska, A., Maczynski, A., *Bull. acad. polon. sci.* I, III 4, 153 (1956); private communication from Y. L. Gladel. Methanol.

(491)   Zieborak, K., Olszewski, K., *Ibid.*, 4, 823 (1956); 6, 115, 127 (1958) *Chem. Abstracts*, 51, 7789g, 52, 13373-4. private communication from Y. L. Gladel. Acetonitrile, Acetic acid.

(492)   Zil'berman, E. N., *J. Appl. Chem.*, (U.S.S.R.), 24, 883 (1951); *Chem. Abstr.*, 47, 4172i. Cyclohexanol.

(493)   *Ibid.*, 26, 941 (1953); *Chem. Abstr.*, 48, 6223h. Adiponitrile.

(494)   Zil'berman, E. N., Skorikova, Z. D., *J. Gen Chem.* (U.S.S.R.), 23, 1629 (1953); *Chem. Abstr.*, 48, 4951f. Hexamethyleneimine.

(495)   Zimm, B. H., *J. Phys. Coll. Chem.*, 54, 1313 (1950). C_7F_{14}.-CCl_4.